15.00

Systemic Planning:
Theory and
Application

Systemic Planning: Theory and Application

Anthony James Catanese
Georgia Institute of Technology

Alan Walter Steiss
Virginia Polytechnic Institute

Heath Lexington Books
D. C. Heath and Company
Lexington, Massachusetts

Contents

Figures

Tables

Preface

This book has several purposes. It is written as a textbook for students in planning, systems analysis, public administration, business administration, and the urban-oriented branches of sociology, economics, political science, anthropology, social work, computer and information science, and engineering. The perspective given throughout the book is directed toward urban problems, which is meant to include the national, state, regional, metropolitan, county, and local levels. Nonetheless, an inherent perspective of generalization, achieved by frequent reference to cybernetics and general systems theory, is maintained throughout the book.

The book may be valuable for training courses and continuing education for systems approaches to the analysis and resolution of urban problems. Such courses directed toward elected and appointed public officials, consultants to government, and educators can make use of this work.

The third purpose is to provide a reference work for practitioners in these areas. It may serve as useful library reference material. The applied orientation given to the subject matter extends its utility beyond the theoretical and academic plane.

We would like to acknowledge the collaboration of several colleagues in the preparation of the following chapters: Chapter 5, Cordell F. Bowman; Chapter 8, James B. Grant and Edward N. Kashuba; and Chapters 10 and 11, John W. Dickey. While elements of some of the chapters have been published in various professional journals, we consider this to be a collection of original essays owing to the extensive revision, modification, and development of some of the initial elements.

A. J. C.
Atlanta, Georgia

A. W. S.
Blacksburg, Virginia

Introduction

This book is an attempt to integrate a variegated array of subjects dealing with contemporary planning within the theory of *systemic planning* that we have developed. Systemic planning is both a theory and a set of real-world applications that provide a convenient and efficient way of looking at the planning process. Systemic planning is a hybrid of general systems theory, systems analysis, operations research, decision theory, cybernetics, and urban and regional planning (city planning). We seek to develop an optimal process of planning, along with its techniques and methods, personnel, and the proper or desirable environment for functioning, by taking the best strains from the above-named branches of the "new science."

Two dangers always lurk for those who attempt to develop hybrid theories. The first danger is that one will go too far into an area and try to carry away too much of a good thing. The record shows that whole-cloth transfer of "hard science" into "soft science" has been deadly. The results of the concerted efforts of the "social physicists" of the late nineteenth century, for example, have been little more than a few debatable models for traffic estimation and migration prediction. The second danger, which is equally confounding, is that a theorist will try to interrelate an equilibrium among the various strains in such a fashion that he will develop a theory that is not at all new and that is little more than a hodge-podge of concepts and tools. These two dangers are formidable, and the test of success must rest upon application and performance. For this reason, we have stressed the applications of systemic planning throughout this book.

The first part of this book is concerned with the formulation of the theory of systemic planning. The rudiments of general systems theory, systems analysis, operations research, decision theory, and cybernetic theory that are useful and relevant to the theory of urban and regional planning are explored and synthesized. Comparisons are made among these various elements, and a detailed description of the synthesis is developed. The theory of systemic planning is placed in its proper perspective of compromise, pragmatics, operationalism, application, and optimization. Part One serves as the basis for the remainder of the book and the most convenient umbrella for various other subjects examined.

Part Two is concerned with the common applications of the systems approach to urban problems. The particular applications discussed in this part are related to the relative new approach to public budgeting known as *planning-programming-budgeting-scheduling systems.* (PPBS systems). PPBS systems fall neatly into the systemic planning category because real-world applications tend to encompass many of the elements described in Part One. PPBS systems also provide efficacious means for translating the somewhat heady nuances of systemic planning theory into practical terms and concepts. PPBS systems are generic in application, but we have chosen to deal with governmental applications in order to achieve uniformity and consistency in the evolution of theory into practice.

The third part of this book is concerned with physical development models and tools. The bulk of this part involves an examination of the types of models that are being used in systemic planning for urban and regional development problems. The emphasis is on physical development, particularly urban structure and form, land use and traffic, and housing. Essentially case studies, these chapters demonstrate the usefulness of modeling and simulation in systemic planning. The models are preceded by a discussion of computer graphics as an aid to the analysis and presentation of model and simulation output. It helps to demonstrate one of the newer uses of the computer in the systemic planning process.

Part Four examines in detail the often nebulous environment in which systemic planning must function. The book would be somewhat lacking if it did not deal with the real-world political, social, and economic environment and the ways in which planning interacts and is limited by this environment. The discussions are empirically derived research findings on the structure, function, and communications of planning in American cities. These findings set the basic parameters for the establishment of systemic planning as an evolutionary form of city planning. The research findings are summarized and a general empirical theory is developed along with several recommendations for improvement of the environment better to enable systemic planning.

The final part of the book is both a summary and a set of conclusions. Some prospects for the near and distant future are presented. Directions for action and suggestions for the next few steps are presented.

**Systemic Planning:
Theory and
Application**

Part One
Theory of Systemic
Planning

Part One consists of four chapters dealing with the theory of systemic planning. Chapter 1 deals with the search for a systems approach to the planning of complex urban systems that was conducted among the fields of general systems theory, operations research, decision theory, and cybernetic theory. Chapter 2 deals with the formulation of the theory of systemic planning as compared with the traditional planning process, and poses its challenges to the new generation of planners. Chapter 3 relates systemic planning to the theory of decision–making as it has been the traditional focus of planning. Chapter 4 places the theory of systemic planning in the realm of implementation of plans and decisions and presents an actions program model.

1

The Search for a Systems Approach to the Planning of Complex Urban Systems

Few professions have been confronted with as rapidly changing arenas of practice as has the planning profession. In the past fifty years in which the field has been organized as a profession, urban and regional problems have become manifold, increasing both in their scope and complexity.

The foundations laid by planning's founding generation — men like Bassett, Bettman, Nolen, Olmsted, Bartholomew, Stein, Comey, Howard, Ullman, and others — served the profession well in its formative years. The emphasis, however, of the founding generation on the independent planning commission, the master plan to guide the physical development of the city, and zoning as the principal tool of implementation reflect the tenor of the times. These tools of the profession were applicable to an era of growth responsive to conditions of the past.

As the further complexities of the urban environment became evident in the years of the Depression and the war years of the Forties, it became the task of the senior generation — members of the profession born after World War I — to seek the necessary adjustments in planning principles and philosophies. One of the significant contributions to this adjustment came from Robert A. Walker's study in the early Forties, which gave substantial evidence to show the relative ineffectiveness of the independent planning commission in influencing community development.[1]

Interpreters of Walker's proposal place the planner in the role of confidant to the chief executive. This view gives emphasis to the advisory nature of this staff-aide relationship, thereby delegating the planner to the role of a technical expert. From this position of technical expertise, planners of the senior generation introduced many important modifications, such as (1) the expanded concept of the master plan — the comprehensive plan; (2) the new focus on programs of public capital investment, renewal, and rehabilitation as more positive steps in guiding future development; (3) the deemphasis of the negative aspects of "police powers"; and (4) the expanded concern for the social and economic dimensions of urban problems. Although the concept of the planner as an adviser on matters of public policy — rather than an innovator of public action — has come under sharp criticism, it remains a fundamental precept of the majority of senior generation planners.

While the senior generation still occupies a position of leadership in the profession, a new generation of planners has begun to make its presence felt. This new generation, born since the Depression, has been raised in a climate of rapid scientific and technological advancement. When they were children, the war effort called upon science to develop sophisticated tools for the annihilation of the enemy. After the war, such fields as communications engineering, computer sciences, cybernetics, operations research, and management science rapidly developed to improve the operations of business and industry. While many of the new generation were still in college, the launching of the first Soviet Sputnik prompted all Western nations to accelerate teaching and research in mathematics and the physical sciences. And now, in the early years of their professional experience, new sophisticated tools of analysis — generally grouped under the label of systems analysis — are finding wide areas of application.

A Growing Interest in Systems Analysis

It perhaps was inevitable that pressures would emerge from all levels of government to apply a "systems" approach in an effort to resolve the problems of cities. The word "resolve" is used here advisedly. Few members of the new generation of planners think that many city problems will ever be completely solved. In the United States and Great Britain especially, the call has gone out for a more scientific approach to the planning and development of our urban areas — from congressmen and members of Parliament to small-town mayors; from cabinet members and ministers to community welfare workers; from labor leaders to professors.

Systems analysis grew out of an intensive and highly technical field known as systems engineering. In recent years, systems analysis more and more has become a catchall phrase for applied science (especially by the nontechnical people who call for its use in urban areas). This overgeneralization is not a serious problem, because the approach and methods of systems analysis are becoming sufficiently universal as to include a wide range of applications.

The Rudiments of Systems Analysis

The first obvious step in discussing the possible applications of systems analysis in the field of planning is to spell out more fully the terms that will be used. A *system*, for example, may be defined as any entity, physical or conceptual, that is composed of interrelated parts. This is a widely held definition of a system; yet it is so broad as to include virtually any interdependent set of activities or things. A computer is a system composed of a processor, data-receiving elements, data-emission elements, control elements, and a memory. An automobile engine is a system that uses several resource inputs such as air, gasoline, oil, and electricity; that has a structure composed of pistons, valves, spark plugs, a crankshaft, and so forth; and that has certain measurable performance outputs. A community is a system composed of interacting units designed to meet basic human needs such as the family, the economy, government, religion, education, and so forth.

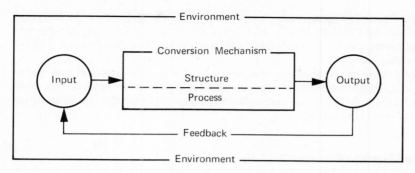

Figure 1-1 The Fundamental Components of a System.

These somewhat diverse examples of systems have several characteristics in common (see Figure 1.1). Each has a *structural configuration* (an arrangement of component parts), and each performs certain *functions*. Each operates in a larger environment (or as a subsystem of some larger system) and requires certain *inputs* from this environment. A system can be thought of as moving through various states, following some definable *process* or set of procedures (the dynamic aspects of a system). Each of the systems cited produce a set of *outputs* that are related to its functional aspects. These outputs, in turn, have a *feedback* effect on the system as a whole by providing new inputs in subsequent cycles and suggesting necessary modifications in structure and process to improve performance. While many disciplines choose to focus on one particular aspect of a system as a vehicle for analysis, a complete understanding of a given system can be derived only by taking cognizance of all these aspects.

As has been noted, a city is composed of interdependent component parts and, therefore, can be viewed as a system. Since each of these components has a group of interrelated parts within themselves, they are also systems. To reconcile this semantic problem, the components can be thought of as subsystems of the larger urban system. Much more could be said about the system characteristics of a city in their generic sense. It could be shown that cities exhibit both physical and conceptual subsystems, and that there is a certain randomness in the way an urban system works. Many other such clarifications and extensions of the concept could be made. The salient point for this discussion, however, is that a city is a system capable of being analyzed and planned.

Analysis is a term familiar to planners, roughly meaning the act of investigation or examination. In its generic sense, analysis is derived from the Greek verb of the same spelling meaning "to separate anything into its component parts or elements." In a rigorous sense, an analysis consists of breaking down the whole into its parts in order to find out their nature, proportion, function, and relationship. In chemistry, for example, compounds or mixtures are broken down into their constituent substances in order to determine their composition (qualitative analysis) and proportion (quantitative analysis). In mathematics, problems are broken down into equations and the relations among the variables are examined; e.g., through differential calculus. In planning, when a city is examined for relations among the component parts, it is also called an analysis.

Systems analysis is thus the conjunction of the two concepts and their operational definitions. Systems analysis involves the separation of a system into its component subsystems in order to examine their relationships one to another and to the system as a whole.

Essential Elements of Systems Analysis

The concepts of systems analysis most often are associated with such people as Robert McNamara, Charles Hitch, and the "whiz kids" of the Rand Corporation. In this context, images are evoked of such things as high-speed electronic computers, large-scale mathematical models, multidisciplinary teams of military strategists, and elaborate cost-benefit and cost-effectiveness analyses. None of these factors, however, is an essential element in systems analysis. To be sure, some were very instrumental in the development of the techniques of systems analysis; but as has been noted, systems analysis is a generic term which can be applied to any explicit, theoretical, or deductive approach to problem analysis. Thus, in some cases, good systems analysis can be performed by a single individual, making some elementary arithmetic calculations on a scratch pad, and without once mentioning cost-effectiveness or cost-benefits. Such an individual, of course, would have to deal with the concepts of cost and effectiveness, or risks and gains, or some other criterion for evaluating various alternative solutions to the problem at hand, but he would not necessarily combine these into a measure called cost-effectiveness.

Charles Hitch has described systems analysis as an approach which defines and attacks a problem explicitly in terms of the following essential elements:[2] (1) an *objective* or a number of objectives; (2) alternative means (or "systems") by which the objectives may be accomplished; (3) knowledge about the "costs" or resources required by each alternative; (4) a mathematical or logical *model* or models which describes a set of relationships among the objectives, the alternative means of achievement, the environment, and the resource requirements; and (5) a *criterion* for choosing the preferred alternative which usually relates the objectives and the costs in some manner; for example, by maximizing the achievement of objectives for some assumed or given budget.

G. H. Fisher, a major spokesman for the Rand Corporation in the application of systems analysis, suggests that it is an analytical process having the following major characteristics:[3] (1) a systematic examination and comparison of alternative courses of action which might be taken to achieve specified objectives for some future time period; (2) critical examination of the cost (in the sense of economic resource cost) and the utility (benefits or gains) pertaining to each of the alternatives being compared to attain the stipulated objectives; (3) an extended time context of analysis — often five, ten, or more years; (4) an environment with considerable uncertainty; (5) numerous interactions among the key variables in the problem; (6) quantitative methods of analysis most frequently applied, but often supplemented by qualitative analysis; and (7) the focus of systems analysis most often is on research and development and/or investment-type decision problems.

While a fundamental characteristic is the systematic examination of alternative courses of action, an equally important output of systems analysis is the information base that may lead to the design of additional alternatives if those examined initially are found to be insufficient in light of identified objectives. The analysis, particularly if done thoroughly and imaginatively, frequently may result in modifications of initially specified objectives. Thus, systems analysis is a dynamic process; as the problem unfolds through analysis, the desired solution or "objective function" may undergo a number of redefinitions of the basis of new information brought to light.

As Fisher has noted, the time context of systems analysis is the future — often the distant future. Because of this extended time horizon, the environment is one of uncertainty — very often great uncertainty. Since uncertainty is an important facet of the problem, it should be recognized and treated explicitly in the analysis from the outset.

The context in which systems analysis takes place frequently is fairly broad, and the environment is very complex, with numerous interactions among the key variables in the problem. As a result, simple, staightforward solutions are the exception rather than the rule. In simple problem situations, the methods of systems analysis sometimes show no obvious advantages over those problem-solving techniques that have long been known. It is chiefly when the systems become complex that the new methods reveal their potential advantages.

While quantitative methods of analysis should be utilized as much as possible, because of the uncertainty of the extended time horizon and the complexity of the environment, and also because of inadequate data and information sources, purely quantitative work often must be supplemented by qualitative analysis. The importance of good qualitative work and the use of appropriate combinations of quantitative and qualitative methods cannot be overemphasized.

The essential elements enumerated above pertain to the analysis itself; in practical applications of systems analysis to problems of the real world, two more essential elements are worth noting. The first — one which perhaps should head the list — is the need to address the right problem in the first place. The second — coming at the end of the list — is the need to interpret the results of analysis in terms of the real-world decisions or other problems.

As Peter Drucker has suggested, the most common source of mistakes in management decisions is the emphasis on finding the *right answer* rather than the *right question*.[4] As Drucker has observed: ". . . the important and difficult job is never to find the right answer, it is to find the right question. For there are few things as useless — if not as dangerous — as the right answer to the wrong question."[5] Thus, Anatol Rapoport asserts that the first step in solving a problem is to state it. "The statement usually involves a description of an existing state and desirable state of affairs where the factors involved in the discrepancy are explicitly pointed out. The success with which any problem is solved depends to a great extent on the clarity with which it is stated. In fact, the solution of the problem is, in a sense, a clarification (or concretization) of the objectives."[6]

Vague statements of the situation lead to vague methods, where success is erratic and questionable. The more a given situation is extensionalized, the better the classification of the problem, and the greater the promise of a successful solution.

If the problem cannot be stated specifically, preferably in one interrogative sentence that includes one or more goals, then the analysis of the problematic situation has not been adequate or of sufficient depth. Emotional bias, habitual or traditional behavior, or the frequent tendency of human beings to seek the path of least resistance may result in a superficial analysis, followed by a statement of the "apparent" problem instead of the "real" problem. An excellent solution to an apparent problem, of course, will not work in practice, because it is the solution to a problem that does not exist in fact. Consequently, a short-circuiting of this state of the analysis process may actually result in more time being spent later to get at the real problem when it becomes painfully evident that further analysis is required.

One possible use of systems analysis is in unambiguously providing the answer to the real-world problem — telling the client, for example, what his decision or plan ought to be. This is the most satisfactory kind of assistance to be rendered by systems analysis; it also is the rarest. Some writers have suggested, however, that it is not rare enough; that is to say, the answer is given through analysis when, in fact, the analytical results are not all that conclusive or clear cut.

Even the best systems analysis, properly applied, has its limitations. Bad systems analysis, improperly applied, can be worse than useless. It is all too easy for the analyst to begin to believe his own assumptions, even if drawn out of thin air, and to attach undue significance to the results of his analysis, especially if it involves some sophisticated mathematics and much hard work. Some clients are too easily impressed by analyses, especially if the results come out of electronic computers and are agreeable or plausible and impressively presented. There are, to be sure, some hard-nosed skeptics, but not enough of them. Moreover, some people are skeptical for the wrong reasons; for example, because the results are unpleasing and not because of questionable features of the analysis process.

In light of these considerations, therefore, it is most important, if not vital, that the results of analysis be interpreted and tested continuously in terms of the real-world problems. This is a responsibility of both the analyst and the client.

The essential elements of systems analysis, as stated above, are little more than statements of rather obvious, explicit, common-sense approaches to problem-solving situations. They do not provide a formula for conducting a good systems analysis. Nor do they preclude the possibility of addressing the wrong problem, or approaching it in terms of the wrong objectives, the wrong alternative systems, the wrong measures of costs, the wrong relationships among various system elements, the wrong criterion of choice, or interpreting the results incorrectly in terms of the real-world problem. The explicit nature of systems analysis can be of some help in exposing deficiencies which might otherwise go unnoticed or have been obscured. Some general precepts and questions, of the sort outlined above, can be useful reminders to the analyst in performing the analysis and to his client in evaluating the results.

Closed and Open Systems:
Limitations to Conventional
Forms of Analysis

Up to this point, it would hardly appear that there is anything "new" about systems analysis as compared to the more traditional approaches to the examination of complex processes or activities. Systems have been studied in the natural sciences — physics, physical chemistry, and biology — for many years; in fact, "systems analysis" is the foundation of the "hard" sciences. However, the approaches pursued in the natural sciences, until recent years, have focused on parts and processes operating in *closed systems,* i.e., systems studied in isolation of their environment. Thus physical chemistry tells us about the reactions, their rates of change, and the chemical equilibria eventually established in a closed vessel where various reactants are brought together. The processes of such systems achieve an *equilibrium* — a predictable balance between inputs and outputs.

However, many systems cannot be separated from their environment in this abstract fashion. Such systems interact continuously with other systems in their environment and, further, experience processes which are reversible. The essential problem was to develop a mode of analysis that would permit the organization of relations resulting from the dynamic interaction of the functions and structural configurations of the system and the system as a whole with its larger environment. Modern system analysis provides such an approach.

Living organisms and their organizations maintain themselves (survive) in a continuous inflow and outflow with their environment in which components are built up and broken down. Such systems never exist in a state of equilibrium, in the chemical or thermodynamic sense, but are maintained in a so-called *steady state.* Thus rather than seeking equilibrium, such systems strive to attain *stability.* In short, such systems are *open,* continuously interacting with their environment.

Recognition of the distinction between open and closed systems has led to two important concepts. In any closed system, the final attainable state is unequivocally determined by the initial conditions. For example, in a chemical equilibrium, the final concentrations of reactants depend on the initial concentrations. Ten parts of hydrogen and five parts of oxygen will produce five parts of H^2O, not four or six. If either the initial conditions or the process is altered, the final state will also change. This is not the case in open systems. Here, the same final state may be reached from different initial conditions and in different ways (through different processes). This characteristic of open systems is called *equifinality*.[7]

The concept of equifinality, based upon dynamic interaction in an open system, has important application in the modification of older mechanistic theories. In the mechanistic view, derived from classical physics of the nineteenth century, the inexorable laws of causality produced all phenomena in the world — inanimate, living, and even mental. There was no room for notions of directiveness, order, or telos. Correspondingly, causality was essentially one-way. In recent years, however, an expansion of physics, in order to include open systems, has taken place. This has shed light on many obscure phenomena in physics and biology and has led to the abandonment of many causal theories.

The mechanistic view of causality is insufficient for explaining most social phenomena. One cannot begin to understand a living organism, much less its behavior or the complex activities of human society, without taking into account what rather loosely is called adaptiveness, goal-seeking, purposiveness, and the like. Teleological behavior, directed toward a characteristic final state or goal, can no longer be avoided by mechanistic or other causal theories. This means that the investigator's focus can no longer be on simple cause-and-effect relationships. Rather, careful attention must be given to the parameters of the system within which change can take place.

The second important concept to be derived from the distinction between open and closed systems relates to what was once thought to be a violent contradiction between Kelvin's principle of degradation and Darwin's theories of evolution. According to the second principle of thermodynamics, the general trend of physical events is toward states of maximum disorder, with a leveling down of difference among the component elements. Eventually, the process comes to a stop at a state of equilibrium. This notion lies at the foundation of the so-called "heat death" of the universe. At this final state, all energy is degraded into evenly distributed heat of low temperature, and the world process comes to a stop.

This concept had an important influence on the thinking of many early writers in the area of urban development theory. They postulated that the conditions evident in the emerging city following the industrial revolution were only the first stages of social degradation. As societies became more urbanized, disorder would increase, and differences in social characteristics would decrease. These processes are in contradiction with Darwin's theories, which suggest that the living world, through embryonic development and evolution, shows a transition toward higher order, heterogeneity, and organization.

On the basis of the theory of open systems, however, the apparent paradox disappears. In all irreversible processes, i.e., in closed systems, the range of possible arrangements of elements — the randomness of the system

— continually increases, and therefore, order is continually destroyed. This can be illustrated through the process of shuffling a deck of cards. If, at the beginning, the cards are in an orderly arrangement, with the cards of each suit following each other according to their value, the shuffling will tend to make the arrangement disorderly. But if the shuffling is begun with a disorderly arrangement, it is very unlikely that, through shuffling, the cards will come into an orderly one. This is because there are many more "disorderly" than orderly arrangements, and so a disorderly state of a deck of cards is more probable. The process of shuffling of cards is analogous to the operations of a closed system.

In an open system, however, the process may be reversed, and order can be restored to random arrangements of elements. Thus living systems, maintaining themselves in a steady state, can avoid the continual increase of disorder, and in the process may even develop toward states of increased order and organization.

Uses of Systems Analysis

As noted previously, systems analysis seldom if ever gives to a problem an unambiguous solution that can be accepted without further consideration. The difficulty, of course, stems from the fact that the analytical results typically hinge on some ambiguous factors. A good systems analysis will not suppress this ambiguity. Rather, it will present complete enumeration of the results for various alternative assumptions about the ambiguous factors. A bad analysis may suppress the ambiguity — deliberately or inadvertently — and may present what purports to be the right answer. This solution will not survive careful scrutiny, however. Unfortunately it sometimes does survive the inadequate scrutiny it often is given.

As a result of irreducible ambiguities, systems analysis frequently is limited to a narrowing of alternatives, i.e., it does not completely solve the problems of the decision-maker or planner. The analyst may present a relatively small listing of "better" system solutions from which the decision-maker can choose. If properly conducted, the analysis may reveal a relatively small list of what appears to be the more important measures of system costs and benefits or effectiveness. The analysts may even go so far as to recommend a particular choice based on their own judgment and/or scale of values. Of course, when an analyst does this, he goes beyond his role as a technician.

Another important use of systems analysis is as a disciplinary and educational device. The explicit approach of systems analysis calls for a spelling out — and preferably exposing to full view — of the various elements of the analysis. This provides a framework which can increase the likelihood that the right questions will be asked and the right considerations taken into account.

This process can be highly educational to both the client and the analyst. It provides a greater range of objective information and thereby improves the bases for judgment. Moreover, it can and often does lead to a consideration of elements of the problem situation which might not otherwise have been thought of, including new or different decision criteria and new or different alternative systems.

In many cases, the principal payoff of good systems analysis is not in indicating the preferred system or systems from among a predetermined set of alternatives. Rather it is in the suggestion of promising additional systems to be considered and tested, leading to the development of better systems than dictated by the original problem constraints or "givens." The added systems may be known systems which, for some reason, were overlooked initially or prematurely ruled out of consideration. Or they may be newly invented systems, devised to remedy the major deficiencies in other alternative systems — deficiencies brought to light by the analysis. Systems analysis, of course, does not provide any magic formula for determining which alternative systems should be considered, much less a foolproof method for inventing new systems. Nevertheless, one of the principal benefits of systems analysis can be the stimulation of improved systems design.

Limitations of Systems Analysis

The limitations of systems analysis are given considerable attention in such works as the pacemaker book by Hitch and McKean, *The Economics of Defense in the Nuclear Age* (Cambridge: Harvard University Press, 1960) and by David Novick in *Program Budgeting* (Washington, D. C.: U. S. Government Printing Office, 1965). These writings are not simply an academic formality, noted for the sake of honesty and then perhaps forgotten. The limitations of systems analysis are stressed advisedly, based on sad experience and observation; they are offered in the hope of offsetting a common tendency to perform systems analyses without due regard for the pitfalls, an approach that can be a gross disservice to the client and to the concepts themselves.

Systems analysis in the wrong hands can be like a dangerous weapon in the hands of a child. In this connection, Fisher has suggested that systems analysis is like the little girl in the nursery rhyme who had a little curl, right in the middle of her forehead:

> When she was good, she was very, very good.
> And when she was bad, she was horrid.

The Process of Systems Analysis

In the majority of its applications, systems analysis is concerned with problem-solving; that is, given a problem with certain determinants and desired end results, the process of systems analysis can be employed to seek a resolution

13

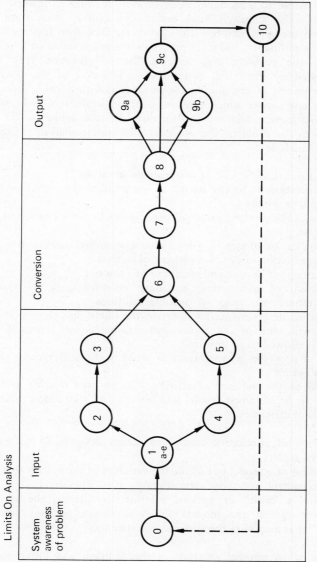

Figure 1-2 The Systems Analysis Procedure. See text for the definition of component numbers.

of the problem. The desired end results are analogous to the states of increased order and organization. If the system under study is assumed to be closed, then it would not be feasible to introduce modifications in order to achieve the desired end results — the system would eventually achieve some state of equilibrium based on the initial determinants. However, since open systems have the characteristic of equifinality, and since processes of open systems are capable of being reversed, the problem may have a "better" solution than the "inevitable" suggested by the initial determinants. The task of the systems analyst, then, becomes one of determining the parameters within which action is feasible, developing alternatives which conform to these parameters, and testing these alternatives to discover which provides the most desirable solution.

Thus, given a particular problem, the procedures of system analysis as shown in Figure 1.2, would include

A. *INPUT*
    (1) Definition and classification of the problem situation
        (a) Specification as to the nature of the problem, i.e., whether it is generic or unique
        (b) Identification of the principal participants in the decision-making process
        (c) Identification of apparent determinants or initial conditions
        (d) Determination of decision-makers' objectives
        (e) Statement of desired end-results to be achieved.
    (2) Identification of parameters, boundary conditions, or constraints which determine the range of possible solutions
    (3) Projection of determinants to ascertain the likely directions that the problem will take in the future and possible consequences if the problem is allowed to go unsolved
    (4) Analysis of processes or operations involved in the achievement of an optimal solution
    (5) Definition of the measure of efficiency to be used relative to each objective to be obtained (goals) and selection of a common measure (standard) of efficiency

B. *CONVERSION*
    (6) Formulation of alternative courses of action designed to reach the desired end-results
    (7) Construction of a model to include the variables of the system that are subject to control, and those variables not subject to control
    (8) Search for a "best" or optimal solution (by testing the various alternatives against the model) so as to determine the "control variables" that maximize the system's effectiveness

C. *OUTPUT*
    (9) Selection of an optimal solution to the problem and initiation of action programs to bring about this solution
        (a) Testing of the solution to determine its effectiveness in predicting changes in the system

  (b) Development of controls for a given solution by establishing procedures for detecting significant changes and specifications as to the modifications to be made in the solution if such changes occur

  (c) Implementation of the selected solution by establishing recommended decision rules and action programs and procedures

 (10) Interpretation of above steps in light of system's expectations and output feedback

The crucial step in these procedures lies in the evaluation of differentials of cost and effectiveness associated with each of the alternatives. The interpretation of this evaluation provides the basis for the recommendation of a particular alternative or set of alternatives. To many planners, these procedural steps may sound quite like the traditional planning process. In a subsequent chapter, a comparison will be made of these two basic approaches to problem-solving situations.

Alternatives to
Systems Analysis

The limitations of systems analysis, good and bad, suggest the desirability of exploring other approaches to problem-solving, as alternatives or supplements to systems analysis. As it usually is employed, systems analysis is an explicit, theoretical, deductive approach — one which starts with some clearly stated postulates or axioms and from these deduces certain logical consequences. Deductive reasoning is necessarily analytic inference which argues from the general to the particular, in that the conclusions drawn are by nature of less generality than the premises. In Aristotelian logic, the function of the deductive process is to establish the first premises. This involves passing from the particulars of sense experience to the universal and necessary principles involved in sense experience. Essentially, then, ". . . knowledge ultimately rests upon an indubitable intellectual apprehension."[8] As applied in the formulation of approaches to the analysis of urban problems, the deductive method has been generally characterized by the use of analogies, paradigms, or general theories derived from other disciplines, although the analytic nature of analogous inference is open to question.

Other problem-solving approaches can be derived from the three basic characteristics of systems analysis — explicit, theoretical, and deductive. That is to say, such approaches can be developed by taking a posture opposite to each of these characteristics — implicit, experimental, and inductive.

An alternative to deductive analysis is inductive or empirical statistical analysis. In this approach, instead of predicting system behavior by applying logic to some fundamental postulates, behavior is predicted by statistical inference and applied to some observed data considered directly applicable to the system in question. Statistical inference, of course, is based on certain axioms and logic, but of a sort quite different than applied in the typical deductive systems analysis.

Through the inductive approach, conclusions concerning problems of a general class are reached by analyzing certain members of that class and thereby drawing an empirical generalization. Levels of sophistication in the inductive process, of course, are determined by the quality and quantity of the empirical data. The emphasis on data quality and quantity in the inductive process is similar to the basic requirements for information systems in computer applications, viz., "that the information sources and data inputs must be continuous, comparable, and consistently accurate."[9]

In practice, systems analysis usually combines the two approaches. The inductive approach is used in formulating the basic postulates (at least those based on fact), and the deductive approach takes over from there. The relative merits of the two approaches, or the best combination of them, depends on the particular problem.

An alternative to theoretical analysis is physical experimentation and other forms of data gathering. Systems analysis typically has to contend with uncertainty concerning several key factors in the systems considered. Some uncertainties reflect a lack of basic, reliable data. Even where the basic data are available, there may be uncertainties reflecting shortcomings in the theoretical relationships to which the data are applied. These shortcomings, in turn, may be attributable to difficulties in describing some features of the system mathematically, or to oversimplification of relationships for the sake of analytical or computational economy or feasibility. Whatever the reason for uncertainty, it leads to ambiguous results.

There probably can be no entirely satisfactory way to cope with uncertainty in systems analysis, although some ways are better than others. The only truly satisfactory procedure is to eliminate uncertainty insofar as possible. Physical experimentation and other forms of data-gathering can be useful to this end. These approaches can either provide the missing basic data or contribute to a bypassing of the shaky theoretical relationships to provide relatively direct and realistic measures of system behavior. The latter case may involve the inductive approach, as outlined above; the present point concerns the acquisition of new data rather than the question of how the data are employed.

The relative merits of, or proper balance between, theoretical analysis and fact-gathering again depends on the nature of the problem. It is important, of course, to get the facts on the proper subject. To this end, a preliminary theoretical analysis can be very useful — in pointing out what information is lacking and most needed. Much effort can be and often is wasted gathering the wrong data, for failure first to do the required theoretical homework. On the other hand, much effort also can be wasted in applying sophisticated analytical techniques to inadequate data — in trying to make a silk-purse analysis out of sow's-ear data.

Physical experimentation and data-gathering activities, in general, are very expensive. Making plans and decisions in the face of great uncertainty — even if aided by the best possible systems analysis — also can be very expensive. A proper balance may well call for much more emphasis on fact-gathering than has been customary.

An alternative to the explicit approach of systems analysis is the implicit application of judgment to the problem at hand. Systems analysis, of course, is pervaded with judgment from start to finish. Judgments must be made in defining the problem, in formulating and carrying out various elements of the analysis, and in interpreting the results. In effect, systems analysis is an explicit procedure for the orderly application of judgment.[16]

Within the present state of the art of systems analysis, there are many practical problems which cannot be readily broken down so as to permit the application of deductive judgment. In these cases, the most effective approach may be to rely primarily on direct judgment, at least to the extent that the judgment is "expert."[a] Even here, however, attempts to attack the problem through the application of systems analysis techniques can be of significant aid in placing the problem in its proper perspective and in improving the basis for expert judgment — providing, of course, that the limitations of systems analysis are kept in mind.

**The Role of
Systems Analysis in the
Long-Range Planning —
Decision-Making Process**

Given this general conception of systems analysis, it is possible to shift the discussion to the more pertinent question which underlies this initial exploration into the search for a systems approach to urban problems. This is the question as to the role of systems analysis in the long-range planning—decision-making process.

Seeking the Optimum

When studying alternative future courses of action, systems analysts always like to try to come up with "preferred solutions." Ideally, this means determining the optimum. An optimum is that point on some well-defined surface where all the partial derivatives are equal to zero and the appropriate second-order conditions prevail.

To put that last statement into less technical terms, most mathematical applications of systems analysis involve some set of conditions that can be expressed as a function of two or more variables. These variables describe some mathematical formula that can be expressed as a surface in two or more dimensions. Linear programming, for the most part, deals with just an X and a Y

coordinates. Once the problem gets beyond three dimensions, of course, it is not possible to express it graphically, although it may be expressed mathematically.

Perhaps an elementary example will provide further clarification. For purposes of this discussion, let us remain with three dimensions. However, to make the problem more interesting, we will examine a nonlinear problem, since this more closely approximates real-world situations.

The problem is to maximize a relationship between two variables, x_1 and x_2, such that

$$\max \left\{ f(x_1, x_2) = 10\, x_1 + 20 x_2 + x_1 x_2 - 2 x_1{}^2 - 2 x_2{}^2 \right\},$$

subject to:

$$7 - x_1 \geq 0$$

$$8 - x_2 \geq 0$$

$$10 - x_1 - x_2 \geq 0$$

$$x_1, x_2 \geq 0.$$

The figure described by this formula would have the appearance of an inverted bowl or helmet (see Figure 1.3). The value of the objective function $f(x_1, x_2)$ — that which we seek to maximize — determines the height of the bowl. What we are seeking, then, is the high point on this curved, three-dimensional surface. The constraints provide information as to the feasible region in which the solution lies. Looking down from the top of the bowl, we know that x_2 cannot exceed 8, that x_1 cannot exceed 7, and that together they cannot exceed 10. Graphically, this can be illustrated as shown in Figure 1.4.

The first step is to solve for the first partial derivatives. This is done by ignoring any term with just x_2 (or x_1) in it when solving for x_1 (or x_2).

$$\frac{\partial f}{\partial x_1} = 10 + x_2 - 4 x_1$$

$$\frac{\partial f}{\partial x_2} = 20 + x_1 - 4 x_2$$

The maximization point is the point where these two derivatives are equal to zero. By multiplying the first partial derivative with respect to x_2 by 4 and adding the two equations, it is possible to eliminate the x_1 variable and to solve for x_2. By substitution, we can then solve for x_1:

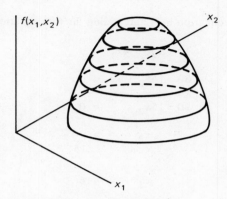

Figure 1-3 Figure for $f(x_1,x_2)$.

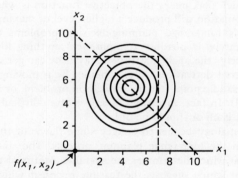

Figure 1-4 Top View of $f(x_1,x_2)$.

$$10 + x_2 - 4x_1 = 0$$

$$20 - 4x_2 + x_1 = 0$$

Multiplying the second equation by 4 and adding the two equations:

$$10 + x_2 - 4x_1 = 0$$

$$\underline{80 - 16x_2 + 4x_1 = 0}$$

$$90 - 15x_2 = 0$$

$$x_2 = \frac{90}{15}$$

$$x_2 = 6$$

$$x_1 = 4$$

Thus, the solution which maximizes the objective function is where $x_1 = 4$ and $x_2 = 6$. No other combination will produce a higher level of maximization.

In most of today's long-range planning-decision problems of any consequence, however, it rarely is possible to approach anything like a hard-core optimization. Most likely, the analyst will be lucky if he can get some notion as to the signs of the partial derivatives — i.e., whether he is moving "up the hill," so to speak, toward a saddle point in a maximization problem, or away from the saddle point (downhill). In fact, in many cases, it is often difficult to determine what "hill" the analyst is on or should be on!

This rather crude analogy begins to convey some flavor of the problems of the role of analysis in the long-range planning process. The statement of the objective function (that which determines the overall contours of the "hill") and of the constraints (that which suggests the feasible region in which the solution might be found) may be a most difficult undertaking. As may be seen from this simple example, once these aspects of the problem are determined, finding the solution is a rather mechanical process.

The Role of
Analysis in
Decision-Making

It might be said that there are two extreme positions regarding the role of analysis in the decision-making process. On the one hand, it might be argued that the types of long-range planning-decision problems under consideration are just too complex to be handled by the current state of the analytical art. Decisions must be made purely on the basis of intuition, judgment, and experience. This is the *zero analysis* position.

At the other extreme, there are those who tend to think that all problems should be tackled in a purely analytical, quantitative fashion, with an eye to essentially "making" the decision. Such a view implies explicit calculations (usually meaning "quantitative") of costs and benefits for all the alternatives under consideration. At times, this may be possible for very narrowly defined, low-level suboptimization problems; but even here the application is questionable.

More generally, in dealing with major problems of choice, if the analyst approaches the analytical task in an inflexible "hard core" frame of mind, he is likely to be in for trouble. For example, he may soon give up in complete frustration; he may wind up with such a simplified model that the resulting calculations are essentially meaningless; or the result might be that his conclusions are presented two years after the critical time of decision and therefore they are useless to the decision-maker.

Contrary to what some of the more enthusiastic advocates of quantitative analysis may assert, it is the authors' view that systems analysis can play a somewhat modest, though very significant, role in the overall decision-making process. In reality, most major long-range planning-decision problems ultimately must be resolved primarily on the basis of intuition and judgment. Therefore, it might be suggested that the main role of systems analysis should be to try to sharpen this intuition and judgment.

In practically no case should it be assumed that the results of the analysis will "make" the decision. The really critical problems are just too difficult, and there are too many intangibles (e.g., political, psychological, and sociological constraints which cannot be fully qualified) which cannot be taken into account in the analytical process.

In most cases, the relevant range of analysis is between the two extremes mentioned above. In such a context, there is a wide scope of analytical effort that can be useful. Furthermore, even when only a relatively incomplete set of quantitative calculations of cost and utility can be made (probably the general situation), much can be done to assist the decision-maker. In sum, the analytical process should be directed toward assisting the decision-maker in such a way that his intuition and judgment are better than they would have been without the results of the analysis. It is conceivable that only a small amount of sharpening of judgment, on occasion, may have a high payoff.

In that rare circumstance where a fairly complete set of calculations of costs and benefits is possible and a resulting conclusion about a preferred alternative is reached, it just may be that the conclusion itself is not the most useful thing to the decision-maker. In the first place, the analysis usually cannot take everything into account — particularly the more nebulous, nonquantitative considerations. These the decision-maker must allow for himself. But more important, most high-level decision-makers are very busy men, with the result that they do not have time to structure a particular problem, think up relevant alternatives (especially the more subtle ones), trace out the key interactions among variables in the problems, and the like. These services the analyst — if he is competent — can and should provide. And it is precisely this sort of contribution that may be most useful to the decision-maker. The fact that the analysis reaches a firm conclusion about a preferred alternative, in many instances, may be of secondary importance.

Applications of
Systems Approaches to
Urban Problems

To date, efforts to apply systems analysis to the general class of problems in the urban system has not produced an all-inclusive deductive hypothesis — one which would identify the existence of a system which could explain and/or suggest interactions relative to problems of an urban magnitude. A number of "systems" approaches have been postulated, however; approaches which in their development go beyond the mere application of systems analysis techniques to isolated urban-problem situations. Without exhausting the present compendium of techniques, models, and processes, some conclusions should be drawn concerning the nature of analysis within certain methodologies to ascertain whether there is a commonality of technique and commonality of inference from qualitative and quantitative data.

W. Steger's model, the "Urban Systems Simulation Flow Chart,"[11] deals with data inputs of a comparative simplistic nature. The use of input-output analyses and allocation models in the process stage requires inputs which can be ascribed a certain value and/or spatial location. These inputs essentially must relate to quantifiable economic and physical variables. The model inputs, controls, and restrictions, however, do not take into account the impinging influences of politics, human behavior, and society in general (value systems, norms, and so forth). Therefore, it must be concluded that Steger's model, at best, offers a partial theory, but it does not provide the basis for a general theory.

The general design process, a generic model frequently applied by planners and urban designers, encounters some fundamental obstacles when applied to problems of an urban magnitude in that it is extremely difficult to model the system or define its objectives in the terms required by this process. Further, there is a necessity within the process to establish constraints to the problem. To complete the modeling of the general design process, it is necessary to test and evaluate the system's performance; yet within a deterministic model, the range of outputs is established by consideration of the inputs and evaluative judgments which follow from judgments implicit in the inputs.[12] The setting of values to the controlled variables, of course, is always open to question, and it is this phase of the general design process that most resembles the transportation planning process, especially insofar as criticisms are concerned.

Swinburne, in his "Theoretical Model of the Architectural Process,"[13] makes the same fundamental error as many of his architectural contemporaries in that he refers to the realms of politics, society, environment, and physical entities in the goal segment of his process, yet fails to identify their roles, influences, interactions, or in general their structure and functions. This criticism holds further in the analysis phase, where Swinburne establishes the human and environmental programs. If he is successful in defining the segments in the goal-definition phase of the process, then he must be able to deal with the "black box," i.e., the processes of synthesis and simulation. As with all approaches outlined thus far, the theoretical model of the architectural process fails to establish the basis for evaluation and judgment of unquantifiables.

The analogies approach has tended to look at the city in two ways: first, as having a certain form or dynamic that is comparable to a physical system; and second, as containing certain processes which are comparable to specific functional models in the natural and social sciences. The biological, ecological, and mechanical analogies are based upon a structural view of the city, while cybernetic, linguistic, and historic analogies compare the functional aspects of the urban system.

Another approach that has been applied to the solution of urban problems is the systems engineering process. However, this process too is open to serious question. For the defined problem area, it is very difficult to identify the relevant subfunctions. Further, the process or problem of developing systems models remains. As with other methodologies, the systems engineering approach falls short in its ability to define the criteria for the problem area under analysis when dealing with problems of urban complexity.

At this point, an apology may be due for the brief presentation of the above methodologies, for in seeking brevity, there is a tendency to overstep the boundaries in which a particular process was designed to be effective. However, the method of analysis in all five approaches is essentially the same; they all follow the basic outline of systems analysis in seeking a "systems" approach to large-scale urban problems.

Applications of "systems" approach to complex urban problems have been essentially deterministic in nature. They have dealt with functional systems and quantifiable data. Although they have been derived from the basic framework of systems analysis, in application they have followed a line of logic which essentially is inductive. Einstein, in his *Method of Theoretical Physics*, maintains that "... there is no inductive method which could lead to fundamental concepts in physics ... in error are those who believe that theory comes inductively from experience."[14]

This discussion is not meant to rule out the application of systems analysis or approaches derived from its conceptual framework to urban problems. It is meant as a cautionary note, however, for such applications are more beneficial and have greater possibility of accuracy on the functional subsystem level.

The implications to be drawn from "the state of the art" should be fairly obvious. It is easier to advocate a systems analysis approach to the problems of urban areas than it is to apply such an approach. The way in which city problems have been handled traditionally — through city planning — is much different from contemporary systems analysis. A great deal of work must be undertaken before systems techniques can be transferred to the field of planning. In fact, it may well be that such outright transfers are not possible; rather it may be necessary and desirable to formulate some hybrid of systems analysis and planning in order to retain the scientific applications of the former and the value orientations of the latter.

2

Systemic Planning:
A Challenge to
the New Generation

While the concepts of systems analysis have had a relatively short history, within the brief span of fifteen to twenty years, these methodological approaches to problem-solving have become almost a legend, acquiring an aura of omniscience. Through mathematical formulation, it is often presumed that the most complex elements of any problem can be organized, in their proper relationship to one another, so that order may appear where chaos existed before.

The "Scientification" of Planning

In view of the great currency enjoyed by the methodologies of systems analysis and other "systems" approaches, in both the natural and the social sciences, it is not surprising that there is a growing self-consciousness among theorists and practitioners alike concerning the need for a more systematic approach to the field of planning. Most planners recognize that the subject matter of their field involves extremely complex problems of ever evolving and rapidly changing urban systems. Those concerned with complex urban systems are aware of the great need for improved methods of research and application that would enable the planner and decision-maker to deal more effectively with these problems. The application of the systems approach has been heralded by many as a more effective means of deriving at least partial solutions to these complex problems. Its attention to *scientia* is part of the growing demand for planners to be consistent and rational in a profession which, in the past, largely has been an art.

In recent years, the planning profession cheerfully has adopted many analytical techniques from other disciplines. For the most part, however, this has been a process of *adoption* without *adaption*. As Richard Snyder has observed in a similar context: " . . . those who venture into other disciplines on foraging expeditions often come back with superficially attractive loot, in some cases exemplified by a shiny new vocabulary ripped from its theoretical context and disciplinary home."[1]

The proliferation of planning studies involving the use of descriptive and predictive models, simulations, game theory, cost-benefit and cost-effectiveness analysis, and other systems methodologies gives evidence of the interest in and eager adoption of these approaches. These studies also stand in mute testimony of the inherent dangers in hurriedly proceeding toward such applications without first developing the philosophical and theoretical bases needed for a systems approach in planning. This is not to suggest that the disciplines of systems analysis, operations research, and other systems approaches should not be brought into the field of comprehensive planning. Undoubtedly, there are mutual benefits to be derived from a careful blending of the concepts and techniques from these related fields.

A great deal of work, however, must be undertaken before any wholesale transfer of systems techniques can be made to the field of comprehensive planning. In fact, it may well be that such outright transfers are neither desirable nor possible. As suggested at the conclusion of the previous chapter, it may be necessary to formulate a hybrid of systems analysis and comprehensive planning in order to retain the scientific applications of the former discipline and the social and human value orientation of the latter.

The Traditional Planning Process

In an effort to explore more fully the nature and character of this hybrid, we can begin by briefly discussing the evolution of the planning process. Of necessity, this discussion must avoid the temptation to dwell upon many interesting and relevant points — points that have been covered in greater detail in other contemporary writings. In the interest of brevity, only the most sketchy outline can be attempted. Current techniques of planning are the result of an evolutionary process which began many years ago. The momentum required to advance to each new stage in this evolution, however, has been derived from developments in the tools of analysis that have taken place, for the most part, outside the planning profession.

Although couched in terms of long range and comprehensiveness, early planning efforts were tied to the simple goal of improving the existing physical environment of the city or region. No systematic procedures for forecasting future requirements or impacts had been developed at this point. Gradually, public decision-makers began to realize that a planning decision could have implications for many years to come, and that the designer should be obligated to give at least some consideration to predicting and providing for future needs. Techniques were available for forecasting aggregate demographic characteristics, and these were utilized in order to predict the aggregate characteristics of future demands.

At this stage in its development, the planning process could be viewed in four simple steps: (1) goal identification; (2) physical analysis; (3) aggregate prediction; and (4) physical design. Because of the weaknesses of analytical techniques, various alternative plans could be compared on only the simplest basis. As a result of this limitation in planning technology, conflicts among alternative proposals most often were resolved in the political arena. Major innovations — since they could not be proved to be good investments — only rarely were approved.

In the middle and late fifties, great strides were made in the technology of analysis and operational simulation. This ability to simulate systems behavior with an acceptable degree of accuracy — combined with improvements in economic analysis, principally in the form of cost-benefit analysis — afforded the planner an opportunity to consider, test, and evaluate a greater range of alternative plans. The widespread availability of high-speed digital computers made the use of these forecasting and testing methods feasible.

Pleased with their newly developed ability to predict and simulate many aspects of future complex urban systems, even though they were unable to simulate the totality of the system, many planners have tended to view the output of their models as the primary basis for evaluation. The techniques of economic analysis permit the selection of that alternative which involves the lowest total cost, or the highest ratio of user benefits to total costs.[2] Minimizing costs has become the most important goal in many quarters. Here again, this emphasis stems from the limitations of planning technology — the inability to quantify more fundamental measures of system effectiveness. The process of identifying goals from the aspirations of individuals, families, and other social and political groups is just beginning to be utilized in the planning process.

Since the real purpose of providing public service is to maintain stability and promote controlled growth of social and economic activities, reliance on simple projections of demand and on cost minimization in the evaluation process has placed the planner in the position of following the trends, rather than undertaking to improve upon these trends where necessary. He is not planning, but projecting, and where his plans might end up — the final goal — is still a relative unknown.[3]

While it often is difficult to achieve agreement on an operational definition of planning, there is a certain amount of consensus on what the process of planning entails, at least in its conceptual form. Reduced to its basic components, the planning process, as shown in Figure 2.1, involves:

A. *INPUT*
   (1) Identification and definition of problems and their interrelationships
   (2) Determination of goals and objectives associated with each problem situation and the problems in totality
   (3) Appraisal of existing policies and procedures designed to achieve goals and objectives
   (4) Formulation of available alternatives to reach agreed upon goals and objectives
B. *CONVERSION*
   (5) Evaluation of alternatives

(a) Identification of by-products and side effects
(b) Determination of approximate benefits and costs associated with each alternative

C. *OUTPUT*

(6) Recommendation of appropriate alternatives
(7) Unstructured feedback and reaction to proposals

Planning involves a continuous study of the urban environment as it is affected by growth and shifts in population, technological developments, changes in economic activities and their distributions, shifts in the preferences and value systems of various classes and social groups, and so forth. It is from this continuous, ongoing activity that problems are identified and defined. Thus, planners must anticipate trends and needs, in advance, in order adequately to prepare to meet these changes in the urban environment.

In a somewhat similar vein, Britton Harris has formulated what he calls "a 7-D description of planning" (see Figure 2.2)[4]. In his diagrammatic presentation, there are five boxes in a vertical line surrounded by a heavy border which comprises the planning process itself. This process is linear but cyclical, and the most important feedbacks are shown in the diagram by dashed lines. Within the planning process, Harris places five D's: Desires (goal formulation), Design (development of alternatives), Deduction (prediction of consequences of plans), Decision (plan selection), and Deeds (plan implementation).

Outside the planning process, enclosed in an overlapping dashed box are two additional D's: Data and Description (theory). These, Harris suggests, " . . . form a part of the community of understanding of the total environment which is accessible to everyone."[5] The distinctive use that the planner makes of information and the theories that underlie his analysis are governed by his particular orientation, which in turn is dependent upon the sequence presented on the vertical axis, i.e., the planning process.

How Planning and Systems Analysis Differ

Despite the striking similarities between the processes involved in planning and systems analysis, as demonstrated above, there are significant differences. The most crucial of these differences are (1) the problem-solving nature of systems analysis; (2) the methods of alternative evaluation; and (3) the extent to which alternatives can be quantified.

Although a "systems" approach can be used as a method of "pure" analysis (as opposed to "applied" analysis), systems analysis is concerned primarily with problem situations. In part, this characteristic stems from its mathematical orientation. If no immediate problem exists, then there is relatively little need for the rigorous procedures of systems analysis.

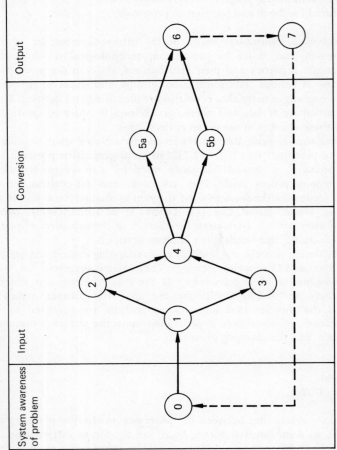

Figure 2-1 The Traditional Planning Process. See text for the definition of component numbers.

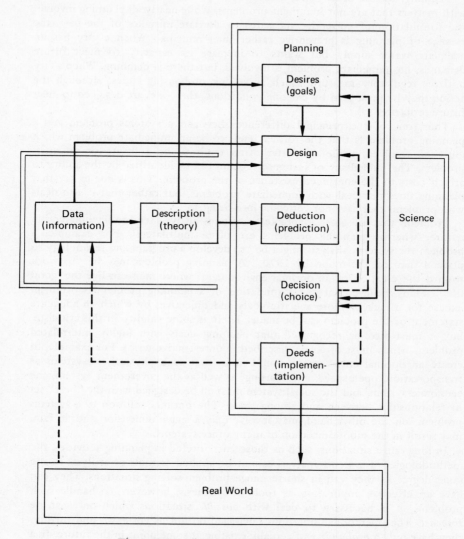

Figure 2-2   The Harris 7—D Planning Model.

Planning, on the other hand, is often anticipatory in its orientation, dealing with matters that are not imminent problems. While nearly all planning involves the formulation of corrective measures to alleviate mistakes of the past, the essence of planning is preventive rather than remedial. When a city has an adequate water supply but wants to increase its capacity to meet future demands, no immediate problem is involved, but there is planning. When a city initiates regulatory measures, such as zoning or housing codes, although the action may be prompted by existing conditions, the codes are designed to meet future problems.

Thus, one of the principal differences between a systems problem and a planning problem is that the former tends to be an immediate problem which must be resolved, while the latter often tends to be a future or potential problem. The immediacy of systems problems can be identified by the ability to attach costs to the continued existence of the problem. This is not to say that planning does not deal with immediate problems, but rather that it also deals with problems that have not yet come into being.

Problems that are most adaptable to systems analysis tend to be unilateral in nature, whereas planning problems are often multilateral. For example, a problem for systems analysis might be "to develop a program and technology to place a man on the moon by 1970." A planning problem may be "to work toward the creation of an optimal environment, where men can live the 'good life.'" Many believe that the formulation of a planning problem is often an excuse for a lack of more specific goals and objectives by which an adequate statement of the problem can be made. There is some validity in this criticism, but it must also be recognized that planning deals with highly interrelated problems which must often be described in unrestrictive terms. For example, to create an optimal environment would mean that such physical subsystems as transportation, open space, and housing, as well as the government system, the economic system, and the social system must all be designed with the "best" set of relationships between and among them. The optimal solution to a systems problem, on the other hand, may involve only a single dimension and, in fact, may result in the suboptimization of many other systems.

In long-range situations, such as those encountered in planning activities, the methodologies of systems analysis cannot be applied as tools of analysis to the same degree as they can in shorter-range problem-solving situations. They can have an effective application as tools of synthesis, however. To handle such problems, it is necessary to deal with *possible* situations which only can be *forecast*. The operational situations envisaged do not as yet exist, and further, they have only a *probability* of actually existing at some point in the future. In a very real sense, it may be said that the systems to be analyzed do not exist but must be "invented." By the same token, the operational laws governing the behavior of these systems may be brought into being by proper manipulation of the operational environment. This means that both the "invented" systems and the operational laws must be conceptualized and analyzed.

These efforts require a *synthesis*. This synthesis must include not only the means already existing which might be gainfully preserved for use in future operations, but also many new means which must be constructed in order to achieve a competitive advantage that does not now exist. These new means must be identified if the synthesis is to be truly creative.

Most aspects of future systems are *probabilistic* in nature. This characteristic necessitates the development and study of alternative future systems. It is important to seek an optimization of each system, but it is also necessary to consider how to optimize the future by comparing the values and objectives associated with an interrelated set of optimized future systems.

There is relatively little difference between the ways in which planners and systems analysts formulate alternatives — perhaps only the detail of the alternatives is different. In both approaches, there are liberal doses of objectivity and subjectivity. There are differences, however, in the way in which these alternatives are evaluated. Systems analysis uses cost-effectiveness as the principal measure of alternatives. Hence, all other things being equal, the alternative which exhibits the greatest effectiveness at the least cost would be considered the optimal solution to the problem. This is not a narrow dollars-and-cents technique of evaluation, for very interesting examples of systems analysis using broad definitions of both costs and effectiveness are available. The salient point is that in order for a cost-effectiveness evaluation to be performed, some measurable expenditure of resources must be made (but not necessarily fiscal resources), and some measurable results must accrue from that expenditure.

Planning often involves a measurement of costs and the anticipated results from the use of resources. By and large, however, the evaluation of alternatives in the planning process does not involve as rigorous examination as cost-effectiveness entails. Planning alternatives may be evaluated only by the logical consistency that is offered, e.g., it is better to have planned communities than unplanned suburban sprawl. Planning alternatives may also be evaluated by population service levels; amount of land available for open space; potential for circulation; or the way an alternative "looks." Thus in planning there is a relatively subjective set of operational criteria which are based upon elicit principles of "good planning."

Attempts have been made to measure the "costs" of planning alternatives, but these attempts rarely have been detailed or exhaustive. Measures of "effectiveness" similarly have been general in nature. For example, the effectiveness of an alternative may be measured by its population-holding capacity; its capacity to accommodate open space and recreational facilities; the amount of freeways included in the alternative; and so forth. While such "effectiveness" has certain associate costs, these seldom are clearly interrelated. Unlike systems analysis, planning involves the expenditure of resources in an attempt to create an environment that "should be." Such a normative environment may not provide the best return on a given investment.

The final difference between systems analysis and planning is that of quantification, using this term in a broad sense. There are many who would argue that systems analysis does not have to be quantitative; but, to date, the results of nonquantitative applications have been far from convincing. There are also those who would argue that anything which can be conceptually described is capable of some kind of measurement. Yet, there has been distressingly little evidence that such concepts as beauty, amenity, happiness, excitement, and so forth can be effectively measured. Efforts to apply artificial indices have been unconvincing and often humorous (consider the Washington bureaucrat who attempted to develop a measurable index unit for the amenity which open space offers to motorists, which he called a "beaut").

In systems analysis, the interrelationships that exist among subsystems within a system must have a proclivity for measurement and quantitative expression. When evaluating alternatives, a systems analyst will use such terms as optimize, minimize, maximize, or hold to a steady state. Such terms reflect the mathematical nature of the tools; to attain any of these conditions, a set of quantified relationships must be at hand. There are, of course, planners who use these terms, but it is with a certain amount of glibness. It is doubtful that we know enough about urban conditions to optimize, maximize, or minimize, or even hold anything in a steady state. When planners use these terms, it is with the maximum of poetic licence.

A great deal of work in planning has been initiated in the lifetime of the new generation of planners, aimed at quantifying relationships that exist in urban systems. Elements of the physical system, such as transportation, have experienced some success in this attempt; some work has been moderately successful in quantifying land-use relationships with population, housing, and transportation variables. With most other components of the urban system, however, there has been very little achievement. In very recent years, there has been some attention given to trying simply to identify what variables can be measured within these subsystems. Even this modest objective has produced only minimal progress. It should come as no surprise, therefore, that the quantification of urban systems is at a very crude stage of development.

The Systemic Planning Process

Systems analysis is concerned with scientific methods, as such, and not with any particular field of science. It is a matter of methodology rather than content. Planning, as an activity, also is basically concerned with a process.[a] For this reason, a systems view of planning should provide a more logical basis for the creation of a proper philosophy and methodology of planning, which, in turn, should lead to far better performance in planning.

Acknowledging the inherent dangers in labeling a conceptual approach before it is fully developed, for the purposes of this discussion, the hybrid of systems analysis and comprehensive planning might be called systemic planning. Such a

[a]As G.F. Chadwick has observed, for too long a time, planning education and planners have been concerned with the *content* of plans. As a result, they have lost sight of planning as a process; their concern has been primarily with the development of a product—a plan.

term conveys the impression that, as planners, we must deal with matters that are system-like in their behavior, and that we are attempting to plan in a systematic fashion.

The systemic planning process, as a combination of the processes of systems analysis and comprehensive planning, may be described in the following manner (see Figure 2.3):

A. INPUT
    (1) Definition and clarification of current and future problems and interrelationships among these problems
    (2) Prediction of future conditions arising from identifiable problems
    (3) Identification of parameters, boundary conditions, or constraints which determine the range of possible solutions to the totality of problems
    (4) Determination of goals and objectives at varying levels
        (a) Maximal and minimal levels
        (b) Optimal levels
        (c) Normative or Utopian levels
    (5) Definition and analysis of subsystems
        (a) Breakdown of the system into its component parts (subsystems), so that subsystem analyses can proceed in parallel
        (b) Identification of particular problems and needs associated with each subsystem

B. CONVERSION
    (6) Formulation of alternatives
    (7) Evaluation of qualitative and quantitative cost-effectiveness of each alternative
    (8) Simulation of alternatives in the projected environment of the urban system in order to test overall performance, as well as to determine possible by-products and spillover effects
    (9) Determination of implementation sequence for each feasible alternative based on the criticality of certain defined subsystem requirements and on the definiteness of subsystem specifications

C. OUTPUT
    (10) Recommendation of (a) minimal; (b) maximal; (c) optimal; and (d) normative alternatives
    (11) Feedback from political and public interests to determine necessary modifications in suggested alternatives
    (12) Selection of alternative course of action and initiation of action programs to bring about the desired conditions
    (13) Development of predictive capacity within the system to identify changing conditions which might necessitate modifications in the selected course of action
    (14) Establishment of a continuous monitoring process to evaluate output feedback

36

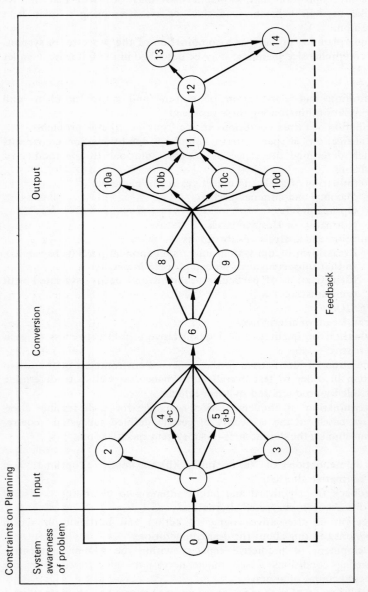

Figure 2-3 The Systemic Planning Process. See text for the definition of component numbers.

The process of systemic planning described above would increase the overall complexity and commitment in understanding the urban system as well as expand the approaches available to improve the system.

The first step in the process would require that the full range of interrelated problems be made discursive. In order to eliminate the near-sightedness of contemporary systems analysis, future or potential problems would also be identified. The most difficult part of this step would be the discussion of interrelationships, since this would have to be undertaken in such a manner as to enable some amount of quantification.

In the second step, a prediction is made largely on the basis of what has been uncovered in the first step. This prediction essentially is an effort to show what is likely to happen if no action is taken. This projection has great utility for the formulation of alternative courses of action as well as for a better understanding of future problems.

The third step involves an identification of the parameters of constraints which set the boundaries for feasible action. In situations where the techniques of operations research can be applied (such as linear programming), boundary conditions can be identified clearly and given numerical values. In many planning problem situations, however, the identification of parameters or constraints may be a difficult undertaking. Nevertheless, this step in the systemic planning process is crucial, for a selected alternative which does not meet the boundary conditions of the problem may have more detrimental effects than one which wrongly defines the problem. It is all but impossible to salvage a recommended course of action that starts with the right premises but stops short of the right conclusions. Furthermore, clear thinking about boundary conditions is needed to recognize when a course of action brought about by a particular analysis must be abandoned. A common cause of failure in action programs lies in the inability to recognize a subsequent shift in the specifications of the problem which makes the prior "right" solution suddenly inappropriate.

Often an alternative is selected in which the specifications to be satisfied are essentially incompatible. In other words, to achieve Goal A through the course of action prescribed by the selected alternative precludes the achievement of Goal B, or at best makes this achievement highly unlikely. This represents a classic case in which the boundary conditions of the problem situation were not fully and clearly identified.

In the fourth step, the various levels of goals and objectives must be determined. The problem with contemporary planning practice is that goals and objectives tend to be a "mixed bag" of varying performance levels. Minimum standards of service, maximum community aspirations, optimal conditions, and utopian goals are all lumped together. If these goals, standards, objectives, aspirations, and so forth could be more rigorously stated so that it would become clear as to the level of generality or specificity attached to them, it would provide a more meaningful basis for alternative evaluation. It should be noted that there may be important differences between the optimal level and the normative or utopian level, because the former tends to operate within the constraints established by the problem definition, while the latter may or may not be affected by the existing constraints.

The sixth step remains largely traditional, because this is an area of objective skill and intuitive "artsmanship." This is as it should be. If standardized techniques were to be developed for the formulation of alternatives (as some authors have suggested would be desirable), there would be little imagination or creativity found in such alternatives. The generation of alternative requires such creativity, as well as a reasonably systematic approach to the description of these alternatives. Such an approach is not only possible, but appears to be within the grasp of many planners at the present time.

The seventh step, involving the evaluation of alternatives, constitutes a major departure from current planning procedures. The cost-effectiveness approach is valuable in that it provides a more practical basis by which choice can be made. However, to overcome the problems of quantification in urban systems, qualitative evaluation techniques must be integrated in this process. Many adequate qualitative evaluation techniques exist in planning. The pertinent need is to integrate them in order that they may be more useful for the evaluation of alternatives. It is also important that quantitative measures be developed, since these measures give a clearer set of evaluation criteria for certain basic components, as well as provide a basis for improving qualitative measures.

A simulation is also needed within an environment that is similar to the urban system. This simulation could take various forms: (1) iconic, e.g., scale models; (2) symbolic, e.g., abstract conveyances of ideas; (3) analog, e.g., representations of ideas using other systems; (4) analytical, e.g., mathematical expressions stored in a computer which generate answers to posed questions. Through a simulation, more can be learned from the various alternatives under evaluation, and some notion of overall performance can be gained. In addition, a simulation of alternatives would produce important leads to determining the possible by-products and side effects that could not be uncovered through more conventional forms of evaluation.

All of the results obtained from the above procedures could be arrayed in a matrix, be it a taxonomic or a value matrix, and certain decisions could be made concerning the fit between alternatives and goal and objective levels. This matching should enable the planner to develop an array of alternatives, ranging from the minimal to the Utopian. In contemporary systems analysis, the alternative that offers an optimal solution is usually chosen, because it represents the "best" that can be achieved within the constraints of the problem. There are many cases, however, where unusual events or conditions make some other alternative more desirable for an urban system. For this reason, more than one recommended alternative should be formulated. The selection of a final alternative for effectuation would be undertaken only after an intensive review effort, involving both public and private decision-makers and a representation of the sentiments of the general public.

3 Systemic Planning for Very Complex Systems: A Proposed Decision-Making System

Operations research and the more generic systems approach have pioneered many important methodological advances in the analysis of very complex systems. Increased understanding has been achieved through the application of these methodologies. A greater cognizance of the interdependencies of complex systems, as well as the laws and operations that govern the behavior of these systems, has evolved in recent years.

It is possible to construct models and simulations which describe these operations and to manipulate variables so as to optimize the objectives desired in the actual operations of complex systems. There are no immutable laws governing the operations of these systems (or, for that matter, no immutable systems). Yet, the "constants" have been consistently fixed and the "laws" have been empirically and intellectually accepted for a sufficient period of time. These are necessary and sufficient conditions to permit the description and subsequent manipulation of operational situations by those concerned with optimizing the operations of such systems for the more immediate future.

Since the "more immediate future" has meant only a few weeks or a few months ahead in time, problems and uncertainties of longer time periods have not been critical. However, operations research and systems analysis have found increasing application in fields of study concerned with situations which will not actually occur until 10 or 20 years in the future (or even longer). It is the explicit function of these fields of study to recommend preparatory action. In order to approach a more optimal system, this action must be initiated between the present time and the more distant future at which time it is anticipated that the situation will actually occur.

The Development of Operations Research as a Scientific Method

Operations research had its origins in the development of operationally usable techniques used in logistic and strategic analyses carried out during World War II, such as those developed by the group of scientists organized by Professor P. M. S. Blackett in 1939 at the University of Manchester. The complexity of modern warfare is so great that new high-powered methodologies have been necessary to provide the raw materials for decision-making. Through the use of a multidiscipline approach, operations research has attempted to provide a basis for comprehensive solutions to these complex problems. Through a group research effort, in which individuals bring to bear upon a given problem their unique experiences and the particular methodologies of their training, a synthesis takes place and new combinations of methodologies emerge to "form fit" the problem. Operations research generates increasing demands for information necessary for problem-solving activities. The complications of communications thus are given greater attention, and this leads to increased activity in investigation of information problems.

The emergence of operations research as a scientific approach to complex problem-solving situations can be traced in the development of its methods, concepts, and techniques. Operations research is concerned with scientific methods as such and not with the field of any specific discipline. On the other hand, operations research is neither a method nor a technique. Rather it must be defined by a combination of the phenomena studied, the methods applied, and the techniques used in carrying out the problem analysis. As Russell Ackoff has observed: "Though it is true that all sciences have certain aspects of method and technique in common, it is also true that each one has unique methodological characteristics which reflect the uniqueness of the subject matter which it investigates. To the extent that a science develops methods and techniques well adapted to its special subject matter, to a great extent that science itself develops.[1]

The Phases of an Operations Research Project

During the early stages of its development — until the mid-fifties — it was difficult to get an operations researcher to describe a procedure for conducting an operations research project. A great variety of methods were being tried; some of these techniques had their origins in much earlier formulations, the application of which was not made possible until the advent of the high-speed computer. At that time, each practitioner's version of the operations research method would differ in some respects.

To a large extent, this still is true today. However, as more books are written on the subject of operations research and as more definitions of its methods are recorded, a good deal of commonality can be identified. Figure 3.1 is an attempt to summarize these common steps or phases of an operations research project. Various writers have identified fewer or greater numbers of phases depending on how they have combined or broken down the various steps of the process, but

42

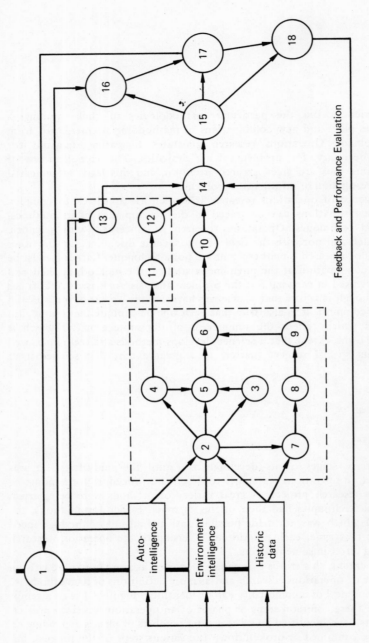

Figure 3-1   Schematic Diagram of the Phases of an Operations Research Project.

we have found that there are essentially five major phases to an operations research project:

I.   Problem Identification (step 1 in the diagram)
II. Formulation of the Client's Problem (steps 2 through 10)
III. Formulation of the Research Problem (steps 11, 12, and 13)
IV. Construction and Testing of a Model (steps 14 through 17 in the diagram) and
V.   Solution Implementation and Performance Evaluation (step 18 plus the feedback cycle).

It is not implied that the steps enumerated in the diagram ever are conducted in this order, or that one step must be completed before another can begin. In many projects, for example, the complete formulation of the client's problem or the research problem (or both) may not be accomplished until the project itself is virtually completed. There usually is a continuous interplay among these steps during the research; that is, there usually is considerable recycling of the results of each step through the preceding steps.

Phase I —
Problem Identification

In order for any organization to survive in the complex environment of modern-day society it is necessary for various "screening devices." These screening devices are designed to alert the organization to the presence of a problem or set of problems. Frequently, when an organization's screening devices are not highly developed or sensitive to incremental changes in the environment, problems may reach crisis proportions before they are detected. However, the more successful organizations have developed highly sensitive devices which act as an early-warning system, identifying the approach of a problem to some threshold of tolerance, and thus alerting the organization to take action before the problem reaches a more critical stage.

Three basic "data files" lie at the foundation of an effective screening process. One of these is an "environmental intelligence system" which should be designed to keep the organization appraised of conditions apparent in the broader environment within which it operates (i.e., the marketplace, client groups, constituencies, and so forth). Such information may come from regular reporting sources or through special studies; it may be consciously sought, or it may reach the organization through less formal channels.

A second element is the "auto-intelligence system," which tells key decision-makers about the internal workings of the organization, its performance output, level of worker morale and efficiency, and so forth. Here again, this system may be formally structured, or it may rely primarily on informal mechanisms such as the "grapevine," "gripe sessions," and the infamous "suggestion box."

The final element is the "historic data file." This is the memory bank of the organization — the records of past performance; information pertaining to past problem situations and the steps taken in seeking solutions; fiscal accounts; and the myriad of other records that fill the files of a modern organization, whether in the private or in the public sector. These data can prove invaluable to an organization, providing that they are organized and maintained in such a way as to be readily accessible and useable for "testing" the acceptability of the current situations confronting the organization.

Phase II —
Formulation of the
Client's Problem

It is useful to distinguish between the client's (decision-maker's) problem and the research problem, in framing an operations research project, even though they are closely related. The latter is a transformation of the former, primarily involving the definition of a scientific basis for selecting a course of action as a "solution."[2]

The client's problem seldom is given to the operations research team. Rather, it is extracted by the team from reported symptoms and the analysis of the system involved. Formulation of the client's problem generally requires the following steps, the numbers corresponding to those in the diagram:

2. Identification of the principal participants in the decision-making process, i.e., those in control of the operations under study and analysis of their decision-making procedures.
3. Determination of constraints of the problem, i.e., the boundary conditions within which a solution must be found.
4. Determination of goals to be achieved. These become a central input into the formulation of the research problem.
5. Determination of the decision-maker's objectives. These fall into two classes: those to be obtained and those to be retained. The former relate to the goals to be achieved; the latter provide inputs as to the restrictions on the problem.
6. Analysis of processes or operations involved, i.e., the processes which fall within the direct control of the organization and which may be modified in order to reach a problem solution.
7. Identification of other participants: those who carry out decisions outside the organization and those who are affected by them, including "competition" or "adversaries."
8. Determination of objectives of other participants which can affect responses to decisions in the area under study.
9. Determination of the alternative courses of action available to other participants, action which can affect the outcome in the area under study.

10. Determination of alternative courses of action available to the client or decision-makers.

It should be apparent from this listing of steps that in the process of formulating the client's problem, the operations research team must analyze the system under control and the organization and procedures by which it is controlled. Consequently, operations research increasingly has come to realize that the types of systems under study involve organized human behavior as well as physical objects and their behavior. More and more, specialists in operations research are turning their attention to the work of others in the area of organizational behavior and have begun work in this area themselves.

Phase III —
Formulation of the
Research Problem

In the most general terms, the objective of the operations research team is to determine which alternative course of action is *most effective* (optimum) relative to the client's set of pertinent objectives. Consequently, in formulating the research problem, the measures of effectiveness to be used and the meaning of "most effective" must be defined. The steps involved may be enumerated as follows:

11. Definition of the measure of efficiency to be used relative to each objective to be obtained (goals).
12. Selection of a common measure (standard) of efficiency and transformation of the measures obtained into the common measure by either (a) finding an objective transformation (e.g., finding the dollar value of the factors to be optimized and the associate constraints); or (b) finding a subjective transformation (e.g., determining the relative importance or utility of the objectives to the decision-maker — client).
13. Definition of "most effective" — this, in effect, defines a "best" or "optimum" solution.

In the early stages of the development of operations research methodology, the principal decision objectives were either the maximization of expected return or the minimization of maximum loss. In recent years, however, studies conducted in the field of decision theory have pointed up the need to develop other decision objectives, which in many practical situations must be used as the criteria of optimality and which are more appropriate than the two mainstays of operations research.

Phase IV —
Construction and
Testing of a Model

Operations research has reached a point in its development at which an OR model can be defined as a mathematical representation of the system under study. This representation takes the form

$$U = f (x_i , y_i),$$

where

U = the utility objective to be attained;

x_i = the variables of the system that are subject to control; and

y_i = the variables that are not subject to control.

The restrictions on values of the variables generally are expressed in a supplementary set of equations and inequations.

During the historic development of operations research methods, certain processes or systems have been encountered repeatedly. The structure of these recurrent processes has been abstracted and analyzed, with the result that seven principal prototype OR models have been formulated: (a) the inventory model; (b) the allocation model; (c) the waiting-line or queuing model; (d) the routing model; (e) the replacement or renewal model; (f) the information-collection model; and (g) the competitive or game-theory model. Although these prototype models seldom can be applied in a specific situation without adjustment, they do provide a valuable point of departure. Recognition of recurrent processes also has led to abstraction and definition of these processes and the problems emerging from them. These are the tools with which operations research has filled its kit.

Problems confronted in reality seldom involve only one of the recurrent processes, however. Therefore, the usual procedure for handling combined processes consists of "solving" them in sequence. Even with successive cyclic adjustments, however, many problems fail to reach a true optimum. Consequently, there is an ever increasing need to combine the abstracted processes and to construct models involving the interaction of several of the recurrent processes.

The next step in the model construction phase (step 15) involves the solution of the selected model (or combination of models) so as to find the values of the "control variables" that maximize the system's effectiveness. This may involve the use of operational experiments and operational gaming. Under certain circumstances, it may be possible to derive a "dual solution" to the model, which provides valuable information as to the effect on the decision objective if certain of the problem constraints are relaxed. For example, if personnel resources provide a problem constraint, the dual solution may suggest the possible increase in the system's effectiveness if additional or improved personnel resources are made available.

It must be recognized that a model is never more than a partial representation of reality. Despite its incompleteness, it is a good model if it can predict the effects of changes in the system on the system's overall effectiveness with acceptable accuracy. Therefore, the model and its solution must be tested (step 16) to determine its ability to predict changes in the system. Such tests may be retrospective, using data from the intelligence system, or may be prospective, usually undertaken on a small-scale or trial-run basis.

A solution derived from an OR model remains a solution only as long as the uncontrolled variables retain their values (i.e., remain constants). The solution goes "out of control" when the value of one or more of these variables has changed significantly. The significance of the change depends on the amount by which the solution is made to deviate from the true optimum under changed conditions as well as the cost of changing the solution in operation.

For this reason, the final step (17) in the model phase of an operations research project involves the development of controls for a given solution by (a) defining a significant change for each variable and relationship which appears in the model; (b) establishing a procedure for detecting the occurrence of such significant changes, thereby providing modifications in the screening device; and (c) specifying how the solution should be modified if such changes occur.[3] This step is vital to the continuing operations of the organization, for without such guidelines and controls, a course of action may continue to be pursued long after it has ceased to be an appropriate solution to a problem.

Phase V —
Solution Implementation and
Performance Evaluation

Proper implementation of a problem solution perhaps still is more of an art than a science. However, one of the more significant contributions of operations research methodologies is the widening recognition of the need to develop *decision-rules* — guidelines which can be turned over to the client and carried out by operating personnel. As Ackoff has observed: "In many cases this means the team must either translate elegant solutions into approximations that are easy to use or to sidestep the elegance and move directly to quick-and-dirty solutions. Operations research is learning that an approximation that is used may be a great deal better than an exact solution that is not."[4]

The development of decision-rules will permit the client more fully to appraise the effectiveness of his organization's performance over time and therefore will sharpen its system's problem-screening devices. A solution must be stated in terms that are understandable to those who will carry through the recommended action programs. In the process of making this translation, various aspects of the situation that had not been taken into account may be found, requiring a recycling of the project or adjustments in the proposed solution.

Operations Research
Procedures in
Systemic Planning

In earlier times, technical innovation was achieved largely on an unorganized, accidental basis and usually without any concerted basic research. This was as true with respect to the innovation and design of complex systems as it was for the invention of particular consumer or other material items. It was a sort of natural growth, occurring at a slow, but steady, rate over long periods of time. Since the Industrial Revolution, however, there has been an increasing concern with innovation. Especially since World War II, full appreciation of the importance of systems innovation, combined with the great increase in fundamental knowledge, have led to our present rate of change and innovation — from the lowest level of consumer products to major systems themselves.

Technical innovation has served as the catalyst of systems growth and development. The amount of catalysis has become so great, however, that there is need for concern about the general reaction resulting from rapid growth and cognitive overcrowding. An important step taken by operations research in World War II was the recognition that operations of the future could be treated as a formal research problem and, therefore, could be studied through the applications of scientific methods. This advance, in turn, has led to a more orderly and systematic approach to innovation. Through research and development activities, innovation can now be directed toward meeting specific needs and solving specific problems.

A Proposed Decision-Making System

What has been outlined to this point in procedural terms obviously will be extremely difficult to achieve in application to complex urban systems. There are many inputs which first must be developed, as well as new techniques to enable a better quantification of the components of large complex systems. Another important methodological development is in the area of prediction. It is almost platitudinous to observe that planners project past trends into the future. But it must be recognized that there is often little reason to believe that these trends should or could continue.

The technical forecast provides the first and fundamental part of a rational basis for future planning. The forecast for any particular time period is based on existing trends in their relation to the values and objectives chosen. It makes a prognosis of situations that may arise in a future period if trends continue. It may be argued that with skill and experience, such formal forecasts can be made with sufficient certainty to provide a far better basis for rational action than the present informal and almost random decision-making system.

Three specific areas of information provide the data inputs for the formulation of a technical forecast: (1) auto-intelligence, which provides information about the particular system under study and the component elements of that system; (2) environmental intelligence, which provides information about the broader environment — the "out there" — of which the particular system is a part; and (3) historical data, which brings together and analyzes the lessons of history. From intelligence studies in these three areas, it is possible to develop a probabilistic forecast (see Figure 3.2). On these foundations, the forecast represents a weighed and balanced analysis rather than an intuitive impression of current trends and their possible effect on developments in the future.

In view of the predictions, the focus of the search is to determine possible new technical, tactical, and strategic courses of action that will enhance the overall performance of the system. Potential possibilities lie in the area of problem-solving innovations. There is no lack of general ideas for such solutions. The practical difficulty is in identifying and gaining support for proposals that will provide the most significant advances. By applying the techniques of operations research and systems analysis, it is possible to identify and compare more completely the most promising alternatives. Wise and timely decisions on the acceptability of proposed innovations are of the utmost importance.

The forecast outlines the probable happenings in the continuance of hypothetical futures. Using operations research and systems analysis techniques, the possible directions to be taken can be identified in an attempt to suggest ways in which the real world can be manipulated to the competitive advantages of the system. Proposed innovations are directed toward providing specific ways and means of achieving successful manipulation.

A group of highly professional, hard-thinking, imaginative planners must be organized to screen ideas and proposals provided from the forecast-operations research chain and to match these with the resources available to the system, as well as the overall goals and objectives of the system now and in the foreseeable future. It should be the job of this planning task force to select specific and feasible plans to meet identified objectives, taking into account many intangibles not susceptible to research at this stage of our knowledge, and to translate these into recommendations for action programs.

The basic problem of decision-makers today, whether in the public or private sectors, is to achieve a balance in the programs and choices made so as to ensure a *systems readiness* in the short-, mid-, and long-range futures. This requires a posture of sufficient flexibility to meet a wide range of possible competitive actions.

The decision-maker requires all the assistance possible from advanced planning and problem-solving procedures that are now available. To date,

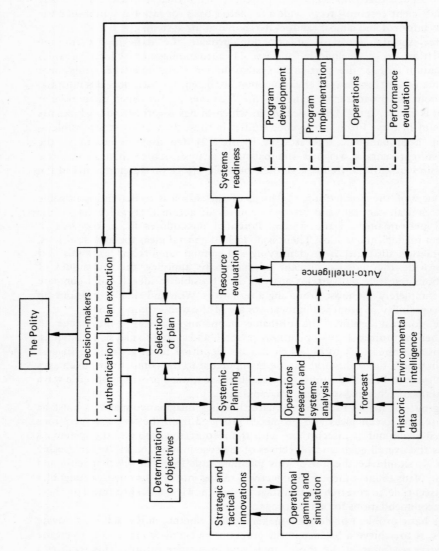

Figure 3-2 A Proposed Decision-Making System.

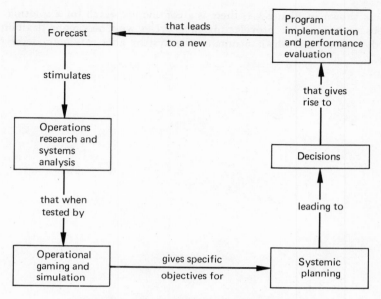

Figure 3-3   The Decision-Making Cycle.

however, too many decision-makers rely on intuitive methods that were sufficient in the past when the problems were comprehensible to a single human mind or a small board of advisers. They have not yet come to recognize that this approach is outmoded in truly complex situations and that the utilization of the available tools of analysis and synthesis must be combined with intuition developed through experience. It should be evident from this description of responsibilities that this planning task force must include more than mere planning technicians. Implicit in this concept is the notion that planning is a principal responsibility of high-level administrative positions. Their participation in this task force approach is vital to the success of the systemic planning process. By the same token, a rapport and level of confidence must be developed whereby the decision-makers can accept the results of the analysis with the assurance that they are valid without having to question the analysis in detail.

The executive should have the benefits of all the sophisticated management and planning techniques when individual plans and sets of objectives covering proposed strategies, tactics, and action programs are submitted to him. The executive, then, has the responsibility for the final decision that determines whether a proposal is to be implemented. This implementation may require further program development and specification before action programs can be put into operation. Finally, some mechanism of performance evaluation must be built into these action programs to provide further inputs into the auto-intelligence system for subsequent problem situations.

Thus, as shown in Figure 3.3, there is a continuous search for a solution, a continuous process which provides planning cycles with maximum flexibility and at the same time which maintains the system at a maximum level of readiness.

4

An Actions Program Model for Systemic Planning

In recent years, there has been considerable discussion as to the possible use of "models" in the planning process. Unfortunately, the term "model" has so many connotations, both to the layman and to the professional planner, that much of this discussion has been thwarted by semantic difficulties. To the design planner, the term *model* may mean a three-dimensional, scale representation of a site plan for a specific area. To the traffic planner, a model may represent a probable distribution of traffic over some future road system. To an economic planner, a model may mean a set of mathematical formulas which permits the analysis and/or prediction of certain events in specific sectors of the economy. Simulation models have been constructed to test, in the "laboratory," certain proposals and recommendations for policy changes before these changes are introduced into the real world. Such models simulate, as close as possible to reality, the sequence of events likely to occur, given some innovation or change in the current direction of observable trends.

While all of these "models" have quite different constructs and applications, they have one thing in common. They represent an attempt to isolate for analysis certain elements from a real situation and to portray these elements in such a way as to make their interrelations more comprehensible. In short, all models are tools for gaining a better understanding of complex situations and for predicting the possible outcomes when certain elements of the situation are altered.

The Cybernetics Model

Models can also serve as useful tools for the communication of complex ideas. Since model-building involves a conscious extraction of selected elements from a real situation, it provides a more exacting focus through which the relationships among these elements can be communicated. The advent and development of high-speed electronic computers for the storage, analysis, and transmission of information has provided a phenomenal extension of man's communication capacity. However, it has also given rise to the need for theoretical constructs to permit a fuller use of this capacity. Thus, in recent years, a number of models have been formulated to provide a clearer understanding and communication of complex concepts.

One such model is the so-called *general cybernetics model.* The term *cybernetics* is derived from the Greek *kybernētikē,* which means, literally, the art of steersmanship. The word occurs fairly often in the writings of Plato, both in its generic sense and in the metaphorical sense of the art of guiding men in society, i.e., the art of government. From this root were derived such Latin words as *gubernaculum,* a helm, and *gubernator,* a helmsman. The French word *gouvernail,* a rudder, derived from *gubernaculum,* retains the nautical meaning. But the majority of the derivations both in French and in English carry a political sense — govern, governor, government, and so on. In 1834, Ampère, in writing his *Essay on the Philosophy of Sciences,* in which he attempted to classify the whole of human knowledge, felt the need for a term to describe the study of government. He chose to appeal directly to Greek, and translated the word *kybernētikē* into the French *cybernetique.* It was not until 1947, however, with the publication of Norbert Wiener's book, *Cybernetics: Or Control and Communication in the Animal and Machine,* that the term was reintroduced into the scientific vocabulary.

As Wiener's subtitle suggests, modern-day cybernetics is concerned with the study of control and communication. Its purpose is to develop a language and technique that will not only attack the general problems of control and communication, but will also find "...the proper repertory of ideas and techniques to classify their particular manifestations..."[1]

The general cybernetics model is built on the assumption that any system can be viewed as consisting of a conversion process by which certain inputs are transposed or converted into outputs. As the term "system" is used in this connection, it may be any definable combination or aggregation of related elements in the real world, united by some form of regular interaction or interdependence.

The Political System as a Cybernetic Model

We often use the term "political system"; but is a political system analogous to the system described by the general cybernetics model? Many political scientists are beginning to accept this analogy as a useful tool for study and analysis. David A. Easton, who has advanced much of the thinking in this area, defines a political system as "those interactions through which values are authoritatively allocated for a society; this is what distinguishes a political system from other systems that may be interpreted as lying in its environment. This environment itself may be divided into two parts, the intra-societal and the extra-societal. The first consists of those systems in the same society as the political system but excluded from the latter by our definition of the nature of political interactions."[2]

The inputs of such a system, Easton suggests, include any event external to the system that alters, modifies, or affects the system in any possible way. Recognizing that virtually every event and condition has some significance for the operations of a political system, such a broad definition of inputs does not help to organize and simplify reality. Therefore, Easton proposes to focus on two major environmental influences as inputs, which he identifies as the *demands* generated by the public and the *supports* which provide stability to the system. In addition, there are demands which are generated from within the system itself, called *withinputs* by Easton, which are usually implicitly related to certain public demands.

The *conversion mechanism* in a political system consists of the decisions and programs of implementation developed by lawmakers and administrators to meet the demands of the public and to maintain its supports. The *outputs* of a political system are thus defined as the decisions and actions of public authorities which result as a consequence of inputs passing through the conversion mechanism. The significance of these outputs is not only that they help to influence events in the broader society of which the political system is a part, but in so doing, they also contribute to a determination of each succeeding round of inputs into the system.[3] Thus, Easton has incorporated the concept of feedback into his conceptualization of the political system.

When applied to the governmental system, the concept of feedback is often manifested in terms of public opinion or public reaction to new laws or programs. These reactions provide the decision-makers, the officials of government, with information as to the effectiveness of these laws and programs. Thus the feedback dimension of the general cybernetics model provides a check by which the adequacy of the conversion mechanism can be judged. If the system does not function properly within the environment, or if the feedback dimension is unfavorable or nonsupportive of the output, it is unlikely that the system will endure or remain stable without modifications being made. Figure 4.1 provides a schematic diagram of the political system in cybernetics model terms.

The Application of the Cybernetics Model to Systemic Planning

The action programs that must be derived in order to carry out the systemic planning process in government can also be examined via the conceptual approach of the cybernetics model. Essentially, the conversion mechanism is the governmental process, and the initial source of inputs is the systemic planning process, in its broadest definition. Through the systemic planning process, demands are identified, goals and objectives are formulated, and planning alternatives or programs are devised and tested. These inputs are then converted by the governmental process into outputs, i.e., action programs. These action

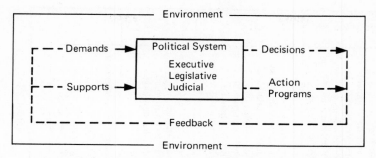

Figure 4-1   The General Political System (after Easton).

programs are essentially public in nature, with related programs in the private sector (i.e., private enterprise, interest groups, certain quasipublic bodies, and certain citizens who do not necessarily represent the general realm of public demands). Once these programs are initiated, the element of feedback provides a means of assessing their effectiveness and thereby making necessary revisions and modifications.

For the purposes of this discussion the systemic planning process can be thought of as focusing on four basic elements: (1) urbanization factors; (2) socioeconomic factors; (3) resource factors; and (4) administrative and organizational factors. Associated with each of these basic elements is a series of planning objectives. While these elements are interrelated in the sense of planning, it is possible to discuss them individually. Associated with each of the objectives of the systemic planning process is a range of derived public and private action programs. These programs are the means by which the objectives are achieved. In the following discussion, the objectives and their related action programs are presented diagrammatically in Figure 4.2 in order to portray the broad range of interrelations among these factors.

Urban Development Objectives

There are essentially five objectives which can be associated with the urbanization element of many plans: (1) to encourage the orderly development of existing urban areas; (2) to provide adequate transportation facilities and channels; (3) to provide adequate open space for the development of the area; (4) to provide a full range of public and private facilities and services for development; and (5) to guide rural development and to define the role of rural service centers.

Urban development is the product of a myriad of individual decisions in both the private and public sectors. Its complexity defies simple cause-and-effect relationships. The decision of a major industrialist to locate a new plant in a given location produces waves of related decisions which lead to the develop-

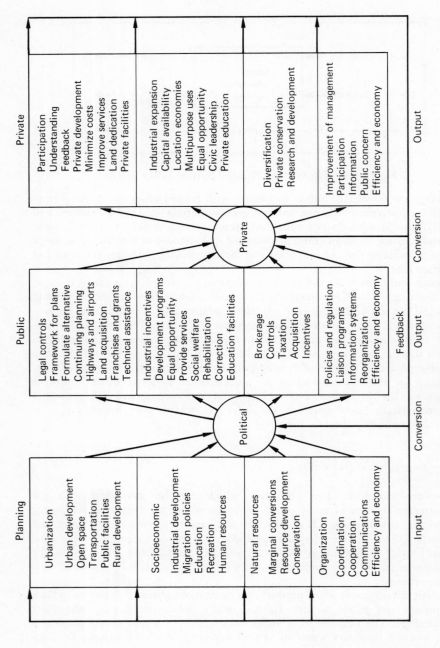

Figure 4-2 An Action Programs Model.

ment of new housing, new commercial facilities, and new public demands for facilities and services. By the same token, a public decision, such as the selection of an alignment for a new highway, has its repercussions in both the public and private sectors.

While the total flow of these decisions cannot be fully predicted, certain regulatory devices can be initiated to help guide these decisions along those lines deemed most beneficial to the public at large. These devices, initiated in the interest of public health, safety, and general welfare, include such controls as zoning, building codes, housing codes, health and safety codes, subdivision regulations, and the official map as well as the more general synoptic device of the comprehensive plan. All of these must be based upon a general understanding of public policy objectives, which in turn should be based upon the examination and testing of relevant alternatives to development. The systemic planning process, itself, is a continuous one which does not terminate with the selection of an alternative.

The private sector plays a vital role in these public programs in three ways. It provides assistance and participation in the systemic planning process at all stages. The private sector must also understand the plans and policies that have been formulated and the necessary devices that have been initiated for carrying out these policies. And finally, the private sector must provide the necessary feedback to provide a basis for determining the adequacy of public policy and to give inferences as to the feasibility of effectuation. Feedback also can serve as a predictor of plan implementation.

The objective of providing adequate open space is accomplished through public programs of acquisition and through the use of controls, both legal and regulatory. The private role is clear for several types of open space. One of the most undervalued roles for the private sector in this area is that of land dedication (gift, donation, etc.), or private development of open space. There was a time when this was perhaps the most important source of open-space lands. Further, there is no reason why the private sectors could not own and operate open-space areas, although it would probably be combined with some commercial recreational activities. As to the transportation objectives, the primary role of government is the provision of highways and airports, although there may be a larger future role for other types of transportation, i.e., mass transit. The provision of highways and airports can be of value, however, only if a comprehensive plan is used as the framework. There is also a complementary role for the private sectors. Since the primary locational objective is to minimize transportation costs of goods and services, proper industrial and commercial location could aid in the minimization of overall highway costs. Similarly, the private sectors must provide the necessary facilities that are not presently within the realm of government, i.e., airlines, trains, and so forth.

In order to obtain adequate facilities and services as an objective of the systemic planning process, the public-action programs would be concerned with the provision of technical assistance to public and private sectors, as well as such duties as issuing franchises, making capital grants, and establishing policies concerning the scope and quality of facilities and services. This is the traditional role of government, especially with regard to public utilities, although there are many signs that this role must be redefined in order to achieve even minimal levels of quality. The latter point is especially seen in the problematic areas of water and sewage treatment.

For all facilities and services, the private role would be concerned with the self-regulation to provide adequate services without defaulting to public regulation. The private sector also must perform a basic innovative role. For example, in a new residential subdivision, if the private sector would provide adequate sewerage systems and adequate water supply and treatment that precludes septic tanks and wells by definition, there would be but a minimal public role, assuming that the development is within the framework established by planning. When these facilities and services are not adequately provided, the public role becomes maximized because of the failure or apathy of the private sector.

While this element of the model is concerned with urban development, it is to be noted that rural development plays an important and complementary role. There are a number of rural centers which are proposed for development in order to service the agricultural sectors of the economy. Thus, there is a specialized role for rural centers, but this does not warrant plans for major industrial expansion. The more logical functions of these rural centers would be to improve upon agricultural service potentials. One approach could be through redevelopment of some centers, which could be interpreted in a broad sense. The public role could be concerned with the formulation of rural redevelopment programs as a counterpart of the urban renewal programs. The bulk of this redevelopment effort, however, should be left to the private sector, which would conceivably act in accordance with market demands. This might obviate the redevelopment of some rural centers which do not play a significant role in servicing surrounding agricultural areas.

Socioeconomic Objectives

The second element of the systemic plan is concerned with the socioeconomic aspects of planning. Specifically, this element can be related to five objectives: (1) to form an industrial-based economy; (2) to provide for an orderly outmigration of marginal agricultural areas; (3) to provide a full range of educational opportunities; (4) to provide adequate recreational facilities for leisure time enjoyment; and (5) to fully develop the human resources. These objectives are directly related to the perspective of an urban-centered pattern of development and provide for an orderly conversion of marginal nonurban areas to types of land uses that would be consistent with urban needs.

In order to strengthen the industrial base, public programs should be concerned with establishing a stable group of dominant industries that would not be subject to cyclical shifts in the long run. This would necessitate, however, a vital role for the private sector in the actual physical expansion of industries, as well as the provision of adequate industrial financing. Both of these aspects tend to be cyclical, so that it may be necessary for some public countercyclical programs, in the Keynesian dimension, to alleviate hardships and instability. Nevertheless, the predominant role would still be undertaken by the private sectors as aided by public policies and programs. Further, in an aggregate sense, it is clear that national countercyclical policies would predominate. The effective application of these policies would necessitate certain kinds of intergovernmental activities.

In addition to the expansion of the certain sectors of the industrial base, it would also be necessary to attract new industries. At the same time, it would be necessary to convert marginal agricultural areas to other types of uses, which would explicitly call for a policy of selected outmigration. In order to attract new industries, the industrial development programs would have to be expanded, within the guidelines of the systemic planning program, and certain kinds of incentives offered. This could be complemented by the private sector in which programs could be formulated to influence the location of industries which are "linked" to those already existing. This type of program is currently being pursued in many areas. These programs are all related to general public objectives designed to encourage job expansion and to provide employment opportunities to persons who are migrating from marginal agricultural areas.

Also interrelated would be a program of vocational training to provide the skills and knowledge that are requisite in an industrial economy. This could be accomplished through a network of vocational training centers in the public sphere, as well as private vocational and technical institutes. Funds for scholarships and other costs of education would come from both the public and private spheres. Further, the private sphere could also formulate programs of on-the-job training to facilitate the acquisition of skills.

Implicit in an industrial economy is a distinct need for higher education. This is clearly the trend in recent years, and it can be expected that public education will someday go beyond high school, as is already being discussed. This would mean that public programs for financing higher education, as well as for providing educational facilities and services, would have to be improved and enlarged. The leadership basis of these programs would enable the inputs to be geared to an industrial entrepreneurial economy. The private sphere could fulfill a role in higher education by developing private colleges and universities as well as providing funds for scholarships to all colleges and universities at the undergraduate and graduate levels.

Recreational outlets for leisure-time activities are important in an industrial economy, and the adequate provision of such facilities is as important as any other program formulated. Public programs should be concerned with the provision of technical assistance, acquisition of land and facilities, and the development of recreational facilities. The private sphere could also be active in the provision of recreational facilities through multipurpose uses of land, especially in those open areas that are privately owned. This could include a full range of recreational activities. At the same time, the private sphere could develop types of recreational facilities that are not generally undertaken by public actions. These types of activities would include such activities as skiing, private hunting and fishing, certain types of camping, and developing resort areas.

Finally, but perhaps overriding all of the above socioeconomic elements, is the development and maximization of human resources. This is the "inner environment," or the humanistic elements of a political system. It is clear that most of the public programs in this area are still in an experimental stage, and much research and development is still needed. Nevertheless, there is a full range of social welfare programs which are inherent in the maximization of this resource. In addition, the need for certain correctional and rehabilitation institutions must be met through concerted public action. It would not be possible to maximize human resources without an explicit role for the private sphere, where most of this resource is utilized. The private sphere must provide action programs that would lead to equal opportunities in employment and advancement, as well as mobility among the various social strata. Further, it would appear that the leadership for the programs must come from both public and private individuals, with little differentiation or cleavage among duties and responsibilities. More than any other element, the maximization of human resources is truly a public-private undertaking. To attempt to have either sphere provide a disproportionate amount of leadership would be inherently self-defeating.

Natural Resource Objectives

The resources element of the systemic planning program has had a long history of importance. It may still be valid to say that the natural resources exhibit the highest correlation between urban and industrial development. Within the resources element, there are three objectives: (1) to convert marginal lands into conservation and resource development areas; (2) to protect agricultural areas with high productivity and prime soils; and (3) to protect and conserve the natural resources of the state. Again, it can be seen that the objectives of the resources element cannot be achieved in isolation from the other elements. If an urban-centered industrial economy is to be developed, certain kinds of programs are necessary to fulfill the role and functions that natural resources can take.

In order to convert marginal lands, especially agricultural and forest, into more useful activities, public programs of an intergovernmental character should be developed. A clear need has been expressed elsewhere for a state brokerage role in this conversion process. Similarly, legal powers, especially the police power of zoning, can be called upon to facilitate conversion. Also, certain types of taxation policies could facilitate conversions, but primarily these policies can be used to curb speculation in these areas. The private sphere could complement these programs through diversification activities aimed at more fully utilizing existing resources, as well as seeking new markets and products. Similarly, it can be shown that there are agricultural areas which should be conserved for this purpose. In many cases, these areas are already under competitive pressures for development. Public programs of zoning and taxation, as well as management, acquisition, and incentives, could be called upon to aid in this conservation. In the private sphere, diversification and private resource conservation programs could be brought to bear at a more significant degree than is presently seen.

In a general sense, the protection of resources is a vital component of the systemic planning program. This resource protection would necessitate management, acquisition, and incentives in the public sphere. On the same objective, the private sphere could be active in research and development, as well as in private conservation. It is unfortunate that in the past conservation and protection of resources have been considered as solely public programs. There is clearly a private role that must be fulfilled. Many examples of this role are already present. It is becoming clear to many private groups and industries that the benefits of resource protection by far outweigh the costs involved. This has been made possible through advanced entrepreneurial calculations as to what constitutes costs and profits in the resource-associated industries. Thus, it would seem that a joint public-private program more fully to utilize existing resources and conserve scarce resources is desirable.

Objectives Related to
Administration and Organization

The last element of the systemic planning input side of the model is concerned with administration and organization. There are many who would argue that this is a key element in that no planning program can be useful without an organizational framework and proper administration. There are essentially four objectives of this element: (1) to coordinate development; (2) to formulate methods of cooperation; (3) to provide for adequate communication networks; and (4) to maximize efficiency and economy in administration. As can be noted, this area of the planning program exhibits both short-range and long-range aspects. This is the critical area for action by various public and private agencies.

The primary objective of this element is to coordinate future development. This goal can be approached through the formulation of policy guidelines and regulations, all within the framework of the plan. Yet, it is most important to develop a system of liaison to ensure that cognizance is taken of the many aspects of the systemic planning process. In the private sphere, there is a need for private assistance and participation in these programs. The most direct way to accomplish interagency cooperation is through a strong administrative liaison.

It is frequently found that underlying all administrative and organizational problems is the lack of communication. The communication networks in planning are ill defined and often quite problematic. While liaison programs would serve to alleviate these problems somewhat, it is also necessary to develop an intelligence system so that the technical aspects of the communication networks are adequately maintained. When this is achieved, the liaison will be based upon adequate informational foundations. Again, private groups should be concerned participants in this development. It may also be desirable to establish input-output stations in selected private sources so that vital information for planning can be codified, stored, and retrieved.

The final objective of the administrative and organizational element of a systemic planning program is concerned with increasing efficiency and economy in government. This is the traditional goal of administrators, yet it is also related to the long-range planning process. Through reorganization and reorientation, problems that impede planning can be resolved. For example, through school district consolidation, reorientation of vocational training, and other measures, the basic urban-centered, industrial-based economy can be achieved. There are several other examples which are quite short range by nature, but well within the systemic planning process as defined. Further, this is not limited to increasing efficiency and economy in the public sphere alone. By approaching this objective in the private sphere as well, it is obvious that the economy can be bolstered and expanded through the better use of the available resources.

Part Two
Application by PPBS

Part Two consists of three chapters dealing with the major application of the systems approach to planning which has been made through planning–programming–budgeting–scheduling systems. Chapter 5 deals with the formulation of PPBS systems in a historical sense as well as with a concern for problems and potentials of the application. Chapter 6 examines procedures for the program analysis elements of PPBS systems and discusses the methodology and techniques. Chapter 7 examines the scheduling and work programming elements of the PPBS systems and presents the methodology and techniques as well.

5 The Planning-Programming-Budgeting-Scheduling System: Potentials and Problems

The widening of the scope and the increased complexity of the public services offered by the several areas of government have been matched by the difficulties of guiding and coordinating functions of government. Because the context in which a government — whether it be federal, state, or local — seeks to provide services for its citizens is one of scarcity of public resources in relation to over-all demands and objectives, the decision-makers in government are forced to choose among many competing programs. A rationally discriminating decision as to how best to serve the public interest can only be reached through the use of improved tools of public decision making.[1]

Public Budgeting

Governments, like private individuals or organizations, are constrained by a scarcity of economic resources at their disposal. Modern government must be concerned with the broad objectives of law and order, health, education, welfare, and economic development. Regardless of its fiscal resources, no government can avoid the need for compromise among objectives — both in terms of the present and of the future. To make these compromises, it is necessary that various desirable governmental activities be expressed in terms of some common denominator. This common dominator most frequently is money.

Some government decisions relate only to the immediate future. If they turn out to be wrong or ineffective, they can be readily reversed or modified. Other decisions, however, relate to a more distant future — a future that at best can only be guessed. Governments may differ in the relative weights they give to the formulation of goals and the attainment of efficiency by minimizing costs of particular activities. Yet, all governments are confronted with the problem of scarcity; therefore, the logic of the decision-making process is independent of the form of government, even though outcomes may differ widely. A government can determine its policies most effectively if it chooses rationally among alternative courses of action, with full knowledge of the implications of these alternatives. To achieve such knowledge, quantitative information must be collected, organized, and analyzed to cast light on the consequences of spending limited resources in various directions.

What method does government use to organize and communicate this information so as to make correct decisions concerning the allocation of fiscal resources? Frederick Mosher has suggested that:[2]

The budget process is just such a system of communications, regularized and cyclical. Its purposes are *POLICY* and *ADMINISTRATION,* and it is the only device invented in democratic governments which:

(1) Brings about periodic reconsideration of governmental purposes and objectives.
(2) Facilitates comparison of programs and purposes and their costs.
(3) Examines the total role of government and its cost in relation to the private sector.
(4) Provides a link between administrative organizations and the people.
(5) Provides a legal basis for the spending of funds.
(6) Provides for public accounts and fiscal accountability.
(7) Examines internal operations for efficiency and economy.
(8) Delegates financial authority and responsibility, yet controls these centrally.

Contemporary attitudes differ considerably from those of the past on such questions as (1) what constitutes prudent fiscal policy; (2) what is the proper role of government in providing public services and facilities; and (3) what government can or should do to foster sound economic growth and development. Historically, annual balancing of the budget has been regarded as a fundamental principle of sound fiscal policy. This policy frequently has had a restraining effect in economic growth and development.

During the past thirty years, economists have come to realize that government can increase, as well as redistribute wealth — while at the same time attaining other social objectives — without displacing private investment. The weighing and evaluation of alternative programs are important factors in budget policy. The same dollar spent on different programs may yield greatly varied results, both in economic and social achievement. Wise budget policy generally seeks to spend money where it produces the greatest net benefits. As David Page has observed: "A budget should be a financial expression of a program plan. Setting goals, defining objectives, and developing planned programs for achieving those objectives are important, integral parts of preparing and justifying a budget submission."[3]

The decisive problem, therefore, confronting all levels of government, as well as agencies within government, involves the allocation of resources in an optimum fashion to meet selected physical, economic, social, and cultural needs and demands. The complexity and severity of this problem are well illustrated by noting those factors that would be necessary to resolve this problem effectively: (1) unlimited resources; (2) unambiguous, quantitative indicators of physical, social, economic, and cultural needs and demands; (3) a social, democratic mechanism for identifying the preferences of a jurisdiction's constituency; and (4) valid data on the capacity of alternative means available for meeting specified needs and demands.

The Budget Process —
Input and Output Relationships

Resource allocations in local government through the "budget process" basically involves an adversary-type process between departments. Significant criteria and controls applied in the budget process usually are of a financial nature and focus upon the expenditure of money. Controversy and analyses of objectives and alternative methods of achieving these objectives generally are based upon money-related considerations rather than on policy issues. There are no major budget problems if there is enough money to pay for the "inputs" — the resources — requested by departments. Seldom, if ever, are projections or estimates made of the impact or effects that these inputs will have in meeting public needs and demands. As a result, there is no guarantee that the decision process is coherently responsive to any comprehensive objectives. No formal or explicit mechanism operates to assure responsiveness to comprehensive objectives. In short, the traditional methods of budgetary decision-making are input-oriented rather than output-oriented.

These traditional budgetary mechanisms are designed to pursue efficiency at the expense of effectiveness. This shortcoming may be observed in the continual efforts of agencies to achieve economies without decreasing services or outputs. The focus is the elimination of waste: with fixed resources, of producing more of A without decreasing the production of B. Questions of efficiency generally are defined and answered purely in economic terms with minimum consideration of priorities or relative worth. By pretending that technical analyses — analyses which focus on efficiency — are sufficient for political decisions, decision-makers may lose the very information that is necessary to determine effectiveness.

Recognition of these shortcomings in the more traditional approaches to the budget process has led to the development of budgetary techniques and concepts that are output-oriented and that consider the impact of resources as well as the resources themselves. These more contemporary techniques make a clear distinction between efficiency and effectiveness in an attempt to supplant financial-type controls in favor of unambiguous and nonpecuniary accounting techniques to measure the output of public investments.

The Evolution of
Modern Public Budgeting

Public budgeting in the United States has gone through three basic stages since the turn of the century. The first stage was that early period in which the major emphasis in budgeting was the central control of spending. The budget was viewed as a safeguard against administrative abuse of public funds. Obviously, this period was under the influence of government reformers, particularly at the local level.

The second stage in this evolution was management-oriented, in which an emphasis was placed on the efficient performance of work and prescribed activities. The performance budget — officially introduced by the · Hoover Commission in the forties — was a major contribution of the management-orientation period. Performance budgeting is designed to prepare and interpret the financial plan embodied in the budget in terms of service to be performed rather than in terms of things to be bought, whether personnel services, supplies, transportation, or others. Performance budgets direct attention to ends, not means, as the significant element in financial planning and expenditure authorization.

The third stage is reflected in more recent developments in public budgeting, which have their roots in Keynesian economics and the new technology of systems analysis. Keynesian economics was important in its transition from the utilization of fiscal policy to achieve economic objectives to the utilization of the budget process to achieve fiscal objectives. If there were some way to build computers with even greater capacity than those which are operational today, systems analysis might be applied to the operations of government programs as a whole. Since this is not technically feasible at this time, much more narrow problem areas within programs are defined and analyzed. These separate analyses then are brought together for broader study.

In modern budgeting, all three of the above discussed stages coexist in government. "Coexistence" best describes the interrelationships among these three concepts. The information requirements of each of these viewpoints is quite different. Often these differences in information needs are suggested as reasons why the three concepts, to date, have not been more closely integrated.

The types of questions raised by each of these viewpoints also differ considerably. The following questions are typically considered important by each approach.

If the orientation is toward fiscal control, (1) How can agencies be held to the expenditure ceiling established by the legislature and chief executive or some other fiscal "watch-dog"? (2) What reporting procedures should be used to enforce the rules in expenditure limitations? (3) What limits should be placed on agency spending for various line items, i.e., personnel, equipment, supplies, etc.?

Under a management orientation, (1) What are the best ways to organize to accomplish prescribed tasks? (2) Which of several staffing alternatives achieves the most effective relationship between the central office and various field offices? (3) Of the various grants and projects proposed, which should be approved, i.e., what are the priorities?

In the case of a planning orientation, (1) What are the long-range goals and policies of government, and how are these related to particular expenditure choices? (2) What criteria should be used in appraising the requests of various public agencies? (3) Which programs should be initiated or terminated, and which ones should be expanded or curtailed?

Clearly, each of these questions should be raised in some quarter of government and in some phase of the budgetary process. Unfortunately, quite often only one viewpoint is treated — that is to say, the budget process is often channeled through narrowed perspectives. As a result, some of these vital questions go unasked, either because they do not come to mind or they do not appear important to those with responsibility for making of the budget.

Historically, long-range planning and program evaluation questions (i.e., the central focus of the more contemporary approach to public budgeting) have not been emphasized. It must be remembered that the budgetary process is an evolutionary process. As such, certain conditions and procedures have become entrenched. In handling public monies, government has tended to be somewhat conservative, and budget officials have persisted in using outmoded techniques in evaluating and preparing budgets. Moreover, the orientation of planning is considered to be a radical departure by many governmental officials.

As noted, in the early phases of budgeting, budget officials were concerned with the inputs — concerned with the line-item requests of agencies. During the period in which management orientation flourished, the stress was laid on the output of programs — to ensure efficiency of operations, to determine least-cost methods of performing certain tasks. Under a planning orientation, with program budgeting, the emphasis has shifted from varying inputs and outputs to obtain a specific objective to an examination of the objective itself. Program analysis may lead to a new statement of objectives through constant reevaluation.

The Origins of PPBS

Perhaps the approach that has received the greatest attention in recent years in terms of innovations in the budget process is the planning-programming-budgeting-scheduling system approach (or PPBS). Heralded as an innovation in comprehensive budgeting procedures, PPBS was first brought to public attention in August 1965, when President Lyndon B. Johnson proclaimed that by fiscal year 1968, all federal departments would adopt the budgeting procedures that has been followed successfully for some years in the Department of Defense.

In spite of the attention that PPBS systems have received, the fundamental concepts are not radically different from earlier program evaluation methods. As David Novick, who often is credited for formulating the PPBS approach, has observed, the concepts of program budgeting "have rather ancient and hoary origins."[4] These concepts did not start in the Department of Defense or in the Rand Corporation, as many have suggested. Rather, there are two basic roots of these concepts and methods: one in the federal government, where program budgeting concepts were introduced as part of the wartime controls systems by the War Production Board in 1942; the other root — an even longer and older one — is in private industry. There is evidence to suggest that large corporations, such as DuPont and General Motors, were applying program budget techniques in the early twenties.

The basic concepts underlying program budgeting — that of presenting budgetary requests in terms of program "packages" rather than in the usual line-item format — have been adopted as a central focus of the PPBS system. However, these concepts have been broadened to encompass a structuring of programs according to objectives regardless of agency responsibility. Further, under the PPBS approach, a conscious effort is made (1) to state end objectives; (2) to seek a wider range of alternatives; and (3) to link program and financial plans.[5] In short, PPBS systems give recognition to the notion that planning and budgeting are complementary operations. The need for planning, programming, budgeting, and scheduling arises from the indossolvable connection between the allocation of resources and the formulation and conduct of governmental policy. When undertaken in the proper "mix," these processes constitute the means by which objectives and resources, and the interrelations among them, are taken into account to achieve a more coherent and comprehensive program of action for government as a whole.

Major Components of a PPBS System

The PPBS method, according to Novick, is to set forth certain major objectives, define programs essential to these objectives or goals, identify resources to the specific types of objectives, and systematically analyze the alternatives available.[6] Therefore, it might be suggested that there are five major components to a PPBS system: (1) an identification of major goals in program terms; (2) an across-the-board governmental program structure, i.e., programs are analyzed as units regardless of the number of agencies which might be involved in implementation; (3) an extended time horizon involving multiyear program and financial plans; (4) program analysis through which alternatives are systematically examined in terms of both supply and demand for resources and effectiveness requirements; and (5) program up-dating procedures through which program analyses during operations are used to determine needed program modifications and improvements.

The *across-the-board governmental program structure* is perhaps an ideal to strive toward — in reality, such a goal should be considered as a long-range objective in many governments. This structure focuses on identifying the fundamental objectives of government in terms that can be related to all activities of government regardless of where they may be carried out within the organizational structure. Some departments simply cannot make the shift to this approach in a short time span. Nevertheless, for the PPBS system to have its fullest measure of success, major governmental agencies should be brought together in the system as soon as possible. In order to gain the maximum potential of this approach, all agencies should be incorporated into the system to assure that the interdependencies of the various agencies can be examined, and that each goal of the government is programmed for in a comprehensive manner throughout the agencies.

The *multiyear program plan* is needed to indicate the proposed outputs of facilities and services according to the objectives outlined. The magnitude of each program is determined through this phase of the process. Most important, this approach permits programs to be related directly to the established objectives of government.

The *multiyear financial plan* projects the cost of each program as outlined by the decisions which are made — usually these costs are measured in dollars. Cost estimates for future years need not be as detailed as those for the current budget presentation. Also included in the long-range financial plan are some estimates as to sources of revenue to support the proposed programs, including an examination of the adequacy of current sources of revenue for future demands.

Program analysis or systematic analysis of alternatives is the cornerstone of the PPBS system. It is through this systematic analysis that programs are selected for the multiyear plans. Program analysis may take several forms — systems analysis, cost-benefit analysis, cost-effectiveness analysis, cost-utility analysis, and so forth. Regardless of which form is applied, this phase essentially involves the reduction of complex problems into their component segments or parts so that each can be studied in greater detail, followed by a synthesis of these parts back to the whole. Those aspects of the problems that involve value judgements can be identified and the basis of such judgement, can be made more explicit.[7]

Program analysis is composed of several basic elements:

1. *Definition of the public problem.* This would include a statement of the goals as established and toward which the government is working, and the identification of criteria and quantitative measures with which to evaluate the progress being made toward the stated objectives.

2. *Projections of the determinants of the problem.* In particular, the future social and economic factors influencing or having an effect on the problem should be examined.

3. *Generation of alternative approaches that government might use to attack the problem.* In the past, analysis has been very inadequate with virtually no alternatives studied in depth. The emphasis should be on innovative methods. The objectives themselves must be liable to scrutiny in order to determine if a completely different approach might hold a better solution to the problem.

4. *Cost-benefit or cost-effectiveness analysis and evaluation of alternatives.* This entails the development and use of quantitative measures of the performance (effectiveness) of an alternative and measures the resources (costs) required to be met in achieving the program objectives.

5. *Interpretation of quantitative results.* The most important element in this phase of the PPBS approach is an awareness of the limitations of the quantitative studies. Certain assumptions must be made; associated with those assumptions are uncertainties which can be quantified only to a limited extent. There are many variables which cannot be quantified but which decision-makers must weigh if they are to make intelligent decisions.

The political process is one of compromise and adjustment. While the allocation of fiscal resources can be further illuminated by the continuous assembling and analyzing of statistical data on the nature and capacity of the economy and the objectives and needs of government and its public, there is danger of becoming mesmerized by the techniques of a "systems" approach. It is better to have fiscal decisions that are nearly right than ones that are perfectly wrong.

This is not to minimize the potential contributions that can be derived through a PPBS systems approach. Rather it is to suggest that PPBS systems must be taken in proper perspective in relation to the other components of the policy-planning process.

What Is New about PPBS Systems?

Many persons, including budget officials, have attempted to discount the PPBS approach, suggesting that it has not made any new contributions to the budget-making process. They argue that a PPBS system is merely a collection of techniques and concepts that have been used in the past singly and in various combinations. As indicated previously, PPBS has sought to bring the various elements of planning, programming, budgeting, and scheduling together into an integrated system. Thus the key word or *sine qua non* of PPBS is *system.*

Daniel Alesch, who was actively involved in the development of a PPBS system for state government in New York State, outlined three new ingredients that PPBS systems have brought to the budget process:[8] (1) advances in technology and techniques, especially in the areas of systems analysis, cost-benefit and cost-effectiveness analysis, and linear programming; (2) an expanded horizon in planning, encompassing physical, social, and economic aspects as well as the fiscal dimensions of budgeting; and (3) continuity and process.

The *new techniques* that have been added to the budget process have permitted complex fiscal problems to be broken down into smaller, more manageable parts. The use of the computer has increased tremendously with the demand for large quantities of information which must be processed.

The *expanded horizon* in planning has two important dimensions. One dimension of this matrix is composed of the functional types of planning — transportation, health, education, economic development, public safety, welfare, etc. — those elements which comprise the so-called "comprehensive plan." The other dimension of the matrix is comprised of activity, spatial, and financial planning. Activity planning is planning for the programmatic action of government throughout the set of functions. Spatial planning is the distribution of activities and the coordination of spatial implications of each of these governmental activities. Financial planning (not to be confused with economic planning) encompasses current and long-range budgeting, revenue and expenditures, and long-term public investments. The interaction of these two dimensions is an interfacing, then, of comprehensive planning and spatial program planning.

As used in the context of PPBS, *continuity* refers to the ongoing, constant reevaluation and readjustment over a time period which is an integral part of any effective PPBS system. *Process* refers to the flow from the overall plan to very specific budgetary allocations of line items. The planning stage sets certain limits by the formulation of objectives, while the program stage sets further limitations on specific allocations.

Potentials of PPBS Systems

PPBS systems, according to definition, have as their objectives the assistance of decision-makers in making more rational decisions involving a choice among various alternative courses of action. John Haldi, former Chief of Program Evaluation of the Bureau of the Budget,[9] suggests that PPBS provides (1) better program information and reports, including better financial and statistical information and better integration of this information; (2) better methods of displaying, comprehensively, program decisions, including estimates of program costs and program outputs, and also making visible the future implications of current decisions; and (3) better analyses of complex issues requiring top-level decisions and direction.

Daniel Alesch suggests several benefits derived from PPBS in the state of New York:[10] (1) increased incentive for advance planning in line agencies; (2) increased interagency communication and data sharing and more clearly identified relationships among agencies; and (3) a logical and practical means of implementing plans by use of the annual executive budget.

Problems and Limitations of PPBS Systems

Although the distinctions are not always clear, the problems and limitations of PPBS arbitrarily can be divided into problems external and problems internal to the PPBS system.

In the realm of external problems, one of the paramount considerations is the reception that comprehensive, long-range planning has been accorded throughout government and by the public. Such a long-range planning perspective is an essential element in a PPBS system. As planning has gained in strength over the past few decades, some government officials and segments of the public have become wary of its power to control. There is fear of a growing overcentralization of authority — concentrated in the planning impact. Quite obviously, there are dangers of overcentralization in the implementation of the PPBS system. Nevertheless, the growing complexities of the government and the advancing state of technology demand a more rational approach to decision-making. Means must be found to deal with the complexities of government without imposing excessive government controls.

A second serious problem is the wide gulf that traditionally has separated planning and budgeting. Frederick Mosher (speaking of budgeting and planning) has said that ". . . in the extreme form, the one means saving, the other spending." Budgeting tends to be conservative and negative in its orientation, while planning is innovative and tends to expand horizons of expectations. Traditional budgeting takes the viewpoint of: "This is where we are, where do we want to go?" Planning in PPBS sees it as: "Where do we want to go?" and "What do we have to do to get there?"[11] Traditional budget officials tend to be leery of dreaming planner-types who court financial disaster with their planning schemes. Indeed, someone constantly has to look over the shoulder of some planners, for they have not devoted enough time to the financial aspects of their plans.

Politics permeates throughout the budgetary process. With legislators voting on the funding of public endeavors, it goes without saying that political dealings play a substantial role in budget-making. Aaron Wildavsky would have us believe that the budget-making process is almost totally politically determined, and furthermore, that this is the way it should be.[12] Wildavsky defends the traditional budgeting process as being that method which best epitomizes the democratic process. Wildavsky holds the opinion that PPBS is the product of a new breed of technocrats who seek to take politics out of budgeting. As mentioned above, PPBS is not a decision-making apparatus but a means to develop better information for the decision-makers. In the end the decisions are made by politicians; hopefully more rational decisions as a result of the application of the PPBS system.

Another problem that confronts the PPBS system is that too much confidence has been placed on the system aspects of the approach, important as they may be. There are those who would suggest that PPBS is the answer to all the budgeting problems. Furthermore, even the users of PPBS tend to overemphasize the importance of the techniques. A single, very important point to remember is that PPBS is a tool, and as such, it is subject to manipulation by anyone having control of it — be he legislator, chief executive, budget-maker, planner, analyst, programmer, or other.

There are loud cries of the increased costs of gathering and relating the huge quantities of information generated. PPBS systems will not be inexpensive with regards to the benefits to be derived in the early years. The initial investment, however, in the development of the PPBS system will be bringing additional benefits in the future, making the varied governmental programs more and more effective in relation to cost. Certain interest groups will balk at the possible long-range or short-run consequences of the planning proposals. Closer scrutiny of appropriations might jeopardize programs which could not be easily justified for their supposed high priority.

PPBS has many internal problems to overcome if it is to be even moderately successful. The first group of problems to be considered are conceptual in nature, encountered in designing the program budget and attempting to relate it to the decision-making process:

1. Societal goals are elusive. It is very difficult for any group to decide what the goals of a government should be. In fact it is somewhat undemocratic for a group to make such decisions. But this is the role of the elected officials — the chief executive and the legislators. The planners must develop sets of goals for the consideration of the decision-makers. Moreover, throughout the planning process, there should be attempts to determine what are the goals of the society.

2. There is a problem of translating societal goals into agency goals, which are usually quite different. In the past, and even in many of the initial stages of PPBS, agencies develop their own priorities, not based on any generalized

governmental objectives. There is a danger that these agencies' goals will be adopted without adequate consideration of whether they do, in fact, reflect societal goals. It seems more rational that general goals be developed which are then broken down into subgoals and objectives proposed to reach these goals. Agencies, then, can gear their programs to meet these established objectives.

3. Of course, decision-makers and their staff are always plagued by inadequate knowledge of the effective means to achieve the goals established.

4. In the development of alternatives, the ends or goals that supposedly are being sought frequently are not explicitly stated; therefore, it is difficult to compare alternative methods of accomplishing a prescribed goal.

5. It is impossible to bring about a complete separation of factual elements from value elements. If value elements are to be scrutinized, what must be done is to give them some weight that is quantifiable. In the end, however, where there are considerable value elements involved — and such cases are numerous — the decision-makers must rely on their own or others' judgment.

6. It is often difficult to determine the time span of a project, thus making it hard to define whether a program is of long or short-run duration, and whether its impact will be short run or long run.

7. A serious pitfall that should be avoided is for the planning to become too conservative as decision-makers strive to "play it safe" on long-range commitments. Many good and necessary programs may never be tested because of their unproved character.

A second group of problems facing PPBS implementation are concerned with operations — the actual development of the budget:

1. Classification is difficult. There are goals and objectives which overlap, programs which are aimed at solving the same problem from a different viewpoint, and so forth. However, it may be expected that program analysis will discover more of these duplications of effort than are presently uncovered by coincidence and happenstance.

2. Related to the first problem is the location of activities needed to effect a particular program. These activities are often dispersed and diffused among several governmental agencies, bureaus, or divisions, and even among levels of government. Where the consolidation of these efforts under a single program would seem to be justified, the agencies frequently may be reluctant to relinquish their control of certain activities.

3. Cost-benefit analysis often does not provide desirable weighing of the relative effectiveness of programs and alternatives. The techniques are still in the developmental stages, and they may never yield the type of information necessary for rational decision-making.

4. Prediction is an arduous task whether it is based on past experience or on the knowledge of the dynamics of a process. The number of very unpredictable variables make forecasting quite vulnerable to attack.

5. Gathering appropriate information is especially perplexing in the early years of PPBS implementation. There may be enormous quantities of information which are superfluous or valueless.

6. A danger exists that a PPBS system will result in overcentralization of authority with a consequent neglect of possibilities for improvement ideas from the lower echelons as well as the possible loss of morale at these lower levels.

7. In order really to integrate the various elements of the budget-making process, there is a need for a common language. Presently each component element seems to talk mostly to itself.

8. There is a dire need for trained personnel. The sophistication of techniques requires highly skilled technicians which are few in number and much in demand.

9. In the area of program analysis, there are a number of pitfalls that must be evaded: (a) the use of arbitrary standards; (b) failure to include important criteria in determining effectiveness; (c) failure to account for the impact of a program on other program areas; (d) ignoring future impacts on all areas; (e) developing assumptions which are grossly inadequate for the analysis to be meaningful; and (f) avoiding discounting the uncertainty of data — uncertainties must be clearly identified and quantified if possible.

10. Most assuredly, there will be opposition from within the governmental structure to a system which is geared to seek out redundant activities and inefficient or ineffective employment of resources, thereby leading to a possible reduction in funding or a curtailment of activities.

6

Procedures for Program Analysis

As noted in the previous chapter, program analysis is the cornerstone of the PPBS system. However, it is in this phase that the greatest difficulties are most often encountered. And it is here that the system most often aborts. For these reasons, it is desirable to explore some of the problems which may be encountered in the process of program analysis.

Program Planning and Program Analysis

Once general governmental goals and objectives have been established, they must be reduced to operating programs. The formulation, evaluation, and carrying out of effective programs designed to implement the responsibilities delegated to governmental agencies are key elements in the successful operation of such agencies. Such activities may be labeled "program planning" to distinguish them from the long-range planning process, which contributes to the identification of goals and objectives.[a] Program planning, in the sense that it is used here, is the process of devising specific steps and procedures necessary to bring to fruition some agreed-upon policy or program. A "program" may be broad and general, such as the improvement of health, or narrow and specific, such as the eradication of typhoid-carrying vectors in a particular district.

There are at least four basic reasons for effective program planning. The first is to provide a vehicle for relating public decisions to established program activities and to the long-range goals of the programs. Current decisions, if not carefully considered in their relationship to long-range program goals, can seriously hamper the efficient achievement of those goals.

The second reason for program planning is the need for better coordination of operating programs. Since World War II, the range and scale of functions performed by governments have expanded vastly, increasing the possibilities for

[a]This activity of public agencies has been referred to by other writers as "departmental planning," "operations planning," or "functional planning." It may be suggested that the concept of "departmental planning" extends beyond that of program planning to include the interrelating of various programs within a single agency. "Operations planning," on the other hand, has been used in a slightly different context to refer to subparts of the program–planning process. "Functional planning," a relatively new term, suffers from the problems of any constructed concept, i.e., a lack of consensus as to its definition. More recently, Dr. Coleman Woodbury has suggested the term "services planning" to distinguish these activities from the overall, long–range planning responsibilities of government, which he suggests should be labeled "capital facilities planning." Both of these forms of planning, Dr. Woodbury suggests, result in programs. Acknowledging the problems in semantics and definitions which arise from the use of any shorthand label, the term "program planning" will be used throughout this discussion.

duplication among various public agencies. If every program of every agency has a properly established set of goals and clearly thought-out plans for achieving these goals, a meaningful comparison may be made among similar programs in different agencies, and excessive overlap will be exposed. An agency also may be duplicating not only the work of other agencies within a given level of government, but that of other levels of government as well. Program plans can be helpful in assessing the specific need for intergovernmental cooperation.

A third reason for program planning is that effective work in this phase of the PPBS system is the only basis on which accurate appraisals of long-range needs for public facilities can be made. Unless there is a systematic and continuing appraisal of program objectives, changing technologies affecting program effectuation, and changing size and location of the clientele groups to be served; and unless these many and ever-changing factors are translated into such terms as the kind, number, and location of physical facilities needed at stated periods of time extending well into the future; and unless these future requirements for physical facilities and related service programs are considered in their relationship to a well-maintained inventory of current physical assets, any attempt to formulate an effective capital budget for an agency or for government as a whole is meaningless. Such an inventory must include information as to the kind, capacity, location, and remaining useful life of all public facilities.

The final objective of program planning is the improvement of government's capacity for fiscal planning. Modern government operates within a complex financial structure and must have detailed knowledge of anticipated expenses and expected revenues. Through program planning, it is possible for public agencies to provide this information, thus ensuring increased economy in governmental operations.

The need for program planning and program analysis arises from the limitations of human beings and the obstinacy of the physical environment. In the first place, it is not sufficient, for example, to invoke the Constitution and to seek to promote the general welfare. More explicit goals and objectives must be formulated, and the general welfare can only be understood in terms of its components. Programs must be developed and evaluated which permit a choice among alternatives — alternatives designed to achieve agreed-upon objectives.

Second, the process of relating ends to means is extremely complicated in a modern, complex society. Herbert Simon has suggested that all decisions, whether in the public or the private sector, are based on two types of premises: (1) factual premises — subject to empirical testing in order to ascertain their truth or falsity; and (2) value premises — not subject to testing, since they are concerned with what "ought to be" rather than with what "is."[1] The former have to do with the choice of means, the latter with the choice of ends. Thus Simon concludes that rational decision-making may be viewed as consisting of means-ends chains, that is, given certain ends, appropriate means are selected for their attainment; but once reached, the ends become the means for the attainment of further ends. Unraveling these means-ends chains may be a very difficult and complex undertaking. Yet it is a most important undertaking if programs are to be effective in achieving their objectives. The process must be broken down into a hierarchy of optimizations and suboptimizations. And fairly systematic and carefully organized procedures must be applied in establishing this hierarchy and in evaluating the possible courses of action to be taken.

Finally, program results cannot be achieved instantaneously, and frequently long lead times are involved in program planning. Programming in an uncertain future dictates that procedures be devised which permit an appraisal of possible spillover effects and by-products of various courses of action. Moreover, once resources are committed to a purpose, particularly when they involve capital facilities, they are not readily transferable elsewhere. Consequently, careful programming is required as a prerequisite to effective decision-making.

What is a Program?

Before effective program planning can be undertaken, it is first necessary to delineate clearly program responsibilities. In government, the terms "program," "activity," "function," and "performance" frequently are used more or less interchangeably. While there may be many subtle shadings among these terms, there is no consistent pattern. For example, some organizations may designate research as an activity, while other organizations may call research a program. These inconsistencies and ambiguities of language reveal the vagueness of the underlying situation. Before effective and meaningful program planning and program analysis can be formulated, a number of criteria for the designation of a governmental operation as a program must be understood.

Perhaps some light can be shed on the problem of program identification through a hypothetical example drawn from outside the framework of government. Many modern manufacturing corporations represent a highly integrated complex of programs, because of the product linkages and the economies to be achieved by being a self-supplier of basic inputs to final stages of production. Consider, for example, the organization of a highly integrated appliance manufacturer. Such a corporation may not only produce appliances, but also may fabricate steel products, assemble electrical systems, manufacture plastic and rubber products, produce service parts, and so forth. The objective of the corporation, of course, is to maximize profits. But a successful corporation rarely would conduct its operations simply by reference to this fundamental objective. If several brand names are produced, the corporation is likely to have a separate program and a separate organizational structure for each of them.

Each brand name, presumably, is intended to appeal to a separate sector of the market, and therefore, approaches to marketing, advertising, and even production may differ with the product. The company even may, as General Motors does in the automotive field, put brands in active competition with each other.

Programming of final products, however, hardly is likely to offer a sufficient basis for program organization. Increased demands for major production inputs, such as fabricated steel or plastic and rubber products, or for more or less standardized parts, resulting from increased production in one or more final-product programs does not evoke automatically parallel increases in supply. The required supply may not be forthcoming unless a capacity to produce these component products has been "programmed" in anticipation of increased demands for appliances. Consequently, the corporation would likely have programs for steel fabrication, rubber and plastics, and other products in which attempts are made to anticipate final demands. However, there would be little point in having a separate steel fabrication program and a separate rubber and plastics program for each of the final products. Economies can be achieved and errors avoided by having a single program organized to supply these materials to the several final-product divisions. Moreover, personnel concerned with the manufacture of final-products are unlikely to be expert in the technology required to produce these intermediate products. Efficient and effective operations commend a vertical division of functions.

The long-run future of the manufacturing concern may depend heavily on the research and development it conducts. Some research and development activities may be associated with specific products or brands, the production of which readily can be anticipated. In such cases, these activities are likely to be included in the final-product programs, perhaps as subprograms. But some research will be of common benefit to all final-products; some will be undertaken in connection with the improvement of intermediate products; and some will relate to models of the future that might come into production beyond the foreseeable time horizon of any current plans for production. Consequently, separate research programs are likely to be initiated to embrace these activities.

From this example it should be clear that questions of program identification, programming, and organization structure are highly interdependent. A central management might oversee and control the entire operation, in which case the separate program categories would assist management in its deliberations about particular production problems. What is more likely is that the need to program these various activities also will influence the administrative pattern of the organization and will dictate some decentralization of decision-making authority.

The identification of an area of governmental concern as a program or activity implies that its components are more closely in competition with each other than they are with elements outside the program. The term *competition*, as it is used in this context, should not be equated with the notion of conflict; rather the implication is that the component elements perform similar or related functions. For example, an urban transportation program might include different modes of travel, all serving a similar clientele.

This example leads to a fundamental question which frequently lies at the heart of the program definition problem. Should all forms of transportation in an urban area be handled under a single program umbrella, that is, should urban transport be linked more closely with international transport than with other aspects of urban development? Or should international transport be regarded as a component of foreign trade rather than of transportation? Or should it be included under both types of programs? Should programs in mass transportation and highway construction be the responsibility of a single public agency or of separate agencies? In much of the current discussion, it would seem to be taken for granted that transportation is a natural program category. However, as the foregoing questions indicate, this conclusion is by no means obvious.

Similar difficulties and problems arise in connection with other aspects of urban development, such as housing programs or programs in health, education, welfare, or other public service areas. Should urban housing programs be handled separately from rural housing, or should housing programs for different consumer groups within the urban market be handled under different program organizations? Current programs at the national and local levels, of course, reflect the uncertainty of these program definitions. The Departments of Agriculture and Housing and Urban Development have divided the territory according to the urban-rural dichotomy, while at the local level the housing authority and the agency reponsible for the administration of zoning and subdivision regulations in effect have divided the market according to economic clientele.

This general discussion is offered by way of pointing up the fact that the designation of activities as programs is not an easy or trivial matter. The manner in which a program structure is established for government as a whole, or for any major segment, can have a significant impact on the decisions that are reached in planning, evaluating, and implementing such programs. Therefore, the design of programs should be regarded as an important part of the decision-making process.

Criteria for the Development of Program Structure

One of the most fundamental criteria for a program structure is that it should permit a comparison of alternative methods of pursuing imperfectly determined policy objectives.[2] This is the framework of program analysis. Policy objectives seldom are articulated with sufficient clarity that the course of action to be pursued is self-evident from the decision. If this were the case, there would be little need for the more elaborate techniques of program analysis that have emerged in recent years.

Thus the need for public assistance can be clarified and analyzed more fully by breaking down the problem into the needs arising from various client groups:

the aged, persons with economic dependents, those with physical handicaps or disabilities, problems of unemployment, and so forth. Limited resources prevent provision fully for all cases under these categories. Despite the absence of a clear-cut concept of social welfare, however, a more satisfactory comparison among these various categories must be formed.

Second, even though objectives may be more clearly defined in some program areas, there may be alternative ways of accomplishing these objectives. Thus, under some circumstances, traffic engineering, street development, and the development and maintenance of parking facilities may be handled as separate and distinct programs, whereas under different circumstances these categories may be integrated into a single program and organized under a single agency's responsibility.

Third, cognizance must be taken of the fact that programs frequently consist of a number of complementary components or functions, none of which can be effective without the others. A health program, for example, requires doctors, nurses, and hospitals in the right proportions. The danger lies in an inability (or reluctance) to establish appropriate boundaries and to continue to expand the "components" beyond what can be properly handled in a program context. On the other hand, an organization's objectives may require it to adopt overlapping program structures. This need is evident in many programs of state government, for example, where recognition of both geographical and functional aspects is required.

A fourth criterion stems from the fact that separate programs may be needed where one part of an organization supplies services to several others. Economies are to be expected if a department has a central purchasing operation rather than separate ones for each bureau. Since the acquisition of capital equipment is likely to require an appreciable lead time, it may be necessary to budget such equipment under a separate program, even though such equipment may be far removed from the overall mission of any department.

A fifth criterion relates to the time span over which expenditures take effect. The uncertainties of the future frequently preclude estimates of requirements for governmental services beyond a limited period. This more limited time period may span five to six years, paralleling the general time schedule of a capital improvements program. Notwithstanding this more protracted time period, research and development and investment programs must be undertaken to provide for a long-range future. Even where such activities can be identified with some major programs, it is often advisable to deal with them as separate subprograms, since the uncertainty of the longer-run future should materially affect the character of the activities to be undertaken. In this event, it is obvious that they should be dealt with separately. In fact, major differences in time spans of various activities may be the leading characteristic of an organization's program structure.

Finally, a general distinction between the final and the intermediate programs of an organization may be useful in program analysis.[3] Final programs are those that contribute directly to the general goals and objectives of the organization.

Intermediate programs are operations that contribute to final programs in the immediate or remote future but that are of sufficient importance or that involve critical inputs so as to require that they be monitored separately. In the Department of Defense, for example, strategic forces, general purpose forces, and air defense often are defined as final programs, while all other programs are considered as intermediate. From the point of view of government as a whole, however, defense becomes the final program, and its components are intermediate.

Who has Responsibility for Program Planning?

In any administrative system, the principal agencies generally are organized on the basis of the substantive functions or programs which they are called upon to carry out. In administrative terms, such agencies frequently are referred to as "line agencies."[4] The line function connotes action — action backed by a certain amount of delegated authority. Line agencies in government deal more or less with identifiable clientele groups, providing services, regulating conduct, collecting taxes and fees, and in general carrying out the programs that have been authorized by legislative bodies and/or the chief executive. As such, line agencies are concerned with the primary objectives and purposes for which a government exists.

The functions that are carried out by line agencies span the full spectrum of governmental activities. Further, these functions constantly are increasing in number as the complexities of government grow. Many of these functions have had a long historical development and are rooted in tradition. As they have evolved, the theory and practice of their administration has emerged gradually over time. As such, some of these administrative practice may no longer be appropriate to the current problems and conditions facing government, and from time to time, these practices require updating and modernizing.

The process of program planning is a continuous one, involving periodic restudy and reappraisal of the programs' goals and the means selected for achieving these goals. In a dynamic society, constant adjustments must be made to redefine both ends and means.

The distribution of the program-planning functions within government shifts as the center of attention moves from strategy to tactics — from broad objectives to ways and means. In its broadest orientation, program planning in line agencies is the responsibility of the chief administrative officer. However, program planning, as it has been discussed here, is primarily the responsibility of the permanent career service personnel within line agencies.

The three categories discussed above broadly constitute the functions of line agencies within the structure of government. The degree to which these functions and related activities are efficiently carried out, in large measure, will determine the effectiveness of government. Failure to properly interpret policy decision, to accept and carry out delegated responsibilities, or to develop and initiate programs to implement policy decisions will seriously impair the overall effectiveness of executive and legislative programs. This, in turn, can result in fiscal waste, obstacles to growth and development, and dangers to the general health, safety, and welfare of the public.

In the most general terms, the function of a line agency is *to execute the law.* In pursuance of this general responsibility, such agencies have a number of important duties. For the purposes of discussion, these duties can be grouped under the following headings.

1. *To make operational decisions under delegated responsibilities.* While operational decisions may be conclusive, in most instances, they are largely dependent upon and confined within the major areas of policy established by the agency's administrative head, the legislative body, and/or the chief executive. These operational decisions are made on a day-to-day basis, usually by career service personnel, acting under delegated authority and responsibility.

2. *To maintain a desirable level of production or service.* Public agencies exist to perform services, in the broadest sense of the term, and the line agency is primarily responsible for providing these services. Therefore, one of the central duties of any line agency is the maintenance of a suitable level of production *at an acceptable level of cost.* A key element in the maintenance of production is the establishment of standards. Standards may be derived to determine the level of service to be provided, effectiveness and efficiency of operations, competence of individual employees, and levels of output or performance.

3. *To plan and program for the execution of delegated responsibilities.* Program planning must begin with a detailed study of the job to be done. Such a study must identify the principal parts of the task, their divisions and subdivisions, the relations between these parts and the boundaries of each part, the types of procedures required to make the program operational, and many other factors. A second phase of program planning involves an estimate of the volume of activity. Such estimates are critical to the operations of line agencies, since volume affects the structure and division of work, budget, personnel, the appropriate forms of program controls, and other related aspects of management. It is necessary to foresee what different skills and experiences will be required, and how many employees of each kind will be needed. A third major aspect involves the forecasting of shifts in the rate or flow of work under alternative conditions. Since many agencies experience fluctuations in work load, these variations must be calculated and plans must be made for the adjustment of personnel and the reassignment of work to carry the program over slack periods. At the same time, there must be assurances that staff will be available for "crash" phases of the program. Thus attention must be given to the timing and organization of work so that its various parts flow in an orderly sequence that permits the full utilization of personnel and other limited resources. This latter phase of program planning is analogous to the "scheduling" phase of PPBS.

Some Considerations Involved in Program Analysis

At this point in the discussion, one might expect the title of the next subject area to be "How To Do Program Analysis." Such a cookbook approach is avoided in this presentation for two main reasons. (1) if such a presentation were attempted, it undoubtedly would require an entire book in itself; but, more important, (2) it is doubtful that even a book on the subject is possible.[b] At the current stage of development, the methods of program analysis — cost-benefit, cost-effectiveness, and other forms of cost-utility analysis — constitute an art rather than a science. As a result, it is not possible to give a definitive set of rules on how to do an appropriate program analysis — rules that would fit every situation. However, some guidelines, principles, and illustrative examples can be suggested.[5]

The Conceptual Framework

In general, there are two principal approaches to program analysis: the (1) *fixed benefits approach* for a specific level of benefits to be attained in the accomplishment of some given objective. The analysis attempts to determine that alternative (or feasible combination of alternatives) likely to achieve the specified objectives at the lowest economic cost; and (2) the *fixed budget approach* for a specified budget level to be used to the attainment of some given objective. The analysis attempts to determine that alternative (or feasible combination) likely to produce the highest level of benefits for the given budget level.

The fixed level of benefits or budget may be specified by someone "outside" the analysis, that is, it may be a "given," and it may be treated as such by the program analyst. Very often, however, a major part of the program analysis will center upon a determination of this constraint. In either case, the analyst generally will use several levels (e.g., high, medium, and low) to investigate the sensitivity of the ranking of alternatives to variations in the level of cost or benefits. Either (or both) of these approaches may be used, depending on the context of the problem. In any event, the objective is to permit comparisons to be made among alternatives, and for this purpose, something has to be held constant.

Construction of a Model

The main thrust of program analysis involves the construction of a model or series of models, using the term in a broad sense. The purpose of the model is to permit an evaluation of alternatives to be made under varying conditions. Depending on the nature of the problem, the model developed may be formal or informal, highly mathematical or nonmathematical, may rely heavily on

[b]It should be noted, however, that books or major parts of books have been or are being written on the subject. A partial listing of these is provided in the Annotated Bibliography.

automated data processing techniques and equipment or only moderately so, and so forth. It must be emphasized that, to be useful, a model need not be highly formal and mathematical.[6] In any event, the following points are important to keep in mind in the construction of a model for program analysis.

The main purpose in designing the model is to develop a meaningful set of relationships among (a) the objectives, (b) relevant alternatives available for attaining the objectives, and (c) the estimated cost and/or benefits associated with each of the alternatives. This central purpose should be kept in mind throughout the model construction and model testing phases.

The construction of a model is an art and not a science. As a consequence, it often requires an experimental process. A major objective of this process is to identify and highlight those factors that are relevant to the problem under study and judiciously to eliminate or hold in check those factors that are relatively unimportant. Unless this is done, the model is likely to be unmanageable.

Since by definition a model is an abstraction from reality, the model must be constructed on a set of assumptions. These assumptions must be made explicit in the construction of the model. Failure to do so must be regarded as a major defect in the model design.

In constructing the model, provision must be made for the explicit treatment of uncertainty. As noted previously, systems analysis as a problem-solving approach is most adaptable to situations in which there is a high degree of uncertainty. In applying these techniques to the budgeting process, failure to take into account explicitly the uncertain nature of resources, of program costs, and of program performance can result in an incomplete analysis or worse yet, an analysis which leads to erroneous decisions and costly mistakes.

Before discussing this final point further, a comment on the use of benefit-to-cost ratios seems in order. The use of such ratios in evaluating alternatives usually poses no problem as long as the analysis is conducted in the framework outlined above (i.e., with the level of either cost or benefit fixed). However, there are occasions when studies fail to do this, with the result that the comparisons essentially are meaningless.

As an example of this problem, consider the following hypothetical illustration:

	Benefit	Cost	Benefit–Cost Ratio
Alternative A	30	20	1.5
Alternative B	450	300	1.5

Under the notion of benefit-cost ratios, those alternatives having a ratio of greater than 1 should be considered, and the alternative with the highest ratio should be selected. If an analyst is preoccupied with ratios, the significance of the above example is a state of indifference regarding the choice between A and B — both yield the same benefit-cost ratio. However, in light of the wide difference in absolute terms between A and B, the analyst most probably should not be indifferent. In fact, with such a great difference in scale, it is likely that the analyst is not even comparing relevant alternatives.

Treatment of Uncertainty

Most of the really interesting and challenging decision situations involve major conditions of uncertainty; therefore, analyses of programs in such situations must provide for explicit treatment of uncertainty. This may be accomplished in a number of ways. For the purposes of discussion, two major types of uncertainty may be distinguished: (1) uncertainty about the state of the real world in the future; and (2) statistical uncertainty.

The second type of uncertainty is usually the least troublesome to handle in program analysis. This type of uncertainty arises from chance elements in the real world. It would exist even if uncertainty of the first type were zero. When necessary, Monte Carlo[7] or other techniques may be applied to deal with statistical uncertainty. Statistical uncertainties, however, usually are overshadowed by uncertainties of the first type, which are dominant in most long-range planning and programming problems. In such cases, the use of complicated techniques to deal with statistical uncertainties may be little more than expensive window dressing.[8]

Techniques for Dealing With
Type 1 Uncertainty

Uncertainty about the state of the world in the future, typically present in most long-range decision problems, is most difficult to take into account in program analysis. Several techniques, applicable under varying circumstances, have been developed for treating such uncertainties, however. These techniques include (1) sensitivity analysis; (2) contingency analysis; and (3) a fortiori analysis. Each of these techniques is described briefly below; here again, the purpose is not to present a "how-to-do-it" approach but to identify the conceptual framework which underlies the technique.

Sensitivity analysis is designed to measure (often very crudely) the possible effects on the alternatives under analysis resulting from variations in uncertain elements. In most problems there are a few key parameters about which there is a great deal of uncertainty. The analyst faced with this situation first would attempt to determine a set of "expected values" for these parameters, as well as all other parameters. But recognizing that these expected values, at best, may be guesstimations, the analyst would use several values (optimistic, most likely, and pessimistic) in an attempt to ascertain how sensitive the results might be (i.e., the relative rankings of the alternatives under consideration) in light of variations in the uncertain parameters.

Assuming a fixed benefits approach, Table 6.1 might serve to illustrate how sensitivity analysis can be used to disclose the variations in rankings among alternatives based on anticipated costs. Two related points concerning uncertainties are illustrated in Table 6.1. First, it points up that the range of uncertainty may vary from alternative to alternative. (For alternative A, the range is 10 to 110; for alternative B, 30 to 115; and for alternative C, 5 to 90.) Second, it underlines the fact that uncertain costs may not always be the critical factor in determining the "best" alternative, i.e., although uncertain costs are lowest in the case of alternative C, it still ranks third except under conditions of "high" or "pessimistic" uncertain costs.

Contingency analysis is designed to examine the effects on alternatives under consideration when a relevant change is postulated in the criteria for evaluating the alternatives. This approach also can be used to ascertain the effects of a major change in the general environment within which the problem situation is operative. In short, it is a form of "with and without" analysis. In the field of public health, for example, various alternative approaches to a state agency's responsibility for environmental health programs might be evaluated with and without a major new program in code enforcement. In a more local context, various possible park sites may be evaluated under conditions of existing population distribution and the configuration of access routes. Additional evaluations then might be made, assuming different population distributions and under various route configurations.

A *fortiori analysis*[9] (coming from the Latin, meaning "with stronger reason") is a method of deliberately "stacking the deck" in favor of one alternative to determine how it might stand up in comparison to other alternatives. Suppose that in a particular planning decision situation, the general accepted judgment prior to analysis strongly favors alternative C. In performing the analysis of C in comparison to other feasible alternatives, the analyst may choose deliberately to resolve the major uncertainties in favor of C and then determine how each of the other alternatives compare under these adverse conditions. If some alternative other than C looks good, the analyst may have a very strong case for dismissing the initial intuitive judgment concerning alternative C. Such analysis might be carried out in a series of trials with each alternative, in turn, being favored in terms of the major uncertainties.

While these three techniques for dealing with uncertainty may be useful in a direct analytical sense, they also may contribute indirectly to the resolution of problem situations.[10] Through sensitivity and contingency analyses, for example, it may be possible to gain a better understanding of the really critical uncertainties of a given problem area. With this knowledge, a newly designed alternative might be formulated that would provide a reasonably good hedge against a range of the more significant uncertainties. While this is often difficult to do, when it can be accomplished, it may offer one of the best ways to offset the uncertainties of a problem situation.

Table 6-1

**Illustration of Sensitivity Analysis
under Various Uncertain Cost Levels.**

Cost Levels	Program Alternatives		
	A	B	C
"Expected value" of uncertain costs (medium)	60	40	70
"Expected value" of all costs	150	120	170
Ranking of alternatives	2	1	3
High value of uncertain costs	110	115	90
"Expected value" of all costs	200	195	190
Ranking of alternatives	3	2	1
Low value of uncertain costs	10	30	5
"Expected value" of all costs	100	110	115
Ranking of alternatives	1	2	3

Checking the Validity of the Model

Another important consideration – often neglected – is to check the validity of the model. Since the model is only a representation of reality, it is desirable to undertake some form of verification to determine if, within the context of the problem under study, the analysis is a reasonably good representation of real world conditions. Such verification may be difficult, especially in dealing with problems having a long-range time dimension.

In general, models of this type cannot be tested by "controlled" experimental methods. However, the analyst might seek answers to the following *a priori* questions: (1) Can the model assign causes to known effects and can it describe known facts and situations reasonably well? (2) Can the model handle particular situations where some indications are already available as to what the outcomes should be? In short, the model can be "tested" using historic trend data to determine how well it can "predict" the present.

It also is possible to check the validity of the model by varying key parameters involved in the particular problem situation and then determining if the results remain relatively consistent and plausible. This approach is somewhat analogous to sensitivity analysis discussed previously. The main difference between the two approaches lies in the elements varied to determine overall sensitivity.

Budget Preparation, Appraisal, and Analysis

Up to this point in the discussion, programming and budgeting have not been clearly distinguished from each other. It now is necessary to rectify this oversimplification. Programming and budgeting may be regarded as different but complementary components of the same general operation.[11]

Every organization – whether in or out of the public sector – finds it necessary to have some sort of budget that represents a plan or program for the use of its resources. Every organization – if it is to survive – also must look beyond the immediate future, to make plans for its long-range activities. In this connection, long-range plans and programs and short-range budgets must be consistent with each other. Program revisions require modifications in the budget; and departures of the budget from the longer range programs may dictate significant revisions in these programs. Ideally, the process of revision should be continuous and comprehensive. Since elements of any program frequently are highly interdependent, revisions of any one element necessitate reconsideration of all other elements. For this reason, revisions must be undertaken in a comprehensive framework.

While in practice comprehensiveness may be too costly in time and effort, in light of uncertainties, and in terms of the organizational demands that it might generate, steps must be taken to guard against the built-in tendency toward rigidity in any budgeting system. In this respect, an approach to budgeting based on a program framework is likely to be more flexible than more conventional budgeting systems. The more conventional systems are particularly responsive to the forces of inertia that exist throughout any organization.

The need for flexibility has important implications for the optimal time horizon for which various program are designed. The very existence of a defined program implies some loss of freedom and flexibility. On the other hand, many activities, such as those involving long term capital investments, must be based on some projection of a highly uncertain future. The time horizon of such programs must be of sufficient duration to encompass the range of activities envisioned by the program. However, long-range projections which border on shaky guesstimations should be avoided, particularly if they lock-in the organization to substantial commitments of uncertain resources.

The primary functions of the capital improvements program are to minimize waste and duplication, to avoid overlap and conflict of programs, to assure that advantage is taken of the range of possible sources for capital funds and annual expenditures for debt service, maintenance, and operations, and to maximize the returns from the long-range capital investments of government. The programming of capital investments will not solve all the financial problems of government, but it should result in wiser and more expeditious use of limited resources, so that each dollar can yield a more effective return of desired improvements.

Failure to plan for capital improvements, including a formulation of policies as to the desired levels of public service, can result in violent fluctuations of capital outlays and operating expenditures. This, in turn, is likely to increase overall financing costs and result in a number of diseconomies in the allocation of personnel and equipment.

The need for staging and coordination of capital facilities arises from the limited tax resources available to any level of government. Staging should permit time for advance planning and design without committing governmental funds years before their actual use. This, in turn, should provide for a more even rate of expenditures, both operating and capital. By anticipating needs in advance, governments should be able to provide more adequate services at lower costs.

While capital programming may be undertaken in the absence of, or prior to, completion of a long-range plan, the dangers inherent in this practice should be readily apparent. Capital outlays represent a long-term investment in facilities and/or equipment which have a substantial "life-span." Once a facility is built to meet an immediate need, it cannot be readily shifted to some other location or expanded without incurring considerable costs. Therefore, the capital improvements program should be based on a long-range and comprehensive plan which embodies the best estimates of future needs and reflects a consensus of policy objectives.

Budget Appraisal

Successful budgeting depends on an ability to appraise and analyze past and current expenditure patterns and to project future implications from these experiences. The direction of future policy often depends critically on the availability of sound quantitative and qualitative data concerning the past, the present, and the near future.

Consequently, a successful budget-making process depends heavily on the systematic accumulation of information about past performance to serve as a guide for the future. Knowledge of the past is necessary not only to provide analogues to present experiences, but also to point to new methods and programs which might provide improvements over past performance. While the point may seem obvious, nevertheless it bears emphasis — past experience can provide an important input to deliberations on future expectations.

However, two kinds of overreactions frequently are found within government. On the one hand, past experience simply is reproduced — extended by a straight-line projection into the future. Failure to analyze the relevance of past experience for the present leads to the reproduction of past mistakes as well as past achievements. Systematic attempts must be made to appraise past performance and adapt these experiences to future requirements. The opposite kind of mistake also is made in government. By failing to recognize that history does afford instances of problems closely analogous to those of the present, each problem situation is approached as if it were a unique occurrence. The result is a great deal of wasted effort and time covering the same analytical ground that has been covered by others in the past.

The foundation of an effective program budget of PPBS system, therefore, is a comprehensive information system. While existing under various designations, such as MIPES (Management Information and Program Evaluation System), IDIS (Integrated Data and Information System), and UGIS (Unified Government Information System), many levels of government are discovering that the establishment of such an information system is a vital precept to the development of an operational PPBS system.

One aspect of the past has been an important preoccupation in the traditional approach to budgeting. A common feature of most public budgeting systems has been their close association with accounting. But government accounting systems largely have been formulated as control devices, to limit the exercise of discretion by public officials and to check on their honesty. This approach to accounting, in turn, has been reflected in traditional methods of public budgeting. Conservative attitudes toward spending and an emphasis on efficiency at the expense of effectiveness have prevailed in budget offices at most levels of government.

In recent years, however, more progressive governments — as have more progressive businesses — have recognized the need for cost accounting. These improvements have been accelerated in some areas by the informational needs of program budgets and PPBS systems. Despite these gradual improvements, it is doubtful that any accounting system by itself will provide all the cost information needed for adequate program and budget analysis.

Measuring costs, however, is only half of the problem. It is far more difficult to obtain information on the benefit side and measures of program effectiveness. How is the success of a long-range economic development program measured? Are government programs in the field of public health keeping pace with the needs of the society? On what basis is it possible to compare a world with public welfare programs with one without these programs? In a rapidly changing, complex urban society, historic analogues may be of little value in gauging the effectiveness of such governmental activities. Questions such as these often defy systematic analysis, with the result that detailed information on costs are matched against crude intuition and value judgments on the benefits side.

Budget Analysis

As attention shifts from the past to the future, two major questions arise, either separately or in combination: (1) How effective is a given budget in attaining the program objectives that it embodies? and (2) Can existing program results be obtained at lower costs? These two questions attempt to draw a distinction between the *effectiveness* of budget allocations in achieving program objectives and the *efficiency* with which programs are carried out. This distinction, when it can be made, is most useful for analytic purposes. Unfortunately, the distinction between effectiveness and efficiency often is made on an arbitrary basis, without careful consideration to true measures of these control objectives. Under such circumstances, the distinction can be very misleading.

In the public sector, the ability to distinguish between efficiency and effectiveness often depends on the feasibility of quantitative measurement of program ·performance. For some programs, such measurements are readily available. However, in many other areas, such as law and order, urban improvement, public welfare, and so forth, it is extremely difficult to formulate a cardinal scale for analyzing and evaluating program effectiveness. Nevertheless, it may be possible to develop ordinal measures or to apply the criterion of "more or less" to such programs. If this is possible, the efficiency of budget allocations can be examined separately at any level of program effectiveness.

As pointed out in the previous chapter, the distinctions between effectiveness and efficiency must be used with extreme care. Programs that purport to increase efficiency may have pronounced effects, good and bad, on effectiveness. Government campaigns for economy of operations, for example, often reduce effectiveness — sometimes intentionally — in the guise of eliminating waste.[12] On the other hand, the elimination of undeniable waste and inefficiency may lead to a general improvement in the overall effectiveness of governmental operations.

7 Operations Scheduling and Work Programming

There continues to be a high degree of inefficient organization in the programming of governmental operations. As public agencies strive to become more effective in carrying out their ever increasing responsibilities, new management techniques must be employed to promote efficiency and economy in governmental operations. Many federal grant-in-aid programs now stipulate that work to be undertaken must be programmed carefully prior to initiation. This work programming requirement can lead to significant cost reductions, as well as provide greater assurances of work completion within the anticipated schedule.

Continued inefficient organization in the programming of governmental operations is somewhat ironic in light of general administrative objectives of economy and efficiency and efforts of governmental planners and administrators to instill long-range planning among operating agencies. Readily available evidence of the above indictment, however, can be found in the number of project deadlines that are missed, often because they are unrealistic in light of the scope of work, in the federally sponsored programs which require project extensions; and in the familiar practice of dropping work items from a project schedule in order to meet overall work deadlines.

The Lack of Understanding and Confidence in Programming Techniques

Much of this inefficiency can be attributed to a lack of understanding of, and confidence in, the use of new programming techniques which have been applied successfully in the private sector. The argument that techniques developed for private enterprise are not applicable directly to public activities — particularly nonproduct-oriented functions — is fallacious by its very nature. It may be valid to say that many activities of government are "process" oriented, and therefore do not result in an "end product" as such. It must be recognized, however, that these processes have some objectives which can be analogous to a project completion. Further, a range of cost and time constraints clearly can be associated with most governmental activities. Through effective programming, these activities, in turn, can be organized in an optimal manner so as to minimize activity cost and utilize time constraints more effectively. Assuming that such a program is followed, it will also mean that the time saved through the minimization of inefficiencies will enable the staff to undertake new and varied activities without increasing in size.

There are two basic requirements for formulating a program for governmental activities applicable to these more advanced management techniques: (1) a clearly stated work program (including a breakdown of jobs or work elements) directed toward one or more definable objectives; and (2) the skill to attach cost and resource estimates to each work element in this program. Given this fundamental information, there are several programming techniques which have been developed to permit the determination of maximum time allotments for each job, as well as costs involved.

The *critical path method* (CPM) and *heuristic programming* are two techniques which perhaps offer the most potential, while at the same time they are relatively simple in their application. Manipulation of a critical path program provides a decision-making tool for determining whether or not "crash" programs — involving significant reallocation of resources — should be attempted. It also improves the ability of management to order activities in a more logical sequence and to identify problems in advance, rather than relying on approaches that, in the main, discover deviations from the program after the fact. Heuristic programming offers a further means of scheduling related activities in light of limited resources, particularly personnel. In effect, it provides a means of leveling off staff commitments, so as to avoid the problems associated with major reassignments during the course of the project.

The Critical Path Method

CPM and PERT — Basic Distinctions

It is important at the outset to clarify the distinctions between the critical path method (CPM) and the *project evaluation and review technique* (PERT). During a brief period in its development, there appeared to be two diverging approaches to the formulation and solution of networks for project planning and control, even though both approaches are derived from basic techniques of network analysis. On the one hand, the critical path method, developed in 1956, was designed primarily for the evaluation of performance time and the total cost of projects consisting of relatively well-defined activities. On the other hand, PERT was formulated in 1958 for the management of very large or long-range projects for which the nature and duration of many activities involved high degrees of uncertainty.

As both methods were later revised for improvement, the attractive features of one were soon incorporated in the other. Thus, while many of the techniques and concepts associated with CPM have been incorporated in PERT (i.e., it is possible to identify a "critical path" in the development of a PERT network), the critical path method is able to stand on its own merits as a work programming device. The techniques of PERT requires substantially more "sophistication" in computer hardware and software, as well as more extensive computer programming. For the purposes of work programming in governmental operations, therefore, CPM offers greater promise, especially in those cases where no previous programming experience is evident.

Basic Components of CPM

Reduced to its basic components, the critical path method is a form of network analysis. The theory of network analysis is not new; scientists and engineers have been using it in one form or another for many years. Some of the earliest work in network theory, for example, began as papers on production scheduling and inventory management. Much of this early work found its way into military applications during the early 1940s and forms a basis for such related fields as operations research and systems analysis.

It is customary when tracing the history of network theory to start with the work of Henry Laurence Gantt. Gantt developed a method of charting production activities and processes in a more orderly manner, and thereby produced one of the earliest forms of modern network analysis techniques. In Gantt charting, however, no effort is made to show the dependency and interconnections among activities and coordinated functions. Further, precedent relationships or the sequential ordering of activities are not clearly identified. Therefore, in recent years, the concept of the critical path method has evolved as a mixture of new ideas and proven experiences.

The critical path method and program evaluation and review technique received widespread application by the military in the late 1950s. While there are still differences of opinion among the various branches of the service as to which first used these programming techniques, the most widely publicized application was that of the Navy in the management of the Polaris missile program. The Air Force also began to make use of these programming techniques during this period, after fifteen years of experience with other network analysis techniques. Today, the Army Corps of Engineers is committed to CPM; the Civil Engineering Corps of the Navy is committed to PERT. Both of these agencies have written a special provision in selected projects which require the contractor to include a CPM or PERT schedule with his bid.

The application of CPM programming to industrial maintenance and heavy construction, as well as managerial decision-making in general, was largely pioneered by the Remington-Rand and DuPont organizations. Early application to governmental operations, outside of the military, have been sporadic in nature, principally in connection with large transportation studies and the programming of capital facilities.

The critical path method, as a technique of graphic network analysis, provides a more systematic approach to the development of information for decision-making. A CPM model is essentially a "graphic plan of action" providing an intelligible, visual picture of the goals to be achieved and their interrelationships. It facilitates the selection of the critical route to be followed to reach these goals. It also permits the identification of where obstacles and delays might be encountered before they actually occur. The critical path approach facilitates logical thought by permitting the administrator and the decision-maker to recognize more fully the relationships of the parts to the whole. While network analysis was originally conceived for application to large programs and operations, usually of a research and development nature, CPM can be used as a relatively simple analytical technique even where operations are on a small scale.

The critical path method divides the management function into two distinct phases: (1) planning — deciding *what* should be done; and (2) scheduling — determining *when* operations should be done. With this separation of functions, it is possible to determine what operations or activities actually control significant completion times. Thus, supervision of any project or program can be managed by exception; principal attention can be given to the controlling operations.

The concept of CPM can be applied to the analysis of several different aspects of any given problem, such as the allocation of personnel, time allocations, operational costs, and reliability of procedures. The critical path method is most frequently applied as a means of indicating the relationships between various events or activities necessary to achieve given objectives and the most effective sequence in which these events or activities should take place.[a]

Application of the Critical Path Method

The problems of planning and scheduling of projects can be represented by networks indicating various activities in the proper order or sequence of execution. A network, showing the dependency or precedence relationships of various activities in a project or program, can be used effectively for the control

[a]The terms "events," "activities," or "jobs," as used in connection with the concept of Critical Path Method, refer to the subparts of any given task or operation. An *activity* is any subdivision of a project whose execution requires time and resources, including manpower and equipment. The time required to perform an activity is called the *duration* of the activity. The beginning and the end of activities are signposts or milestones indicating the progress of the project. The instantaneous time denoting any such beginning or end is called an *event*. The time at which a specified event occurs is called the *event time*.

of performance time and cost of the project. The network provides a master plan in time scale for achieving the objectives of expediting the completion, allocating available resources, and/or controlling the cost of the project.

Identification of Activity Linkages

In applying the CPM, a program is first portrayed in symbolic terms (using circles, squares, or rectangles) as a network of interrelated operations or activities necessary to achieve certain prescribed events. If an activity is denoted by a directed branch between two nodes in a network, an arrow indicates the direction of time flow from one event to another, the events being denoted by the nodes. Either the branches or the nodes in a network may be identified, depending upon whether the emphasis is placed on the role of the activities or on the significance of the events. It also is possible to place activities on the nodes if such an arrangement is preferred.

These various approaches are illustrated in Figure 7.1. In Figure 7.1A, the network is said to be *activity-on-branch,* and the identifiers are *activity oriented.* The network in Figure 7.1B is also activity-on-branch, but the identifiers are *event oriented.* The network in Figure 7.1C is said to be *activity-on-node,* and the branches are used to denote the precedence relationships of activities only. As a generally accepted form of notation, activities are designated by alpha characters (A, B, C, and so forth) whether on-branch or on-node, while events are designated by arabic number (1, 2, 3, and so forth).

To illustrate the procedures for developing a CPM network, in Column 1 of Figure 7.2 seventeen activities are noted by alpha characters A through Q. These activities are then related to one another in terms of their linkages (Column 2). Through this process, it is possible to ensure that all of the important elements, activities, or processes, and their interrelationships have been included in the analysis. At this stage, however, the critical path method merely indicated that activity A is related to activity B, activity C is related to activities D and G, and so forth.

Predecessor-Successor Relationships

Once the "links" between the various activities have been indicated clearly for all operations in the program, three basic questions must be asked about each activity: (1) What must be done before this activity can begin? (2) What can be undertaken concurrently? (3) What must immediately follow this activity? These three questions are summaried for the example in Column 3 of Figure 7.2.

The predecessor-successor relationships of various activities can also be given by a matrix, such as shown in Figure 7.3, which is frequently referred to as the *implicit precedence matrix.* Using this approach, the predecessors of an activity in a column heading are located by the rows in which the X's are marked in that

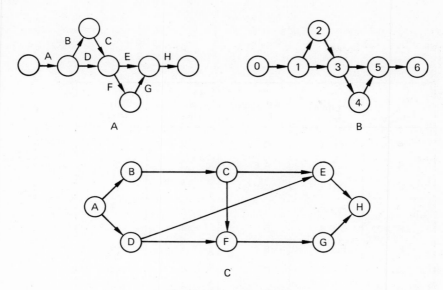

Figure 7-1 Networks.

column. For example, column I has an X in rows D, H, and L, since these activities must precede activity I; Columns A and E also have X's in row D, since activity D is a predecessor of these activities. Conversely, the successors of an activity in a row heading are given by the columns in which the X's are found in that row. For example, row L has X's in columns I, M, and N, since activities I, M, and N are successors to activity L. Using this matrix, all predecessors and all successors of any activity can be obtained by following through both the designated row and column.

By examining the total network in this manner, a series of sequential relationships, called *paths,* can be identified and diagrammed by means of connecting arrows. These paths indicate the flow of activities which must take place in order to complete any given task. Each path must be completed in the indicated sequence in order for the various work items to be carried out in the proper relationship to one another, and in order for the overall program to be successfully accomplished. Once the various connections have been drawn, a critical route can be determined and progress can be more easily followed and measured against a list of key check points or milestones.

Formulating the Arrow Diagram

An examination of selected activities in Figure 7.4 will illustrate how these "arrow diagrams" can be developed. Activity A is linked to activities B, D, and J and must be preceded by Activity D. Graphically, this can be represented by

(1) Activity	(2) Linked to	(3) Preceded by	(4) Length of Time	(5) Staff Required
A	B,D,J	D	2	4
B	A,K,E	A,E	2	4
C	D,G	(None)	1	5
D	A,C,E,I	C	2	4
E	D,F,B	D	1	5
F	E,J	E	1	5
G	C,H	C	1	3
H	G,I	G	2	3
I	D,H,L,M	D,H,L	2	5
J	A,F,K,M,O	A,F,M	1	8
K	B,J,Q	B,J,Q	2	4
L	I,M,N	(None)	2	3
M	I,J,L,O	I,L	1	3
N	L,P,O	L	1	3
O	J,M,N,Q,P	J,M,N,P	1	6
P	N,O	N	1	3
Q	K,O	O	1	4

Figure 7-2 Activity Links.

	Successor																
Predecessor	A	B	C	D	E	F	G	H	I	J	K	L	M	N	O	P	Q
A		X								X							
B											X						
C				X		X											
D	X				X				X								
E		X				X											
F									X								
G								X									
H									X								
I													X				
J											X				X		
K																	
L									X				X	X			
M									X						X		
N															X	X	
O																	X
P															X		
Q											X						

Figure 7-3   Implicit Precedence Matrix.

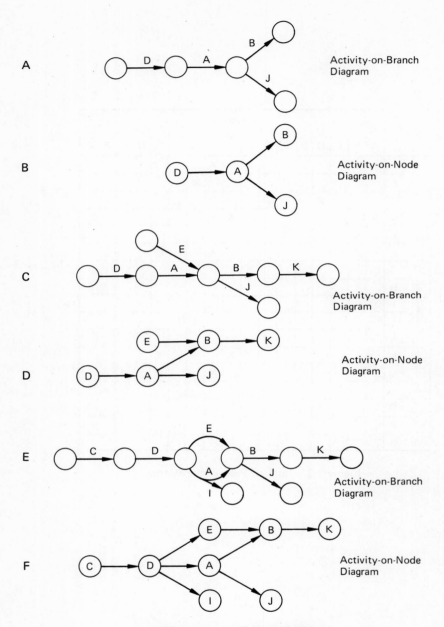

Figure 7-4 Activity Diagrams.

either Figure 7.4A, or 7.4B. However, examining Activity B, it will be noted that it must be preceded by E and is linked to both A and K. Added to the initial arrow diagrams, the new diagrams would take the forms illustrated by Figures 7.4C and 7.4D. Activity D, it will be noted, is linked to A, E, and I and must be preceded by C. This would expand the diagrams as shown by Figures 7.4E and 7.4F. Since activities A, E, and I must all be preceded by Activity D, but have no apparent relation to one another, they can begin at the same time and can be performed simultaneously.

Dummy Operations

Frequently, various operations or activities evidence a dependence even though they are not directly related. Therefore, it may be of importance to include some notion of this dependence in the arrow diagram. Such a case is illustrated by the common dependence of activity B on activities E and A. While E and A are not directly related, these activities must be completed before B can be initiated. A dashed arrow is used in activity-on-branch networks to show this dependence and is called a *dummy operation*. A dummy operation requires no time; it merely is a device to identify a dependence among operations. Dummy operations may be introduced into a network for the purposes of providing unique activity designations and maintaining the correct order in the sequence. Another use of the dummy operation in activity-on-node networks is to prevent arrows from having the same common beginning and end points, as when two operations are initiated at the same time, are carried on simultaneously, and are linked to the same subsequent event. This case is shown in Figure 7.5. The purpose here is to prevent mistakes when the network is used for calculations. In general, dummy operations can be introduced without disturbing the network sequence except at locations where their presence is necessary.

One of the major advantages of the activity-on-node network is that dummy operations are seldom needed except for the initial and terminal nodes in some cases. Although the activity-on-node network is not as widely used as is the activity-on-branch approach, it has gained popularity for scheduling projects with activities that have complicated precedence relationships. Since this frequently is a problem in work programming problems associated with governmental operations, the activity-on-node approach will be utilized throughout the remainder of this presentation. However, it should be underlined that the methods of computation for activity-on-branch networks are very similar to those for the activity-on-node network.

The Arrow Network

Any project consists of many activities and events, or course, and the CPM network for the project consists of many arrows — one for each operation. When

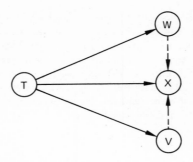

Figure 7-5   Dummy Operations.

all of the arrow diagrams are completed for the project or program, they form an *arrow network*. Networks for the seventeen activities shown in Figure 7.2 are presented in Figures 7.6 and 7.7.

A comparison of these two figures may help to illustrate some of the problems associated with the activity-on-branch approach to projects with complicated precedence relationships. Ten dummy operations are required to show uncertain precedence relationships in Figure 7.6. The term "uncertain" is used here to underline the fact that, until the critical path is found, the network analyst cannot be sure that these dummy operations are not, in fact, directly dependent relationships. For example, the network may have to be modified to shift activity M from branch (10, 12) to branch (9, 12), thereby making the former branch a dummy operation. One of the major advantages to the activity-on-branch approach, however, is that it is more readily adaptable to computerized solution in that the scheduling problem can be stated as a linear programming problem. By solving for both the primal and the dual, the necessary information for the identification of the critical path can be developed mathematically in more elaborate scheduling problems. This may eliminate the need for extensive graphic analyses and network development.

In Figure 7.7 this problem is not encountered. The durations for all activities are placed on the arrow diagram, and computations are made for each path. Therefore, for example, the operational duration of 1 for Activity J is shown on the path from A to J, F to J, and M to J.

At this point, it may be of value to illustrate the advantages of the CPM approach to the programming of related activities over a somewhat less systematic examination of alternatives. As has been suggested, any problem involving a chain of events may be likened to a maze, consisting of a sequence of decision points. At each point, a number of paths are available, but only one can be chosen. One method of finding an optimum solution to such problems would be to enumerate each possible path, evaluate the end results according to some predetermined criteria, and then select the best path. Obviously, if the problems contains many decision points and various paths at each of these points, the number of possible combinations becomes enormous. For example, if the

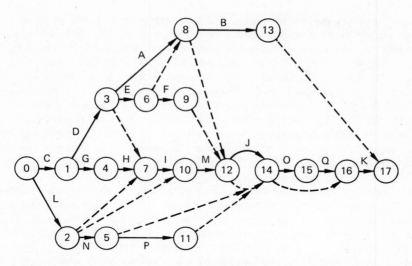

Figure 7-6   An Activity-On-Branch Network for a 17-Event Project.

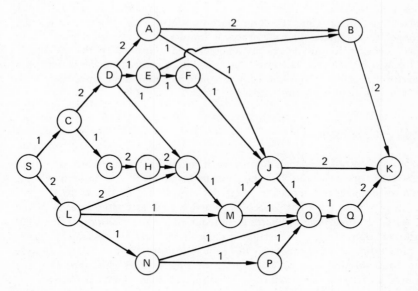

Figure 7-7   An Arrow Network for a 17-Event Project Showing Operation Durations.

seventeen activities shown in Figure 7.2 were to be considered as distinct decision points, each of which could be made in one of three different ways (each having three possible paths to the next activity), it would be necessary to examine over 43 million different solutions or combinations of decisions in a complete enumeration. (Since the decision at each step must be considered to differ from decisions at previous or subsequent steps, the number of branches at each decision point is raised to the power of the number of decision points, or 3^{16} = 43,046,721). The purpose of the CPM technique is drastically to reduce the number of possible alternatives by first establishing sequential relationships and thereby eliminating many of the possible alternatives. The result is a much smaller maze to be searched.

Even with this substantial reduction in the number of possible alternative routes to be searched, the determination of the critical path would be a time-consuming operation if done manually. Over fifty possible paths remain to be explored in Figure 7.7 after the sequential relationships have been diagramed. With the advances in computer software, however, this problem has been minimized. A number of canned programs are available for determining the critical path once a network has been established. Based on the time estimates assigned to each path, the computer program can determine which paths will take less time to complete than others. Such paths have what network analysts call "slack" or "float" time. The one route or combination of paths which will take longer to complete than all others is known as the "critical path." It is "critical" because if any delays are encountered along the path, the whole operation will be delayed. Therefore, the purpose of identifying the critical path is to ensure that elapsed time and delays are held to a minimum, since there is no "float" time to spare along this path.

Calculations on the Network

As previously noted, associated with each arrow in the network is a time estimate called its *duration*. The duration of an arrow is the amount of time required to complete the operation or activity represented by this arrow.

The next step in the CPM process is to assign time estimates to each of the paths. Initially, three time estimates were required in the development of a CPM network: (1) optimistic; (2) most likely or probable; and (3) pessimistic. These three time estimates, together with the probabilities of their occurrences, were utilized to determine a mean value of t or time. Under this approach, the duration of an activity was taken to be the weighted mean value t as follows:

$$t = 1/6\ (t_a + 4t_b + t_c),$$

where

t_a = the most optimistic time estimate

t_b = the most likely time estimate, and

t_c = the most pessimistic time estimate

This relationship, first recognized by the management consulting firm of Booz, Allen, and Hamilton, is equivalent to the so-called *beta distribution,* through which a normal curve can be constructed having a plus and minus of three standard deviations from the mean. After some experimentation, this approach was generally abandoned in favor of developing a single, most likely time estimate. In situations of high uncertainty, however, the three estimates still may prove to be of value.

Suggested "most likely" durations for each of the seventeen activities in the example are shown in column 4 of Figure 7.2. These operation durations can be transferred to Figure 7.7 by writing the duration of each operation near the middle of the corresponding arrow. At this point, it should be noted that no effort has been made to draw the arrows to a time scale.

Objectives of the Network Calculations

Before further explanation, it may be well to review the objectives of the calculations that follow. An effort will be made to determine (1) how long it takes to complete the entire project (completion time); (2) which of the operations establish and control the completion time (the critical path); and (3) how much leeway there is in the operations that do not control the completion time (the "floats"). To meet these objectives, it is necessary to make four calculations for each activity: (1) the *earliest possible occurrence* (EPO) – the earliest possible time for starting all arrows that originate at a given activity node; (2) the *earliest finish time* (EFT) – the sum of the EPO of the activity at the start of the operation plus the duration of the operation; (3) the *latest possible occurrence* (LPO) – the latest possible time that all of the operations that terminate at that activity node can finish without causing the project duration to exceed the value originally calculated with the EPO's; and (4) the *latest start time* (LST) – the LPO of the activity node at which an operation terminates minus the duration of the operation.

To find the EPO of all the activities on an arrow diagram, it is first necessary to assign an EPO = 0 to the first activity node or event in the diagram (this is usually designated as S for "start"). The EPO for each of the remaining events is the maximum of the EFT's of *all* the operations that terminate at that activity node. The EPO for each activity in Figure 7.7 is designated in the arrowhead adjacent to the activity designation in Figure 7.8.

The EPO of the final activity on the diagram has added significance, since it is the earliest possible completion time for the entire project. This follows because each operation in the project was started at the earliest possible time. Thus, the first objective listed previously has been attained, that is, the determination of the project completion time.

Operation Leeway I — Free Float

In calculating the EPO's of each activity, only the maximum EFT pertaining to each was used. The other EFT's are used to calculate a measure of leeway associated with the operations with these smaller EFT's. The *Free Float* of an operation is the difference between its EFT and the EPO of the activity node at which it terminates. In Figure 7.8, the EFT between activities N and O is 4, while the EPO of activity O is 9. Therefore, operation (N, O) has a free float of 9 – 4 = 5. If time is measured in months, this means that operation (N, O) can have a duration of as much as the original estimated duration plus the free float (4 + 5 = 9 months) without disturbing the EPO of activity O. Looking at this another way (if the duration remains in months), (N, O) could be initiated 5 months later than its earliest start time, and the EPO of activity O would be unaffected.

Free float of an operation is the amount of time that the operation can be delayed or lengthened without affecting the EPO of *any* activity on the diagram.

The Critical Path

It should be clear that no operation with a positive free float can control the duration of the entire project. The durations of these operations can be shortened as much as is physically possible or lengthened by an amount equal to the free float they possess without affecting the EPO of any activity. This means that the EPO of the last activity will not be affected and hence that the project duration will not be altered. This observation limits the search for "critical" operations to those that have free floats of zero.

However, all operations with zero floats do not control the project duration. The operations that do control are the ones that have zero free float *and* form a continuous path starting at the first activity and ending at the last one. In Figure 7.9 a small amount of searching will reveal that this path is made up of the links between activities C, G, H, I, M, J, O, Q, and K. If any of these operations are delayed, the project completion time will be increased by the amount of that delay. It is this chain of events that is called the *Critical Path*.

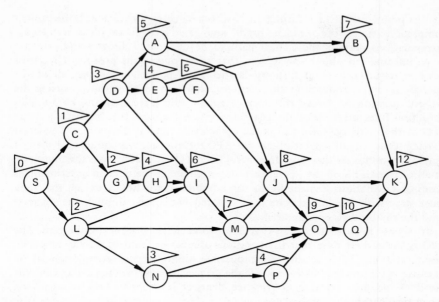

Figure 7-8 An Arrow Network for a 17-Event Project Showing the EPO for Each Event.

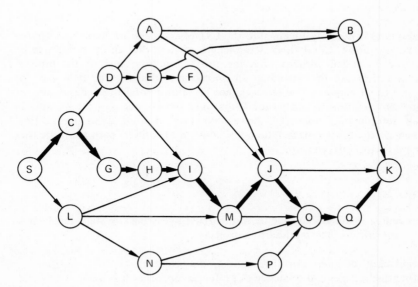

Figure 7-9 An Arrow Network for a 17-Event Project Showing the Critical Path

The LST Schedule

At this point, sufficient information has been calculated to establish the project completion time, the critical path, and the free floats. The remaining manipulations permits the critical path to be designated directly and provides more information about the leeway that some operations possess. The latest possible occurrence of an activity is the latest possible time that all of the operations that terminate at that activity node can finish without causing the project duration to exceed the value originally calculated with the EPO's. This definition fixes the LPO of the last activity (see Figure 7.10). It must equal the EPO of that activity, since this is the completion time of the project. The latest starting time of an operation is the LPO of the activity node at which it terminates minus its duration. In general, the LPO of an activity is the minimum of all of the LST's of the operations that originate at the node in question. This series of calculations is made in the same fashion as the EPO's, except that they must start with the last activity and proceed backwards through the diagram until the first node is encountered.

It is now possible to assign two times to each activity on the diagram. The EPO is the earliest time that all operations originating from an activity node can begin, and the LPO is the latest possible time for the completion of all operations terminating at the node if the project is to be finished on schedule. If the EPO and the LPO of an activity are identical, it means that the activity is on the critical path.

Operation Leeway II — Total Float

The *total float* is numerically equal to the LST of an *operation* minus the EST of the same *operation*. Total float is the length of time that an operation can be delayed or expanded without affecting the *completion time* of the project. Recall that delaying or expanding an operation within its free float did not affect *any* other activity. The same cannot be said of total float. Expanding or delaying an operation within its total float may or may not alter the position in time of intermediate activities. An examination of total float gives a final definition of the critical path. The operations on the critical path are those that have total floats equal to zero.

Summary

The preceding material can best be summarized by listing the steps involved in applying the critical path method to a project:

1. Define all of the operations that make up the project.
2. Define the linkages and sequence of performance for each activity.
3. Draw arrow diagrams that define the sequence of performing the various operations.

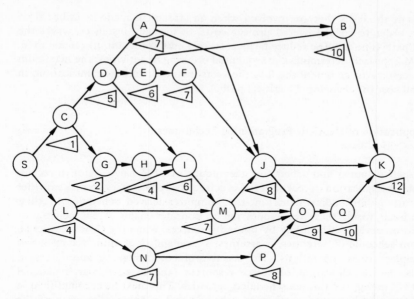

Figure 7-10   An Arrow Network for a 17-Event Project Showing the LPO for Each Event.

4. Estimate the duration of each operation.
5. Calculate the EPO of each activity node or event.
6. Calculate the free float of each operation.
7. Calculate the LPO of each activity node or event.
8. Calculate the total float of each operation.
9. Locate the critical path.

Monitoring the Program with CPM

Once the actual program is placed into operation, the critical path can be continually monitored so that any delays can be determined before they occur. By shifting personnel, materials, or other inputs to the critical path or from those paths which have "floats," such delays can be circumvented. Therefore, the identification of the critical path also provides a dynamic control dimension.

In addition, the CPM network provides a convenient form of shorthand for the administrator, the programmer, and the production manager to express a complex set of relations. It offers a medium of communication and prognostication. It facilitates the subdivision of work so that each person and unit involved in the process may proceed with the more detailed planning of his own part for which he is directly responsible. The CPM approach allows for an analysis of the costs that are involved when an attempt is made to utilize float time in order to reduce overall project costs, or in many instances, where the critical path time is to be reduced, the costs of a crash program. In general then, the CPM approach determines the sequential ordering of activities, the maximum time necessary to complete the job, the costs involved, and the ramifications in time and cost for changing the critical path.

The Application of Heuristic Programming Techniques
To The Critical Path

While such planning and scheduling techniques as CPM have begun to receive widespread application in recent years, it is frequently necessary to make further modifications and adjustments in the computer-derived schedule. In their conventional form, these techniques fail to consider many of the constraints imposed on activity scheduling by limited resources. While the CPM provides an optimum schedule of activities, it assumes an availability of unlimited resources to complete these operations. The usual problem facing the administrator, however, is the allocation of scarce resources (and in particular, personnel resources) among the various scheduled activities. This must be accomplished in such a way to keep the project on schedule and minimize the costs of the resources used. Thus it becomes necessary to apply other programming techniques to bring the decision-making process within more manageable bounds. Such a technique is found in heuristic programming or heuristic problem-solving.

The basic notion of heuristic problem-solving is not new. The term heuristic, as a noun, is derived from the Greek verb *heuriskein*, meaning "to discover." In ancient times, heuristics was the name of a branch of study belonging to logic or philosophy, the aim of which was to investigate the methods of discovery and invention. In its present usage, the meaning has expanded somewhat, so that a "heuristic" is itself an aid to discovery — especially the discovery of a solution to a problem. Thus, a heuristic may be described as any device or procedure used to reduce problem-solving efforts — in short, a rule of thumb used to solve a particular problem.

Although seldom identified as such, most people develop and follow various heuristics in their daily lives. For example, consider the common rule of thumb: "When the sky is cloudy, take an umbrella when going outside." The problem at hand is how to defend oneself against the possible discomforts of the weather. This simple heuristic avoids the more complicated problem-solving procedures such as reading the weather report, calling the weather bureau, analyzing barometer readings, and so forth. For many problems of this kind, we lack the time or inclination to employ more thorough problem-solving procedures. A simple (if not always infallible) rule of thumb usually serves us best.

Some rather sophisticated extensions of this basically simple notion, when combined with the computing capacity of modern electronic data-processing equipment, enable the problem solver to deal successfully with many problems that have not previously yielded to established problem-solving techniques. While heuristics may not lead to the best solution in a particular case, experience over time has proved their general usefulness in finding good solutions to recurring problems and with a minimum of effort.

As shown in column 5 of Figure 7.2, the staff requirements for the successful completion of each of the tasks within the scheduled project vary considerably. When these personnel requirements are applied to the CPM network, as illustrated by Figure 7.11, it may be seen that in the sixth time period (when tasks A, I, N, and E are underway) seventeen staff members are required, while in the seventh time period, fifteen staff members are called for. But suppose there are only ten staff personnel available for the entire project. Some guidelines are required to assist the administrator in his task of assigning these limited resources if the project is to be kept on schedule. These guidelines can be derived from a relatively simple heuristic program, based on the following rules of thumb: (1) Allocate resources serially in time; that is, for the first time period, schedule all jobs possible given staff (or other limited) resources, then do the same for the second time period, and so on. (2) When several jobs compete for the same resources, give preference to the jobs with the least slack time. (3) Reschedule noncritical jobs (those not on the critical path), if possible, in order to free resources for scheduling nonslack (critical) jobs.

For simplicity, let us assume that all of the ten men available are interchangeable in their skills. In practical situations, the various jobs may require men of different skills, as well as other resources such as machines, materials, and money. However, the fundamental techniques applied in this hypothetical example are equally applicable to more complex situations, since the constraints can be manipulated through a computer operation.

In the first time period, only activities C and L can be scheduled since all other activities are dependent upon their completion. These two tasks require eight men. Applying the heuristics to the second time period, activity G, which is in the critical path (and therefore has no slack time) is scheduled first. Activity L, which was initiated in the first time period, is then scheduled. This leaves four members of the staff uncommitted. Thus activity D can be initiated one time period early. In the third time period, activity H in the critical path is scheduled first; D is continued; and activity N is rescheduled from the sixth time period to utilize the remaining three staff members. In the fourth time period, activity H is continued, committing three men. With the early completion of activity D, freeing four men, it is possible to schedule activities A and P.

In the fifth time period, it is necessary to apply the second heuristic in order to initiate activity E, which in combination with activity I commits the entire staff. Thus, activity A must be delayed from completion to the next time period. In the sixth time period, activities I and A are completed and from this point on, the project schedule remains unaltered from the CPM network.

By making these minor adjustments in scheduling utilizing the slack time of various tasks to make "early starts," it is possible to keep the project within the

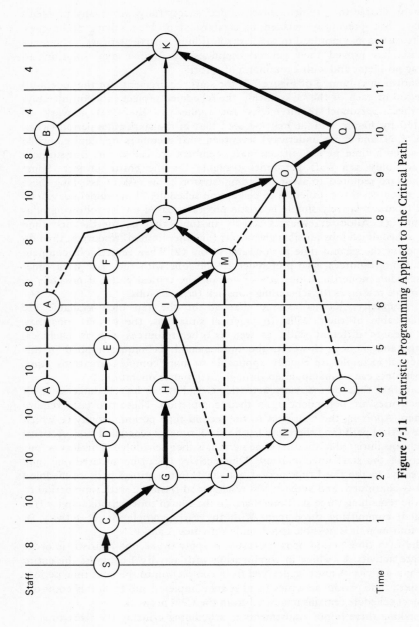

Figure 7-11 Heuristic Programming Applied to the Critical Path.

bounds of the limited staff resources to keep on schedule, and at the same time, to achieve a more even distribution of staff commitments. The new schedule of events is shown in Figure 7.11. It should be noted that in more complex networks, it may be necessary under conditions of limited resources to extend the time period of the project in order to maintain the constraints. However, by utilizing the basic heuristic problem-solving approach, the necessary extensions in time to achieve an optimal schedule can be minimized.

Part Three
Physical Development
Models and Tools

Part Three consists of four chapters dealing with models and tools for the planning of the physical environment that will be of great relevance to urban and regional applications. Chapter 8 deals with the usefulness of computer graphics as a tool for aiding the presentation of information in systemic planning. Chapter 9 discusses a model of urban form and structure that has proved useful in certain types of planning. Chapter 10 is concerned with a model of land use and traffic that is of interest for the programming of physical development plans. Chapter 11, in its discussion of a model for housing in urban areas, concentrates on its application in new town planning – a subject that increases in importance with every passing year.

8 Computer Graphics

As computer science continues to expand, new applications for the computer's speed and precision are constantly being developed. One of the most recent developments has been in the field of computer graphics.

Computer graphics is the art of producing pictures and line drawings on some output medium. In general, such output can be classified as either "soft copy" or "hard copy" drawings. The *soft copy drawing* is generally of an object still under design. For example, new designs can be displayed on special cathode ray tubes with sensitized screens that react to a light pen. Using this pen on the face of the screen, a person can draw or erase lines with immediate response from the computer. *Hard copy,* on the other hand, is output which is permanent. Such copy might be a computer-produced map or graphic plot.

The development of computer graphics and its potential for the planner can be discussed if the subject is subdivided into two main areas: (1) *hardware*, which comprises all devices developed as graphic input or output media for the computer; and (2) *software,* which comprises all methods and techniques of computer programming that are used in conjunction with hardware to translate some input data to graphic form as either soft or hard copy. Before detailing the types of hardware and software that are available for computer graphics, a discussion of the graphic needs of the planner will lend some needed perspective. The desirability of hardware or software can be measured only in terms of applicability in filling a particular need or in solving a particular problem.

Graphic Needs of the Planner

The graphic needs of the planner for soft copy are few. These needs are more often found with architects and engineers as an aid in project design. Soft copy provides an instantaneous means of studying various architectural design alternatives, such as the slope of a roof line or the moment of inertia for a structural member, where changes are commonly made. The need of the planner for soft copy is confined to those areas where he is contemplating physical design alternatives. Site planning is such an area. The ability of the computer to change alternative layouts readily, permitting the planner to study new vistas or arrangements of buildings, has some potential application for soft copy. Similarly, the planner involved in new town development might find some need for soft copy.[1,2]

Soft-copy drawings have proved useful for alternative designs and routing of highways. Experiments using cathode-ray tube pictures of visual perception and esthetic quality of roadside development have been successful for planning purposes.[3] Several attempts at using computer graphics to aid the selections of highway route location have been interesting also.[4]

The primary graphical need of the planner is for hard-copy drawings. The planner traditionally has been predominately land-use oriented and concerned with physical planning. Consequently, his major need has been for permanent drawings, maps, and map-like information. The changes that are afforded by soft-copy drawings are not so valuable to the planner because these graphics are used to influence planning decisions. Graphics are not normally used to select a decision (through experimentation) in planning.

As part of an information retrieval system, the planner can make good use of hard-copy ability to find significant information on a map. In particular, the ability to obtain the elevation of any point in a study area simply by querying the computer can be valuable in site planning or locational analysis. The ability to store a map in terms of a standard coordinate system can be useful. An example of this is the increased use of the address coding guide, which converts street addresses to standard coordinates.

The planner has a very real need to be able to present statistical information in graphic form. The truism that "a picture is worth a thousand words" is significant when a planner attempts to influence a decision-maker through the use of statistical persuasion. The argument is enhanced when cold statistics can be translated into visually recognizable form. For the planner, much statistical data are geographically related. As a result, such statistics may be the basis for a highly informative map.

The predominant interest of the planner in computer graphics lies in the ability of the machine to convert statistical information into graphic form. This may take the form of charts and graphs, but it is most useful when these statistics can be geographically related — that is, converted to a map.

Hardware

Given the perspective of the preceding discussion, hardware can be discussed in terms of its ability to produce hard or soft copy and to fulfill the planner's requirements. Four types of hardware are discussed below: (1) the standard line printer, (2) $X-Y$ plotters, (3) the automated drawing table, and (4) the cathode ray tube (CRT).[5]

Standard Line Printer

The standard output line printer has a considerable ability to produce meaningful hard copy. The printed page is treated as a grid containing 132 cells per row horizontally and six (eight on some machines) cells per inch vertically. A map or other drawing is prepared on a cell-by-cell basis and then printed. As an example, suppose an X versus Y plot is desired.

(1) The machine would operate in this manner:

given,	X = Actual	Y = Predicted
	50	45
	45	50
	39	40
	70	65

(2) The Y is ranked highest to lowest:

X = Actual	Y = Predicted
70	65
45	50
50	45
39	40

The computer would look at the first X-Y pair, call the first line 65, skip 70 cells, and print the plot symbol. In successive steps, the computer would determine the difference between the Y just operated on and the next largest Y and skip the number of lines equal to this difference. On reaching the proper line, X would be read, this value taken as the number of cells to skip, and the proper symbol printed. In this manner, the plot would be produced. Utilizing this technique, it is possible to produce not only simple graphs, but also maps of considerable quality and readability.

X—Y Plotter

The $X—Y$ plotter can produce line graphs or drawings. Generally, these devices consist of a pen that may move only horizontally and a strip of paper that moves vertically. In the example used earlier, the coordinates would have been taken as the end-points of straight-line segments. Having been programmed for this, the computer would produce a magnetic tape, instructing the plotter at what rate the pen was to move horizontally and at what rate the paper was to move vertically, to produce a line graph connecting the coordinate points. This tape is then played back to the plotter, and the actual drawing is produced. Such devices can draw a line 25 feet long in a minute and be accurate to one-hundredth of an inch.

Automated Drawing Table

The automated drawing table is a highly sophisticated drawing device and operates much like the $X—Y$ plotter, except that the pen does both the vertical and horizontal movements. The machine can also do letter drawings with appropriate legends. Speed of operation is about that of the $X-Y$ plotter, but the drafting machine is about ten times more accurate. The automated drawing table may or may not be linked or used in conjunction with a digital computer. Some automated drawing tables function independently of digital computers and are called *analog computers.*

Cathode Ray Tube

The cathode ray tube mentioned earlier is similar to a television picture tube except that lines only are produced. The line is the result of luminescence caused by an electron beam. If this beam moves fast enough, the impression is that of a line or of some geometric shape. The beam is controlled by two perpendicular electrical fields through which the electron beam must pass. By controlling the intensity of the fields, the beam can be aimed to any point on the viewing screen. In turn, each point on the screen corresponds to a unique set of field intensities. Having been programmed for this, the computer can be instructed to adjust these intensities in the same way it adjusted the rate the pen moved, to produce lines. The lines are portrayed on the tube almost instantaneously. It is immediacy that is the most favorable quality of the cathode ray tube. The cathode ray tube is currently the only hardware available for producing soft copy.

Software

Inasmuch as computer graphics are a new area for research and development, there is only a limited amount of software available with which graphic output can be generated. A major portion of the software mentioned in the literature is of an experimental nature, and it is not generally available. The discussion below deals with the software currently operational for which references have been found in the literature. Later discussion considers the questions of cost and availability as these topics affect the planner.

Statistical Graphics

The usual charts found in the planning office are scattergrams and histograms (see Figures 8.1 and 8.2). The Biomedical Center at the University of California at Los Angeles has developed a number of programs that have graphic output of statistical information.[6] The program of particular interest to planners produces scattergrams or histograms on the high-speed line printer. This program has the drawbacks of not being operable as part of a larger program and of requiring the manipulation of input data using a special notation. These drawbacks can be best

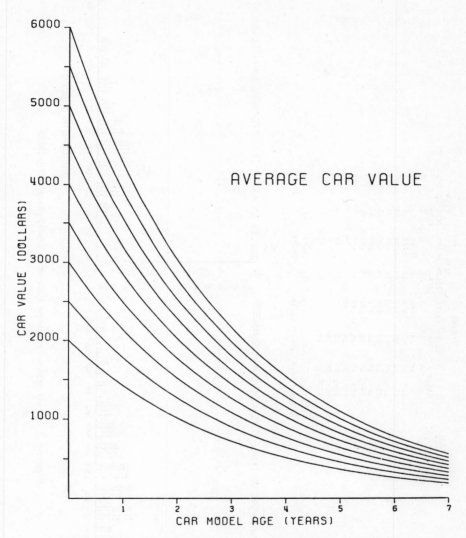

Figure 8-1 Graph Drawn by CalComp Plotter of Car Value Data.

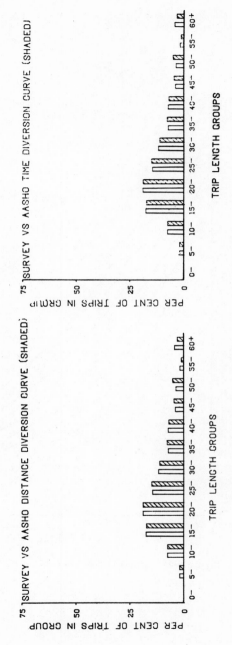

	SURVEY		TIME AASHO		DIST AASHO	
RANGE	ZONE	ZONE-TRIPS	ZONE	ZONE-TRIPS	ZONE	ZONE-TRIPS
0- 5	0	0	0	0	0	0
5- 10	7	3886	7	3946	7	3798
10- 15	27	1475	28	1425	28	1325
15- 20	63	2412	65	2283	65	2180
20- 25	68	950	71	807	71	789
25- 30	52	584	56	473	56	456
30- 35	42	278	42	209	42	205
35- 40	26	173	29	153	25	147
40- 45	26	197	26	168	26	162
45- 50	14	99	19	76	17	70
50- 55	13	84	15	74	15	72
55- 60	6	22	5	14	4	12
60 PLUS	15	49	12	26	11	25
TOTALS	359	10209	377	9654	375	9241
AVE. TRIP LENGTH	16.15		15.36		15.37	

Figure 8-2   Histograms Drawn by Computer for Highway Trip Data.

explained in an example taken from actual experience. An equation was produced of the form:

$$Y = \sum_{K=1}^{5} C_K X_K,$$

where:

Y is the dependent variable,

C is the coefficient of the independent variable,

X is the independent variable, and

K is the index number.

The objective was to plot the actual Y values against the estimated Y values to see if the slope was 1:1, as in theory. Ideally, such a plot should have been produced in the computer development of the equations, but the plotting program requires that this be done as a separate operation. In preparing the data for plotting, the computer must be informed of the value of the coefficients. Normally, two punch cards would have been sufficient, but using the special notation required ten times as many cards.

West and Reynolds have developed a program for plotting on the high-speed line printer.[7] Their description of the procedures needed seems rather straight-forward and seems to produce scattergrams of a quality comparable to those produced using the Biomed program. The advantage of the West and Reynolds' technique is that it is assumed to be used as part of a larger program. Unfortunately, their procedure does not allow the drawing of histograms, as does the Biomed program.

One of the few attempts to develop computer graphics software especially for planning purposes was undertaken by the Urban Data Center of the University of Washington under the direction of Edgar M. Horwood.[8] The research project resulted in a number of programs written for IBM 700 Series computers. These programs permitted array and distribution graphs and data plotted by coordinates of a map (see Figures 8.3 and 8.4). These programs were applied in the Spokane Community Renewal Program and several other planning studies.

Perspectives

Many planning offices are deeply involved with physical design and could make use of the programs listed in the Bibliography that do perspective drawings (see Figure 8.5). Perspective drawing using the computer is possible since the graphical principles involved are amenable to mathematical expression via analytic geometry. This fact has been made use of in the three following articles.

Adamowiez has written what is termed a three-dimensional manipulation

SEATTLE WASH. HOUSING STUDY
PERCENT OF OCCUPIED HOUSING OCCUPIED BY NON WHITE

```
                                          N
                                          U
                                          M
                                          B
                                          E
                                          R

  5.0                                     C.
 10.0                                     4.
 15.0                                     20.
 20.0                                     12.
 25.0                                     14.
 30.0                                     6.
 35.0                                     11.
 40.0                                     8.
 45.0                                     6.
 50.0                                     3.
 55.0                                     5.
 60.0                                     3.
 65.0                                     6.
 70.0                                     1.
 75.0                                     1.
 80.0                                     3.
 85.0                                     6.
 90.0                                     3.
 95.0                                     1.
100.0                                     3.

ACCUMULATED TOTAL =    116.
```

P
E
R
C
E
N
T

Figure 8-3 Distribution Table by Computer from Seattle, Washington, Urban Renewal Study.

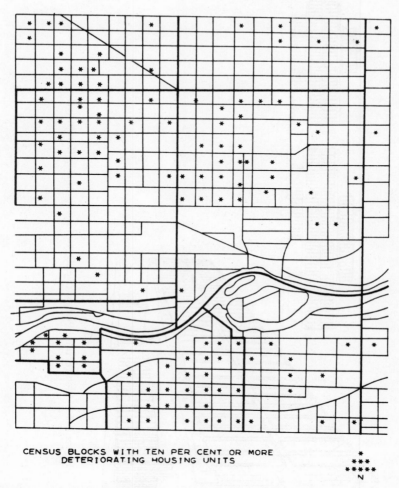

CENSUS BLOCKS WITH TEN PER CENT OR MORE
DETERIORATING HOUSING UNITS

Figure 8-4   Early Version of Computer Mapping Program Developed at the University of Washington.

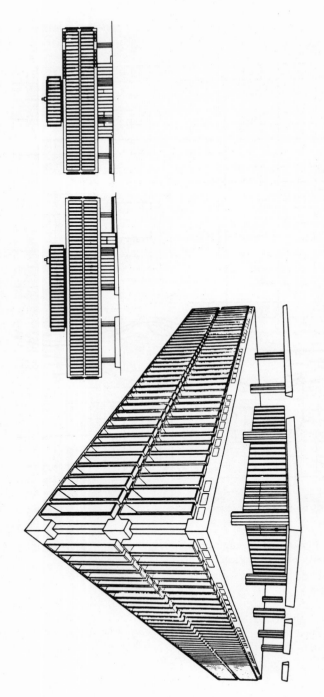

Figure 8-5 Architectural Perspectives Drawn by an Analog Computer.

program.[9] What this means is that the program gives views of an object from various viewpoints. The principle involved is similar to that used in the other two articles. The coordinates of the corners of the object are specified and the computer is informed which corners share a common edge. Also, the imagined position of the viewer is given. Using this basic data, the program instructs the line-drawing device how it shall move. The problem with this program is that it assumes the user is willing to use a PDP-5 computer, which is one of the earlier computers produced by General Electric.

Bernier has written an article that will be useful to persons who might wish to develop their own perspective program.[10] He gives a step-by-step account of the logic involved in drawing a perspective using analytic geometry. He has not involved himself with the actual translation of the mathematical formulas into symbols that can be understood by the computer, nor does he mention any particular drawing equipment to use. This open-ended approach is quite commendable since it makes this article of use to a much larger group than if it had been oriented to a particular computer system. The programming is straightforward once the logic is known. This particular article also discusses how the perspective program can be used to produce axonometric projection.

Unlike the general approach of Bernier, Campion and Robey have written an article on perspective drawing which assumes a particular computer system; and, to compound matters, it is a British computer.[11] The article is useful since it discusses the tradeoffs between manual and automatic production of perspectives. It is pointed out that although setting up the program requires a great deal of a professional's time initially, once operable, it requires a minimal amount of time to use. They also mention that the data preparation takes about two hours, and the machine produces perspectives in three minutes at a cost of about two dollars for the computer time. Overall cost is not mentioned, and this should be considered by anyone seriously interested in automation of perspective drawing.

In considering these three available articles, we feel that Bernier's article is likely to be of use to more individuals than the other two, since it is general in its approach and does not assume that a particular computer is being used. His procedure, along with that of the other two articles, does not remove hidden lines. But as Campion and Robey point out, once the perspective is drawn a tracing can easily be made that does not include hidden lines. Some recent experiments, further, have eliminated the hidden lines, but the costs and time have been prohibitive.

Animated Movies

If a large number of perspective drawings were available of the view presented to an observer through time, an animated movie could be produced. The film is exposed to either hard or soft copy and when projected, the illusion of motion and change is conveyed.[12] This technique has been used with some success in transportation planning (see Figure 8.6).

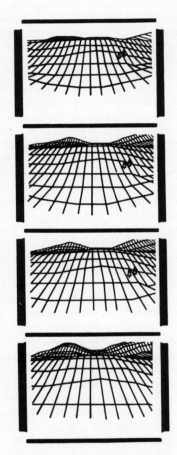

Figure 8-6 Animated Movie of Landscape Drawn by Computer.

Maps

Contour maps using special plotting devices are possible by using programs developed by F. G. Smith.[13] His article describes the data input, which is 2,000 or less *X, Y, Z* coordinate values. These data are then scaled to fit the plotting device. Elevation interpolation takes place, and the data is plotted. Smith has developed three similar programs — a basic plotting program and two others that take into account geologic irregularities.

His first program seems to be the one planners could use. In his article, he mentions that he will supply the programmer information on it to interested parties. These programs are in Fortran IV, the IBM language.

A program that uses the high-speed line printer to produce maps of various projections is available. This was developed at Northwestern University by F. J. Rens while working under a federal contract.[14] Basic input is latitude and longitude. Basic output is small or large sized maps at any reasonable scale and to any projection. To make this work even more valuable, its description has been given in a very straightforward manner. The article assumes the use of the Fortran language. A conceptual extension of the Rens program is the Symap (sim'-map) program, which stands for synographic mapping.[15] This latter program was developed at the Harvard University Laboratory for Computer Graphics. We have used it and have found it quite flexible. Symap produces three basic map types to depict data. This accounts for its versatility, for virtually all data may be plotted as one of these types (see Figure 8.7, which is a typical example).

Contour Map. The contour map is used whenever continuous information is to be presented. The contour map is based on a series of closed curves with each curve representing a uniform numeric level. Uniform variation between contour lines is assumed. Symap takes data from point sources and automatically computes and plots the required contour lines.

Conformant Map. The conformant map is used when data is not continuous but related to certain areal boundaries. All points within these boundaries are assumed to have the same level of information. Different symbolism is used to show distinctions between areas on the map.

Proximal Map. The proximal map looks very similar to the conformant map but has a different theoretical basis. The area of uniform level is determined from point information. Each point on the map is assigned the level of the nearest data point. The area boundaries occur at the point where the *nearest neighbor* (i.e., the nearest data point) changes. Representation is similar to conformant mapping with different symbolism used to show the difference in levels between areas on the map.

We feel that Symap is an ideal method of presenting information on land use, population densities, levels of crime, housing conditions, income levels, and just about every other type of information that is related to a place in the city or region. This program has the additional advantage of producing maps via the

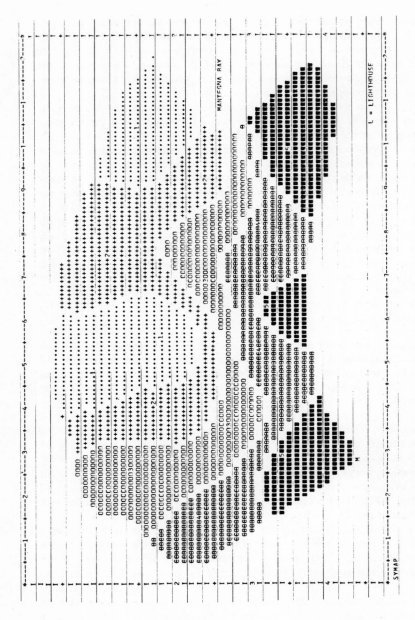

Figure 8-7 Symap Contour Map for Theoretical Data on Economic Production for an Island.

standard line printer. When finished, these maps appear much like a newspaper photo since they are shaded by using combinations of overprinted alphabetical symbols that produce characters of varying intensity.

The type of input data is easy to obtain, though sometimes this data tends to be extensive. For example, the coordinates of the intersection of boundary lines must be known. If the shape is complicated, this can be quite a bit of input. Fortunately, once these are known, they need not be determined again when working with the same area. A variety of maps can be produced for a single area merely by changing the information at the data points. Thus, a complex map shape need be coded only once to produce many different maps. If the point at which data are recorded (for example, the center of a census tract) remains the same, only the actual data need be changed to produce a new map showing new information. Similarly, standard symbols, such as railroads, schools, etc., need only be coded once for a particular study area.

The authors feel that of all automated graphic procedures available, the Symap program possesses the potential for the greatest usefulness to the planner with the least expense in terms of money and expertise needed to make use of it.

Models

Some experimental work has been undertaken using computer graphics and computer-controlled machine tools for making models (see Figure 8.8). There are several types of planning which utilize models, either abstract or iconic, for presentation and study purposes. An agency that does this on a meaningful and repetitive level could possibly benefit from such automation. These experiments, however, have not yet reached the point where applications are fully operational or economic.

Preparation of Data

A critical factor in the use of a particular program or system is the need to convert available data in one form to a form compatible with that program or system. When this conversion process must be done by hand, it quickly becomes tedious and error-prone.

Some of the devices mentioned require a considerable amount of input information to produce only a limited amount of output. This is especially true for the perspective drawing and computer-produced perspectives. The planner should weigh the results of using a particular graphic method against the difficulty of preparing the input data.

One decided advantage of Symap is the ability to use data in whatever form is currently available without the necessity of converting it to a form which is program compatible. In order to do this, a relatively simple Fortran subroutine must be written which will read the data in the current format. It also is possible

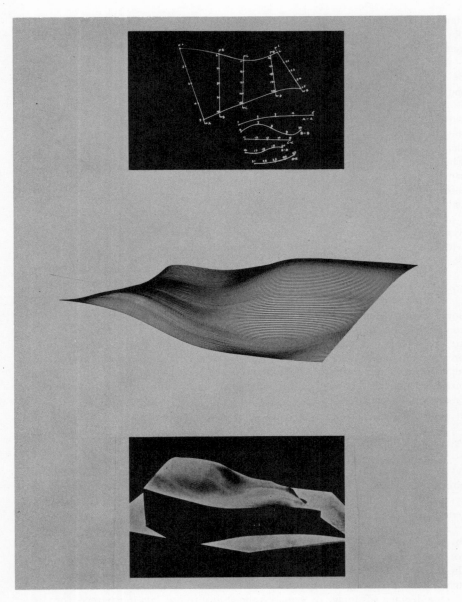

Figure 8-8   CRT Plot of Data (top), Plotter Drawing of the Same Data (middle), and Machine-Tooled Model Controlled by Computer of the Same Surface (bottom).

to convert data in this way — that is, to read data from two different sources and combine them in some way before using the data to make a map. This flexibility may be extremely useful after the 1970 Census of Population is completed. There is a very strong possibility that census information will be available on computer tape. Symap will be able to produce maps from this information merely by using the subroutine mentioned. A wide variety of maps will be possible without any expensive conversion of data.

9   An Urban Form Model

This chapter is the product of an attempt to determine if a basic hypothesis concerning the form of urban areas can be tested through a priori techniques. The basic hypothesis can be succinctly stated — urban functions are organized in a spatial arrangement which interact to create environmental form. The essence of the hypothesis is that there is a set of interrelationships which interconnect urban functions, spatial organization, and environmental form.

The nature of social science is such that a hypothesis, such as the one above, cannot be conclusively proved, as might be the case with hypotheses in the physical sciences. In a sense, the above statement must be treated as a lemma, or a proposition that cannot be proved or disproved, but that can be utilized to examine other interrelationships. After several iterations, the interrelationships may give credence to the lemma itself, which could be construed as a proof.

An organizing principle to such a complex undertaking is afforded through the use of set theory. Urban functions can be considered as a set of elements of finite number, just as the several possibilities of spatial organization and environmental form can also be so considered. There are two ways of specifying the elements of a set, namely, complete enumeration and characteristics specification.[1] Since this approach is essentially a priori, the sets must be described in terms of the complete enumeration of the elements of each, but it is clear that this enumeration is in itself more descriptive of the characteristics of the elements. Further, for operational reasons, it is desirable to limit the scope of inquiry as related to the number of elements in the urban functions set. This is done through an aggregation of elements, rather than becoming overly concerned with the very large number of possibilities.

There is value in this approach because it will enable a certain freedom from the rigor that is necessary with empirical investigation. The a priori approach can be combined with analytical techniques that have become common in the field, as well as with knowledge that has been gained either through personal experience or findings of empirical studies in a variety of places. The approach that is used, then, will serve as a beginning point in the examination of the interrelationships that are found among urban functions, spatial organization, and environmental form. Within the set theory terminology, these interrelationships form the universal set of discourse. Using set theory expressions, the above discussion can be summarized. Let

$$SO_m \quad = \quad \text{the set of spatial organization possibilities}$$

$$UF_n \quad = \quad \text{the urban functions set}$$

$$EF_t = \text{the environmental forms set}$$

$$f = \text{functional relationships.}$$

Then
$$SO_m = f_i(UF_n)$$

$$EF_t = f_j(\ [\ f_i(UF_n)\ ]\ ).$$

While these basic relationships may look relatively simple to the casual observer, the analyst will be cognizant of the very large number of relationships that are being discussed. Again, the nature of social science cannot give the slightest guarantee that a finite series of relationships is possible, nevertheless susceptible to explicit, parametric description. Further, as an investigation in the field of planning, there must be a connection with some type of optimization approach. Yet the nature of the interrelationships may not give the slightest clue as to what or how to optimize. To cope with these problems, an operational device must be established. The approach that appears to be acceptable is the development of an index, or profile of interrelationships. Further, as will be noted, the purity of the a priori approach was violated in order to give a crude testing to the profile technique, which can be considered as a type of simulation. In this case, the Standard Metropolitan Statistical Area of Madison, Wisconsin (not inclusive of the urban fringe areas) was used as a testing area, subject to certain controls and generalizations.

The Basis for Generating Environmental Form

The basis that was used for the generation of the series of interrelationships consisted primarily of a description of the elements of the three sets, the hypothetical urban area, and the a priori interrelationships. The first item, element description, is summarized in Figure 9.1. As will be seen, a kind of hierarchy was afforded in terms of set size. The elements of the three sets would indicate that, for purposes of this analysis, urban functions are the lowest tier of the hierarchy, spatial organization accounts for the middle tier, and the highest tier of the hierarchy is held by environmental forms. A word of caution should be added at this point. The set descriptions that are shown in Figure 9.1 are but one of a very large number of possibilities. It is clear that many other descriptions of these sets would be offered by other analysts. Rather than

Analogue	Urban Functions	Spatial Organization	Environmental Form
	Residential-non-urban	Agricultural groups Non-urban sub-centers Special Groups	Farms Ranches Exurban homes Estates Artisan colonies
	Residential-low	Suburbs Urban neighborhoods Urban sub-centers	Detached houses Townhouses Farm-homes
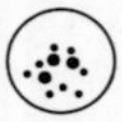	Residential-medium	Suburbs Urban neighborhoods Urban sub-centers	Attached homes Apartments Cluster developments Detached houses
	Residential-high	Urban centers Urban sub-centers	High apartments Multi-use buildings
	Consumption	Service centers Education centers Business complexes Shopping centers	Offices Schools University Retail stores Distribution centers
	Production	Agricultural combines Manufacturing areas	Farms Cooperatives Factories Automated plants
	Transportation	Circulation systems Terminal facilities	Highways Rail lines Water routes Air routes Stations
	Open Space	Active Passive	Urban parks Regional parks Reserves Managed areas Facilities Open land
	Culture	Art and entertainment Institutions	Institutional facilities Private facilities

Figure 9-1   Element Description

defending this set description, it is sufficient to state that this is an operational approach for the a priori interrelationships that were used. In other cases, a different set description system might be more useful. This does not, however, undermine the basic approach.

One other factor of the set description system should be noted in passing. This is the fact that there is a heavy land-use bias throughout the elements. This was intentional, since there is a great deal already known about land use, while there may be lesser bodies of knowledge concerning other aspects of planning. An attempt has been made, however, to give these elements the broadest interpretation; hence the use of the characteristics specification method of set description.

Urban functions are in reality multidimensional. In a mathematical sense, however, they can be considered as unidimensional variables. The spatial organization set is then conceivable as a two-dimensional set. To express two-dimensional or three-dimensional variables, a spatial system is needed. To cope with this problem, a grid coordinate system was generalized to allow for the maximum extent of a priori formulation. Thus, if urban functions and spatial organization possibilities can assume any value R, then the grid coordinate system is adequate for the mappings of the cartesian product, $R \times R$. In this sense, mapping is used in the set theoretic meaning, that is, it is synonomous with function. Further, since environmental form is considered to be three-dimensional, or if assumed also to have any value R, then the grid coordinate system can also be used to express the $R \times R \times R$ mappings because of the theory of imbedded planes.[2]

The grid coordinate system that was used was a 15 x 15 grid, at a scale of one inch to the mile. The individual grids were numbered in order to allow for identification, and, if desirable, computer storage. Each grid or cell was subdivided into sixteen units of spatial identification, or approximately an area simulation of forty acres. Each of these cells in turn can be logically subdivided into sixteenths to a practical limitation of about one-tenth of an acre. The degree of fineness desired in the analysis will depend on such factors as computer memory size, or if the analysis is not automated, the amount of staff time vis-à-vis the benefits expected from the research. While the cells, in the present case, were numbered from 00101 to 22516, only the basic cell, that is, the square-mile grid, was utilized in the testing of the interrelationships.

In addition to specifying the grid coordinate system, it was also necessary to control the a priori nature of the analysis through the constraints of a hypothetical urban area. As can also be observed, a careful specification of this hypothetical urban area would allow for real-world examples to be used as a data source for the simulation. To achieve both of these benefits, the following set of constraints was adapted to control the scope of the interrelationships. The urban areas to be analyzed must meet the following requirements: (1) founded in the early nineteenth century; (2) a metropolitan population of 200,000; (3) no deterministic geographic, physical, or climatological limitations; (4) a diversified manufacturing economic base, with linkages to rural and agricultural industries;

(5) a diversified socioeconomic composition; and (6) an independent sphere of urban influence. These constraints, then, limit the scope of inquiry to the largest group of metropolitan areas, and through some constraint modification, a good deal of the actual metropolitan areas in the country. It does not, however, allow for specific examination of the largest or smallest sized urban areas.

Figure 9.2 shows the areas contained by the hypothetical central city, its suburbs, and its surrounding subcenters. Thus, it was deemed important to include the whole urban area in the sense of nodal structure, even though the interrelationships become more complex. The shapes shown in the plate are arbitrary, although they roughly approximate the central city and subcenters of Madison, Wisconsin, at least in terms of location. The size and shape of the areas differ from the actual Madison situation. To reiterate, the areas shown are relatively unimportant; the concept that is being expounded is what is important.

The Simulation of Environmental Form

A clarification on the meaning of form should be interjected at this point. For purposes of this analysis, there are two types of environmental form. The first is the human scale or perceptual form. This is the type of form that is most often associated with parts of the urban area, rather than its entirety. The other type of environmental form is precisely that of the urban area in its entirety — namely, aggregate form. This is the type of environmental form that cannot be perceived visually, for it covers many aspects of the urban area. Even in a plane, only one facet of aggregate form, that is, mass, can be seen. The set of interrelationships of urban functions, spatial organization, and environmental form, however, can be specified so that the aggregate form can be described in terms of an abstract simulation. When the testing is applied, the simulation becomes less abstract, but still not a visually perceptible phenomenon in the sense of visible aggregate form in its entirety. A model can be constructed visually to represent the simulation, that is, an analog, but this only is a representation, not the abstraction itself.

As was mentioned, an index system can be used to overcome many of the problems of an empirical nature. Essentially, an index of each element of the urban functions and spatial organization interrelationships or functional interactions can be formed. To keep a common underlying framework, a key variable can be selected from the universal set. The most obvious key variable is that of population. These indices can then be aggregated to form a general environmental form index which can be used to interpret the aggregate form of an urban area. Inherent in these indices are the interrelationships among the three sets that were shown above. Further, the magnitude of an index allows for a categorization to any element desired, should the sets need to be described in a different manner.

The properties of index numbers allow for the aggregation of the urban

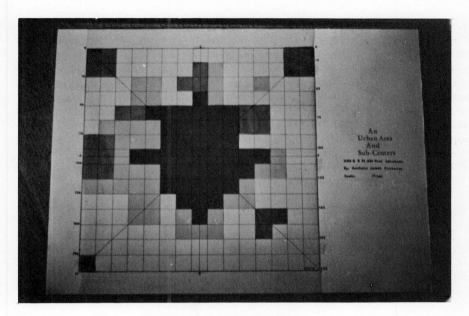

Figure 9-2 Nodal Grid Structure.

function and spatial organization indices to form the environmental form index. It may be argued that in real life, these forms cannot be considered as additive, yet, the nature of mathematics does allow for this type of abstraction.[3] The salient point is that this is an index of an interrelationship that can be used for analysis rather than for the assignment of a specific value.

The specific advantage of this approach is that such nonquantifiable phenomena as technology are implicit within the simulation. Even time is implicit in the simulation, for the indices change over time without the specific input of a separate variable. Thus within the parameters of the index values are factors of time and technological change.

In addition to the specific indices, analog models have been formed to represent these interrelationships. This was done by constructing profiles of the various form indices (urban functions as related to spatial organization) through the use of median values of the three-dimensional squares that were generated. This tends to distort the actual values somewhat, but the final aggregation to environmental form was not profiled and shows the general values more precisely. There were several advantages of generalization, however, which appear to have rationalized the profile nature of the individual form indices.

Residential Form

Residential form accounts for the largest single aspect of environmental form. For convenience, the four elements of urban activities corresponding to residential functions were aggregated. This meant that the spatial organization possibilities were also aggregated. On its face, this method may seem like an overgeneralization. In mathematical terms, however, it allows any arbitrary aspects of the element description to be overcome. Specifically, the magnitude of the index can be classified to the various elements of the urban functions, spatial organization, and environmental form sets by grouping values. Yet, by varying the groupings, any number of different elements for each set can be generated. Thus, the aggregation allows for even greater generalization than is afforded by the set descriptions.

The residential form index can be expressed in the following manner.

Let P_i = population per square mile

PU_i = number of persons per unit per square mile

RU_i = number of residential units per square mile

i = identification of square mile ($1 \leqslant i \leqslant 225$)

RA_i = average area of residential units per square mile

RH_i = average height of residential units per square mile

RD_i = average residential displacement per square mile

RF_i = index of residential form.

Then, the general index can be expressed as follows:

$$RA_i(RH_i) = RD_i$$

$$RD_i(RU_i) = RF_i$$

or,

$$RU_i = RF_i/RD_i$$

This index can be related to population:

$$P_i = RU_i(PU_i)$$

$$RU_i = P_i/PU_i .$$

Thus, it can be shown that

$$P_i/PU_i \;=\; RF_i/RD_i$$

$$RF_i \;=\; RD_i(P_i/PU_i)\,.$$

For the entire urban area, the summation can be expressed as

$$RF \;=\; \sum_{i=1}^{i=225} RD_i(P_i/PU_i)$$

The index can be interpreted as a way of showing through mathematical relationships the way that residential form is related to population, as well as the basic urban functions and the spatial organizations that are relevant. Again, the value of RF_i can enable the definition of any desirable elements of the sets. The other elements of the sets can be similarly evaluated.

Consumption Form

The elements of the urban functions and spatial organization sets that are related to consumption are quite important. While the spatial organization of consumption activities is not as extensive as residential activities, it tends to create extensive nodal forms, many of which give distinctive patterns to environmental form among real-world cities. The primary examples of consumption form are central business districts and shopping centers, but as was shown above, the category includes many other elements.

The consumption form index can be expressed in the following manner.

Let $\quad CA_i$ = average consumption unit area per square mile

$\quad CH_i$ = average consumption unit height per square mile

$\quad CU_i$ = number of consumption units per square mile

$\quad CD_i$ = average consumption displacement per square mile

$\quad CF_i$ = index of consumption form

$$C_i \quad = \text{ consumers drawn to } i$$

$$\overline{C} \quad = \text{ average consumer trips}$$

$$j \quad = \text{ any cell other than } i, \text{ and for the internal trips, } i \text{ itself.}$$

Then, the general index can be expressed as

$$CA_i(CH_i) = CD_i$$

$$CD_i(CU_i) = CF_i \ .$$

The index can also be related to population, but in a different manner than was used with residential functions. Drawing upon knowledge that is already in existence, the "Law of Retail Gravitation" can be most useful.[4] Using a modification of Reilley's findings to express the relations in the traditional gravity model, it can be shown that

$$C_i = \sum_{j=1}^{225} \overline{C} \, (P_i P_j \, / \, P)$$

and,

$$P = \sum_{j=1}^{225} \overline{C} \, (P_i P_j \, / \, C_i) \ .$$

This enables both consumption and residential activities to be related to population. With consumption form, however, there is a more definable limitation than can be seen with residential form. Specifically, there is some upper limit beyond which the consumption area in a cell will not go. It can be hypothesized that this is an S-shaped curve function, best shown by the Gompertz curve. Then the consumption area of a cell is actually limited by the consumers that are drawn into the cell. The upper limit will always exist and is known as an asymptote. In reality, there may be an attempt to increase the level of the asymptote, but this only confirms its existence in fact as well as in theory. Symbolically, this can be shown as

$$CA_i = Ka^{b^{C_i}}$$

or

$$\log \, CA_i = \log \, K + b \, \log \, a^{C_i} \ .$$

In these equations, K, b, and a are statistically determined coefficients which form the parameters of the S-shaped curve. The coefficients are determined through standard procedures. The value of explicitly showing this limiting expression is that it places the consumption element in a perspective which becomes important if the indices are to be projected or subjected to parametric analysis for change. It can be argued that there is also a limiting expression for residential elements. However, the consumption, and other, elements act in a more "rational" manner than do residential decision-makers. There may well be an upper asymptote for residential area in a cell, but it does not appear that this can be stated in an explicit manner in the same way that consumption can. Further, the residential asymptote, if it exists, seems to vary greatly among urban areas, unlike consumption and other functions. Pragmatically, this is equivalent to saying that people act less rationally in living preferences than they do in such activities as shopping and traveling.

Production Form

The urban activities concerned with production are clearly seen in the light and heavy manufacturing industries. Yet there are several other types of production which contribute significantly to the environmental form of an area, that is, agricultural and food processing, rural industries, etc. These are important in the study of environmental form for an urban area.

The index form production functions can be expressed in much the same way as consumption functions. The general index can be shown by letting

PA_i = average production unit area per square mile

PH_i = average production unit height per square mile

PU_i = number of production units per square mile

PD_i = average production displacement per square mile

PF_i = index of production form

PW_i = production workers.

The relationship can be expressed as

$$PA_i (PH_i) = PD_i$$

$$PD_i (PU_i) = PF_i \ .$$

The production form index can also be related to population on the basis of accumulated knowledge. It appears that the number of production workers can be estimated by a linear relationship because of a generally explicit dependence of population on jobs. It can be shown that

$$P_i = a + bPW_i$$

$$\text{or} \quad PW_i = (P_i - a) / b,$$

where a and b are statistically determined coefficients; that is, through correlation and regression analysis. Yet there is also a limit upon the production area that can be found in any single cell which can also be expressed as a relationship to production workers. Like consumption, this relationship is an S-shaped curve which expresses an upper asymptote:

$$PA_i = Ka^{b^{PW_i}}$$

$$\text{or} \quad \log PA_i = \log K + b \log a^{PW_i} .$$

There is much evidence to support the relationships concerning the linear function of production workers and population, as well as the upper limit of production area in an urban unit.[5] Again, this is equivalent to saying that economic forces become much more determining in decisions related to production functions than might be found in the residential functions, where people operate on a more or less independent basis.

Transportation Form

Transportation becomes a rather abstract function in an analysis of urban form. While transportation is clearly a generator of land use which creates spatial organization, it is not generally perceptible as a three-dimensional form. Thus the interrelationships to describe how transportation contributes to environmental form must be expressed in a more theoretical vein than those functions above. The general index can be expressed by letting

TV_i = average transportation volume per square mile

TM_i = average length of transportation unit per square mile

TD_i = average transportation displacement per square mile

TU_i = number of transportation channels per square mile

TF_i = index of transportation form

DS_i = design standards used per square mile (length, right–of–way, and other standards per trip, for all modes).

Then, the index can be shown to be

$$TV_i(TM_i) = TD_i$$

$$TD_i(TU_i) = TF_i.$$

Again, this index can be related to population by

$$T_{ij} = K(P_i P_j /P) ,$$

which is the traditional gravity model approach to estimating the number of trips to i from j (T_{ij}).[6] The coefficient K stands for the average trips per person so that the aggregate trips would be expressed as

$$T_i = \sum_{j=1}^{225} K(P_i P_j /P).$$

It is also quite clear that an S-shaped curve represents the relation of trips to population in a cell. It is explicit in urban areas that the upper asymptote for the number of trips coming into an area has some finite limit beyond which no more vehicles can enter without tip-ups. In transportation, this upper asymptote can be temporarily raised through such devices as street widening, traffic regulations, and one-way flows; yet the asymptote will exist at a slightly higher level. Symbolically, this is

$$T_i = Ka^{b^{P_i}}$$

or $$\log T_i = \log K + b \log a^{P_i}.$$

In the form of a hypothesis, it can be stated that

$$TV_i = T_i(DS_i).$$

Thus, in this context, transportation volume is modified by the design standards that are found in an area which would tend to make it more useful in a form index. Volume in this sense is different than the common technical usage.

Open Space Form

Open space form becomes even more complex than transportation form. Essentially, it can be stated that open space is a kind of negative form since it takes away from the usual height of form that is found in an urban area. Open space is being used in a way that implies public areas, and not agricultural areas. For example, a park near an apartment district will take away from the form of that area in an abstract, mathematical way. This characteristic of open space necessitates that a constant be used for adjustment to allow comparability to the above types of form. The index can be shown by letting

OSD_i = open space displacement per square mile

d_i = demand per person per square mile

k_i = a constant adjustment factor to account for the negative aspects of open space

OSU_i = open space units per square mile

OSF_i = index of open space form.

The general index is

$$OSD_i(OSU_i) = OSF_i.$$

This can also be related to population in a linear manner, owing to empirical findings in this area.[7] The interrelationship is

$$OSD_i = d_i(P_i) + k_i \ .$$

This index is more abstract than others that have preceded, and perhaps it is in need of a more explicit restatement. For operational purposes, however, it appears adequate.

Culture Form

It is an arguable point whether or not a separate function for culture is necessary. It accounts for the least contribution to environmental form in an analytical sense. Its small contribution, however, is more mathematical than realistic. While the form of cultural activities may be small in organization and form, it is perhaps the most distinctive in many urban areas. For example, great museums, entertainment centers, and art galleries are a small part of the environmental form in reality, but perhaps the most perceptible. For operational reasons and consistency, however, cultural form must be treated like any other three-dimensional function, which leads to its small values in the sense of index numbers. The index can be shown by letting

CUA_i = average cultural area per square mile

CUH_i = average cultural unit height per square mile

CUD_i = average cultural unit displacement per square mile

CUF_i = index of cultural form

d_i = demand for cultural units per square mile

k_i = a scale adjustment factor

CUU_i = number of cultural units per squre mile.

This can be related to population in a somewhat crude manner:

$$CUA_i = d_i(P_i) + k_i .$$

The scale adjustment factor depends upon the magnitude of the other form indices. Without this adjustment, cultural units would be too small a part of environmental form to merit a separate functional status.

Environmental Form

The environmental form index is the attempt to incorporate all of the urban functions into a single representation of the form of an area. This can be done through aggregation, because of the manner in which the interrelationships have been framed. The aggregative index is then expressed as

$$EF_i = RF_i + CF_i + PF_i + TF_i + OSF_i + CUF_i ,$$

which can be compared to a total environmental form index by

$$EF = \sum_{i=1}^{225} RF_i + CF_i + PF_i + TF_i + OSF_i + CUF_i$$

The environmental form index is thus the numerical expression of a complex series of interrelationships among the elements of the urban functions, spatial organization, and environmental form sets. The ability to express these relationships can be considered as an intuitive type of proof to the lemma that was posed initially. A more rigorous proof would have to result from attempts to utilize the index in the real world via empirical observations.

A Simulation of Madison, Wisconsin

It is clearly beyond the scope of the present research to subject the environmental form model to a rigorous empirical testing. An empirical testing, the end product of which would be a simulation, would require several researchers, desirably familiar with computer applications, as well as the collection of extensive empirical data needed as input for the indices. A computer would solve many of the problems for a large urban area, but it is possible to test the indices by limiting the extent of the area.

In order to keep within the six constraints for the hypothetical area, the Madison urban area serves as a data source. Rather than considering this as a case study, it is better to regard it as a use of existing data. In keeping with the hypothetical orientation of the approach, it would have been better to formulate a hypothetical data set. This would have been a problem, however, since reality could have been missed altogether, or the data formed in such a manner to prove anything desired. Thus it appeared that the Madison area, since it meets all constraints (by modifying the geographical constraints and rearranging some of the data), could serve as a data source. This data was fitted into the cells in the grid coordinate system, and through a sampling process, profile curves for each index were computed. These profiles are rough approximations of the actual values, but they do allow for an interesting generalization of the empirical data. The profiles have been smoothed where abrupt changes distorted the curves.

The empirical values of the several indices are shown in Table 9.1.[8] Only the highest, median, and lowest values are shown. This is done to emphasize the crude testing that was given to the simulation. Still, for all the shortcomings of the testing, some very interesting findings resulted. As Table 8.1 shows, the values were computed and assigned to the appropriate cells. The 113 cell which accounts for most of the highest values is analogous to the central business district, in the case of Madison, the square mile centered upon the Capitol Square. The 115 cell which is the highest value for production form is analogous to a heavy manufacturing area, in the Madison case, the Marquette area. The

Table 9-1

Madison, Wisconsin Simulation.

Index	Highest		Lowest		Medium	
	Value (10^7)	Cell (i)	Value (10^7)	Cell (i)	Value (10^7)	Cell (i)
RF_i	21.0	113	0.2	214	10.6	115
CF_i	40.0	113	n	214	20.0	115
PF_i	15.0	115	n	214	7.5	111
TF_i	19.6	113	n	214	9.8	083
OSF_i	10.0	141	n	113	5.0	143
CUF_i	10.0	113	n	214	5.0	111

n = negligible, i.e., an index less
than 0.005×10^7.

open space form reaches its highest value in the Madison case in the University Arboretheum area, which could be a matter of definition of open space (although the square mile also includes Vilas Park, a major regional park in the Madison area).

All of the lowest values are found in the most undeveloped cell in the grid coordinate system, except for the lowest open space form index. The 214 cell can be analogous to a very large agricultural area within the urban area. Yet according to the parameters established for the open space index, the central-business square-mile cell emerges as that which has the lowest open space form index. However, there are many other cells which have an equivalently negligible open space form — thus, the central business cell is not the sole cell with the lowest open space form. Further, the median values and an example of a cell which corresponds to the median is shown in the last column. Here also it should be noted that many cells reflect the median values for each form index, the cells that are shown are more exemplary than exhaustive.

Since the values for the form indices were all calibrated to 10^7, it is possible to construct an analog model of each function by taking the value at the median point of each cell area, and establishing a common scale (as was mentioned above, curve smoothing was also undertaken). The scale that was used was 1:32, which enabled many functions to display a value for each cell. The profiles were established along the two diagonals and the east-west, north-south axes. This also enabled a certain degree of generalization. The generalization afforded was that the profiles could be shown as curves in a smoothed fashion, although this was not always possible. Figures 9.3—9.8 show the six analog models that were constructed to represent the profiles along the axes mentioned. It should also be added that each of these profiles could be mathematically interpreted and stored in a computer to enable a wide range of analyses. This would also tend to overcome some of the distortions which result from taking only the median value of each cell.

Figure 9.3 shows the residential form index, and Figure 9.4 shows the consumption form index. As can be noted, residential form shows the highest values occurring close to the center of the urban area with increases in the curve at the various subcenters. The curve is remarkably smooth and well defined. The only significant deviation from the smoothness occurs at cell 111 (in the Madison analogy, this would be the Hill Farms apartments and other residential uses). The consumption form index exhibits a quite different situation. This index is remarkably nonsmooth, even with the generalizations that were attempted. The two major peaks occur in the central business cell and the major subcenter cell (111). This shows that the major subcenter is not only rivaling the central area in consumption form but even may overtake it in the future. The other abrupt increments in consumption form occur at other subcenters, which would include major shopping centers, and some of the satellites and suburbs. In a pragmatic sense, this indicates that consumption form can be viewed as a kind of nodal phenomenon.

Figure 9.5 shows the transportation form index, and Figure 9.6 shows the

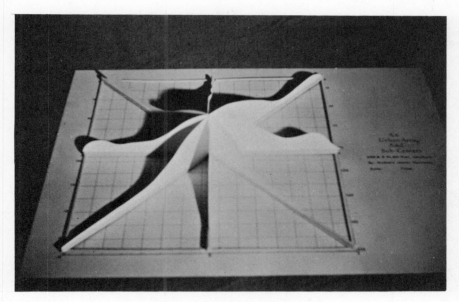

Figure 9-3   Residential Form Index.

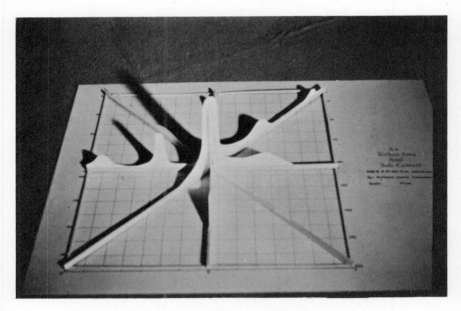

Figure 9-4   Consumption Form Index.

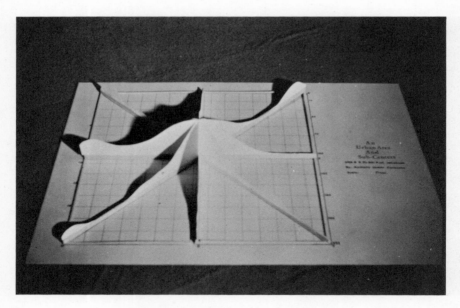

Figure 9-5 Transportation Form Index.

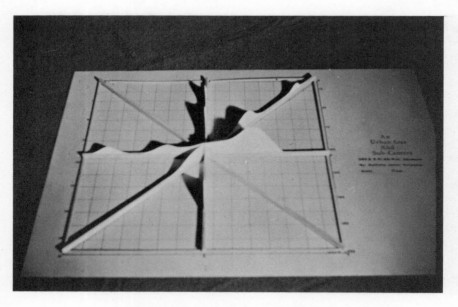

Figure 9-6 Production Form Index.

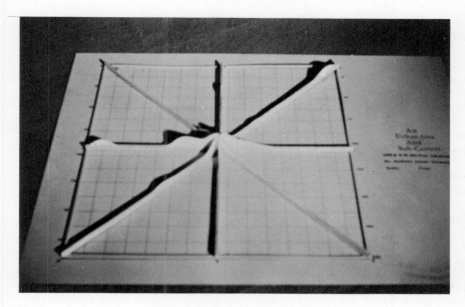

Figure 9-7   Cultural Form Index.

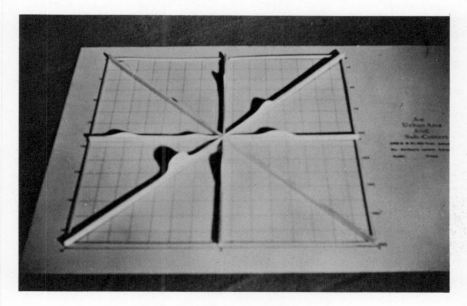

Figure 9-8   Open Space Form Index.

production form index. As can be seen, the transportation form exhibits the smoothest curve, as could be well expected because of the gravity model used in the parameters. This can be interpreted as reflective of the dominance with which the most accessible areas, that is, the central cells, attract a wide variety of trips — business, shopping, work, entertainment. The only deviance from a generally rational curve is the 111 cell, which shows that this area is also beginning to attract a large number of trips. The production form index is quite different from the above. This reflects that the Madison area that served as the data source has a comparatively unusual production form. There is little production form in the centers and in the newer areas to the west, yet there are several nodal cells in the first quadrant. In reality, most of these cells reflect a small number of very large manufacturing functions. It is quite clear that the use of another empirical area would produce different curves.

Figure 9.7 shows the cultural form index, and Figure 9.8 shows the open space form index. As will be readily seen, these two functions, even with comparability adjustments, are in much less evidence than the above functions. Cultural form appears to key on the central cells with a major deviation toward the west. The latter results from the location of the University of Wisconsin, which has many cultural activities. Some of the subcenters exhibit some value for the index, but as can be seen, the majority of cells have a negligible index value. Much of the same holds true for the open space form index, except that the values are even smaller than for the cultural form. The only major nodal area is a cell which consists almost entirely of a University open area and a major regional park. All other cells with significant values are the result of public parks, open areas, and beaches. The open space form indices are small because of the strict definition of open space used. If this definition is altered, however, the agricultural areas would dominate the form of the urban area, which is quite unrealistic. Thus, while open space may exhibit small values, these reflect the specific areas of public concentration; that is, the public does not go to a farm for the enjoyment of open space, but rather to a public facility.

Figures 9.9—9.11 are views of the environmental form index, which is the aggregate of the six forms classified by urban function. As can be seen in the north, south, and top views, respectively, the scale has been decreased to 1:200 in order to enable a value for every significant cell. Still, many cells do not show any noticeable indices (in every case, these cells represent sparsely settled rural areas within the urban area). It will also be seen that the environmental form index has not been generalized in order to allow for detail examination of cells, and especially, the relationships between neighboring cells. If a profile were desired, however, the same type of analog model for the individual functions could be used for the aggregate form index.

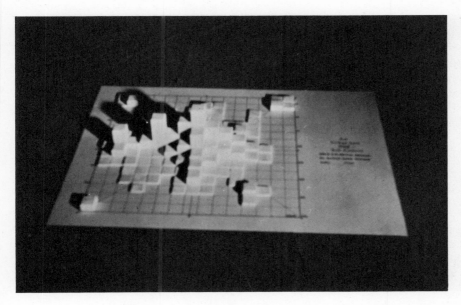

Figure 9-9 Environmental Form Index: North View.

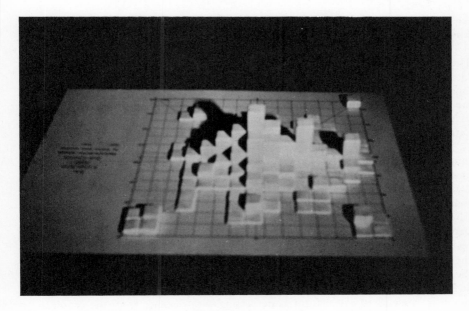

Figure 9-10 Environmental Form Index: South View.

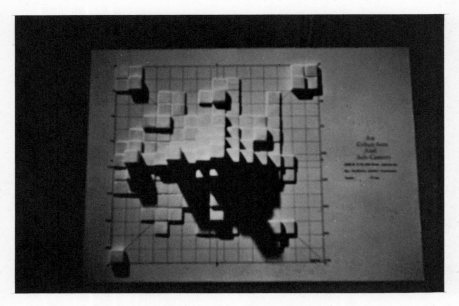

Figure 9-11   Environmental Form Index: Top View.

An Interpretation of the
Environmental Form Index

The index for environmental form is a complex collation of a series of interrelationships, according to the set theory principles advanced previously. One interpretation of this index will be offered, but it is quite clear that there are a large number of ways of using and understanding the simulation. Again, all of the problems that were mentioned with regard to using an empirical area as a data source hold for this interpretation.

The accumulation of high indices of form in the central cells is hardly innovative or surprising. It would seem that when an urban area is being examined for aggregate form, the perception is almost solely related to central areas. More interesting, however, is the strong accumulation of index values that some of the subcenters and satellites exhibit. The most significant is the 111 cell, which is rivaling the central cells for value of environmental form. Similarly, strong values are found for satellites, especially the westernmost satellite (in reality, Middleton, Wisconsin). This would seem to indicate that the traditional theories about the form of an urban area can still be seen in the model, that is, the "pyramid concept," but there are strong signs that the suburbs, subcenters, and satellites are beginning to challenge the dominance of the central cells. The simplistic viewing of urban form as decreasing with distance from the center is perhaps outmoded. Before more detailed assertions can be made, the environmental form index would have to be examined for past years, and projected for future years. Because of the aforementioned inherent nature of time and technology in the parameters, this task is quite feasible.

While the emerging role in environmental form for subcenters and satellites is implied, a finding which is not usually examined, there is little doubt that the central cells still dominate the environmental form of the urban area. The central cells show the highest accumulation over the grid coordinate system, and as such, can be said to be dominant. Yet the uneveness with which gradience occurs, in combination with the emerging subcenters, gives credence to the hypothesis that future environmental form will not be dominated by central cells. If the subcenters increase the values of the index, it would appear that a series of nodes would be found in the urban area, indicating the existence of several "centers" with roughly comparable environmental form indices. Yet, the emerging centers would most likely never surpass the value of the central business cell, unless serious decline occurs. This finding is not at all inconsistent with some of the broader trends found in the literature of urban studies.

The environmental form index has been used to give an intuitive type of proof to the lemma concerning the interrelationships among urban functions, spatial organization, and environmental form. This has been an analytical approach concerned with quantification — but what of the qualitative aspects of environmental form? Could the environmental form index be used to determine the quality of the environment — an undertaking which is never strictly objective?

In its present form, the analog model gives some indication of the quality of the environment. It becomes explicit, for example, that density is correlated highly with the value of the environmental form index. Thus if density is valued, the central cells would have a greater quality, as well as the converse of this value. There are also certain implicit observations concerning quality which can be seen in relating cells to the neighboring cells. The most obvious example is cell 111, which is greatly dominant over its neighboring cells. If it can be assumed that these neighboring cells were settled because people liked the general environment (as can be measured by the index), it can be seen that some may be dissatisfied with the nodal cell, which is clearly growing. This would mean that even though the air may be clean, the buildings attractive, and the area generally well kept, there may be a quality problem because the value of the 111 cell environmental form, which reflects a series of relationships, is so out of proportion and scale to its neighbors. Pragmatically, the cell "sticks out like a sore thumb." This is also beginning to emerge in some other subcenters, to a less marked degree. Yet it can be seen that this does not occur in the satellites. In the satellite areas, the dominant environmental form cell is approached gradually, in the traditional "pyramid" sense. This may or may not be valued by the people in the neighboring cells. The question which is posed is, Since the evolution of subcenters seems to be the long term trend, how will people react, in a qualitative sense, to the environment formed?

This is one way to evaluate quality from the existing interrelationships, but a more detailed examination could come from adding a quality parameter to each of the functional indices. This parameter would not affect the basic relationships or the aggregate interrelationships. It would simply be an additional dimension added to the indices. This quality index could come from a subjective basis, or from a theoretical plane. In empirical applications, it would most likely involve both.

10 The Empiric Programming Model

One of the greatest challenges facing public decision-makers is the preparation of plans that will include simultaneous changes in both land use and transportation. In the past, plans or forecasts of future land-use patterns usually have been prepared somewhat independently of planned transportation facilities. An important missing link in the plan-making process has been the effect that transportation facilities themselves have in shaping future land-use patterns. It is imperative that the planner and engineer design transportation facilities to accommodate not only those land-use activities already in place and those expected or planned for urban expansion, but also those activities which might be induced to redistribute themselves spatially under the influence of proposed transportation facilities.

Collection and processing of a detailed and comprehensive set of small area, time-series socioeconomic data generally is required in order properly to forecast future land-use values. The next step is to summarize and classify such data into specified groupings so as to be usable in the appropriate forecasting model. Once the data are classified and used as input to the appropriate mathematical land-use model, future land-use variables can be obtained.

The value of sophisticated regional planning models lies in the fact that they force the user to define his input and output terms more precisely and systematically. However, such models generally require large amounts of data for their application, and the data collection phase often is a difficult and time-consuming process. Many studies have become bogged down in this data collection phase, and as a result, the fundamental advantages to improved decision-making to be derived from the application of more sophisticated forecasting techniques have not been realized.

Characteristics of Models Useful in the Systemic Planning Process

In the initial iteration of the systemic planning process it is highly desirable to formulate and apply a model which (1) embodies the predictive capacity of basic mathematical models; and (2) takes advantage of readily available data. At the same time, such a model should be capable of being fully integrated into a continuing planning process — a process which can provide general direction to decisions in the initial iterations and more and more detailed specifications in subsequent iterations.

These basic characteristics provide the major guidelines for the development of models in conjunction with the more specific characteristics outlined in the preceding sections. In summary, these characteristics are

1. A multivariate nature, taking into account not only those variables which are of direct concern to any public official but also those in the broader environment which affect or are affected by the originally considered variables.
2. An incorporation of choice or controllable variables, enabling the decision-maker to influence the direction of an open system in which a series of final states can result from the initial state depending on the manner in which controllable variables in the environment are manipulated.
3. The utilization of autointelligence, environmental intelligence, and historical data as inputs to the model formulation and application.
4. The recognization and identification of goals or objectives through which certain trial policy inputs can be tested and evaluated or, in the most desired case, from which optimal policies can be derived.
5. A recognition of constraints, especially those concerning the operation (laws) of the system, which must be met in any drive toward given goals.
6. The ability to synthesize or "invent" situations which may lead to feasible or perhaps optimal states of the system at some specified future stage.
7. A measure of the performance of the system at the specified future stage, especially in relation to the resulting performance if no changes are made.
8. A measure of the sensitivity of performance of the system to changes in goals, constraints, and, most important, to variations in the settings of controllable (decision) variables.
9. The ability to indicate the proper programming of improvements leading to the desired state of the system.
10. The ability to develop the model in accordance with reasonable budget, personnel, and time limitations on the model maker.

A Model Applicable to the Systemic Planning Process

A mathematical model which embodies many of the characteristics delineated above is the Empiric Land Use Forecasting Model. This model was developed by the Traffic Research Corporation (now part of Peat, Marwick, Livingston and

Company of New York) for use by the Commonwealth of Massachusetts in the Eastern Massachusetts Regional Planning Project.[1] To achieve more fully the desirable model characteristics required for systemic planning, however, it is necessary to employ this model in conjunction with mathematical programming techniques. This application will be covered further, subsequent to a more complete discussion of the Empiric model approach.

The Empiric model was designed primarily to satisfy two needs: (1) prediction of *zonal* distributions of *regional* land use activities at some future point in time; and (2) determination of the impact of alternative decisions, especially those concerning the location and capacity of transportation facilities, on zonal land use. Inherent in the Empiric model is the capability of reproducing significant parts of the environment and of predicting the future distribution of land use activities, given as inputs (a) present land uses, (b) estimates of future regional land use totals, and (c) present and anticipated demands for transportation, water and sanitary facilities.

Thus, at the outset, it may be seen that the Empiric model is multivariate in nature (characteristic 1), since it takes into account both land use and transportation variables. The latter set of variables is controllable for the most part, thereby implying a variety of final system states (characteristic 2) which can be achieved depending on the individual control decisions.

The inputs to the Empiric model fall into five general classes:

1. Present value (time t) of land *use* variable i in zone h $V_{ih}(t)$;
2. Present value (time t) of land *area* variable r in zone h, $L_{rh}(t)$;
3. Present value (time t) of *controllable* variable j, $C_j(t)$;
4. Future value (time $t + 1$) of *regional* land use variable i, $T_i(t + 1)$; and
5. Future value (time $t + 1$) of controllable variable j, $C_j(t + 1)$.

The outputs of the model are the future values of each land use variable i for each zone h (designated as $V_{ih}(t + 1)$).

The broad classes of variables used in the model are indicated in Table 10.1. Land-use variables are represented by four categories of population and five categories of employment. The controllable variables relate to automobile and transit travel times (transportation system variables) and water supply and sewage-disposal zonal service indices. Land-area variables include acreage measures for various use activities. Data for all of these variables are readily available from federal census information and transportation and planning studies.

The variables presented in Table 10.1 adequately fulfill a number of criteria specified in conjunction with the desired characteristics for models in the systemic planning process. Focusing on the transportation system as a matter of primary concern, transportation variables represent the needed autointelligence information, whereas the present land use variables fall under the heading of environmental intelligence information since they include factors in the broader environment which both affect and are affected by modifications in the

Table 10-1

Empiric Land - Use Model Variables.

Land Use Variable (i)

(1)   Number of families with an annual income less than $5,000.

(2)   Number of families with an annual income between $5,000 and $9,999.

(3)   Number of families with an annual income between $10,000 and $14,999.

(4)   Number of families with an annual income equal to or greater than $15,000.

(5)   Number of persons in manufacturing and construction employment (S.I.C.* Codes 15 - 39).

(6)   Number of persons in wholesale, transportation, communication, utilities and government employment (S.I.C. Codes 1 - 14, 40 - 50, 91 - 99).

(7)   Number of persons in retail employment (S.I.C. Codes 52 - 59).

(8)   Number of persons in service employment (S.I.C. Codes 70 - 89).

(9)   Number of employees in finance, insurance, and real estate employment (S.I.C. Codes 60 - 67).

Land Area Variables (r)	Controllable Variables (j)
(1) Net residential area (acres)	Automobile travel time between zones
(2) Net manufacturing area (acres)	Transit travel time between zones
(3) Net retail area (acres)	Zonal water supply service index
(4) Other developed area (acres)	Zonal sewage disposal service index
(5) Developable area (acres)	

*The letters S.I.C. stand for the Standard Industrial Classification of land use activity taken from: Bureau of the Budget, *Standard Industrial Calssification Manual,* U.S. Government Printing Office, Washington, D.C., 1957.

transportation system. Similarly, historical data are included in the model for the transportation and land use variables, although the inclusion appears indirectly through the calibration process which requires data from two cross sections in time in order to establish model parameters. Moreover, future regional land use totals are exogenous inputs to the model, and these usually are extrapolated through time series analyses using historical data.

Figure 10.1 portrays the general nature of the input-output relationships in the Empiric model using the previously defined variables. It may be seen that the model accepts trial values for each of the future controllable variables and then produces the resulting future zonal land use variables.

As an example of this process, consider the inputs in Table 10.2, developed for a hypothetical three-zone situation. The future interzonal travel times by automobile and transit have been set at values slightly lower than those which presently exist, the assumption being that these decreases are desirable (policy objectives) and that they can be achieved through possible construction and control schemes which might be proposed. The output resulting from these inputs is presented in Table 10.3.

The data utilized in this example have been presented simply to demonstrate in concrete terms the nature of the factors inherent in the Empiric model and, therefore, have no particular significance. What is of significance about the example, however, is that, despite the fact that a future transportation situation has been "invented" (a feature which is desirable in terms of the sixth characteristic cited above), the model is incomplete in the following respects: (1) no goals have been set explicitly for land use development in any zone (characteristic 4); (2) no measures of performance or sensitivity are given (characteristics 7 and 8); and (3) no indication of how transportation improvements are to be programmed is shown (characteristic 9).

An Empiric-Programming Model

As a consequence of the three "shortcomings" listed above, it would appear that the Empiric model must be combined with some other technique which has the necessary complementary characteristics to make it a suitable tool for systemic planning. Mathematical programming is the logical choice for this complementary technique, since, by means of programming, it is possible to (1) include a priori goals or objectives in a criterion function associated with the program; (2) measure the performance of the system as indicated by the value of the criterion function; and (3) gauge the sensitivity of outputs to various changes in the inputs by means of the dual variables which are concomitant products of any mathematical programming technique. Another benefit of this combination of the Empiric model and mathematical programming, and perhaps the most important benefit, is the determination of the value of each transportation variable which leads to an optimal allocation of land use in the region (in terms of the a priori goals). Thus, the transportation variables are treated as unknowns

Table 10-2

**Input to a Three-Zone Example
of the Empiric Model.**

	Land — Use Variables (i)*								
	1	2	3	4	5	6	7	8	9
$V_{i1}(t)$	1000	2000	500	500	2000	1000	1000	1000	1000
$V_{i2}(t)$	1000	2000	500	500	2000	1000	1000	1000	1000
$V_{i3}(t)$	500	500	1500	2000	500	2000	1500	1000	1000
$T_i(t+1)$	1000	6000	4000	4000	5000	5000	4400	3750	3750

Transportation Variables						

			Travel Time in Minutes			
			Transit		Automobile	
Zone	and	Zone	Present	Future	Present	Future
1		2	12	10	15	10
1		3	21	18	24	18
2		3	21	20	24	20

Other Variables								

	Land Area Variable (r)					Water Index		Sewerage Index	
Zone	$L_{1b}(t)$	$L_{2b}(t)$	$L_{3b}(t)$	$L_{4b}(t)$	$L_{5b}(t)$	Present	Future	Present	Future
1	5000	15000	10000	30000	32000	7	7	5	5
2	4000	18000	8000	30000	32000	7	7	5	5
3	5000	5000	5000	20000	64000	7	7	5	5

*For a definition of each variable
type, see Table 10-1.

Table 10-3

**Output from a Three-Zone Example
of the Empiric Model.**

Land – Use Variable*	Zone 1	Zone 2	Zone 3
$V_{1b}(t + 1)$	400	401	251
$V_{2b}(t + 1)$	2529	2512	1060
$V_{3b}(t + 1)$	850	845	2242
$V_{4b}(t + 1)$	1014	1024	2044
$V_{5b}(t + 1)$	2045	2073	1102
$V_{6b}(t + 1)$	1161	1182	2420
$V_{7b}(t + 1)$	816	800	1581
$V_{8b}(t + 1)$	766	748	1910
$V_{9b}(t + 1)$	1258	1248	1240

*For a definition of each variable type,
see Table 10-1.

to be established and not as preset trial possibilities as in the case of the previous numerical example. Applying these modifications, the process shown in Figure 10.1 can be transformed to that illustrated by Figure 10.2, where each $G_{ib}(t + 1)$ is an a priori goal for land-use variable i in zone b at some future point in time.

An example of the input to the process illustrated in Figure 10.2 is presented in Table 10.4 for one zone (zone five) of a hypothetical six-zone region. For purposes of simplicity in this example, the goals for each land use variable in zone five are incorporated in a linear criterion function and are specified as either increasing (+1) or decreasing (-1) the intensity of the respective land use variables in that zone. No preference weighting of goals has been made, and only future automobile travel times have been treated as decision (unknown) variables.

The outputs from the process are displayed in Table 10.5. A comparison of the $V_{ib}(t)$ and the $V_{ib}(t + 1)$ show that the optimization procedure has indeed produced changes in each land use variable in the direction indicated by the corresponding goal. In fact, the change in all of the variables taken together amounts to 77,906 families and employees, this figure being a *measure* of the best possible performance (characteristic 7) that can be produced by modifying the interzonal highway transportation system. As also can be seen in Table 10.5, the optimal modifications of the transportation networks entering zone five involve (1) the construction of a facility between zones five and three so as to reduce travel time from 39 to 20 minutes, and (2) the construction of a facility between zones five and six to reduce travel time from 24 to 20.3 minutes.

The values of the dual variables related to each constraint are not shown because of the difficulty of presentation. However, as an example, one constraint in the process is designed to prevent the automobile travel time from zone five to zone three from becoming larger than the present value of 39 minutes. If this value were not 39 but instead were, say, 40 minutes, the dual value of -3578 corresponding to this constraint would indicate that the value of the criterion function would be decreased by that amount; that is to say, the desired change in families and employees would be 3578 less than that which was found in the solution shown in Table 10.5. This dual variable, then, does portray the sensitivity of changes in the criterion function in response to possible changes or errors in the constraint values (characteristic 8).

Two characteristics not accounted for directly in the Empiric-Programming Model are (1) the staging of improvements, and (2) the detailed specification of the solution. The first of these could be readily incorporated into the model simply by creating several short (perhaps five-year) temporal stages and using the model recursively in conjunction with some form of budgetary constraint for each stage. This procedure, although somewhat cumbersome, would ensure that improvements would be made in a proper sequence and that short-run budget limitations would not be exceeded.

It is acknowledged that the Empiric-Programming Model is inadequate insofar as detailed specification is concerned, since transportation is presented only in

174

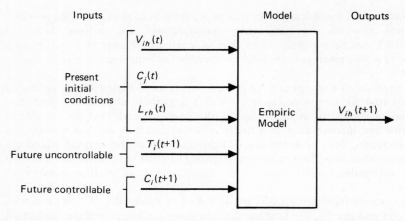

Figure 10-1 Diagrammatic Representation of Input and Output of the Empiric Model.

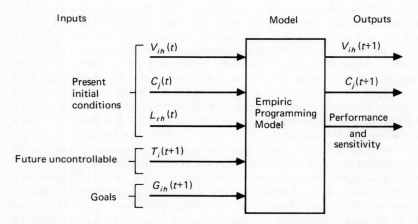

Figure 10-2 Diagrammatic Representation of Input and Output of Empiric Programming Model.

Table 10-4

**Input for One Zone (5) of a
Six-Zone Example of the
Empiric Programming Model.**

Land — Use Variable*	$V_{i5}(t)$	$T_i(t + 1)$	$G_i(t + 1)$
1	25,000	151,500	increase (+1)
2	50,000	303,000	decrease (-1)
3	12,500	75,700	increase (+1)
4	12,500	75,700	increase (+1)
5	60,000	363,600	decrease (-1)
6	40,000	242,400	decrease (-1)
7	25,000	151,500	decrease (-1)
8	20,000	121,200	increase (+1)
9	5,000	30,300	increase (+1)

(continued)

Table 10-4 *(continued)*

Transportation Variables				Land Area Variables (r)	
	Travel Time in Minutes				
From Zone 5		Transit	Automobile		
to Zone	Present	Future	Present		
1	40	38	45	$L_{15}(t)$	10,000 acres
2	28	25	30	$L_{25}(t)$	2,500 acres
3	35	32	39	$L_{35}(t)$	2,500 acres
4	12	10	15	$L_{45}(t)$	15,000 acres
6	21	18	24	$L_{55}(t)$	30,000 acres

Other Variables			
Water Index		Sewerage Index	
Present	Future	Present	Future
7	7	5	5

*For a definition of each variable type, see Table 10-1.

Table 10-5

**Output for One Zone (5) of a
Six-Zone Example of the
Empiric Programming Model.**

Land — Use Variables*		Transportation Variables	
Variable	Value	From Zone 5 to Zone	Travel Time in Minutes
$V_{15}(t + 1)$	26,476	1	45
$V_{25}(t + 1)$	48,598	2	30
$V_{35}(t + 1)$	12,743	3	20
$V_{45}(t + 1)$	14,316	4	15
$V_{55}(t + 1)$	47,304	6	20.3
$V_{65}(t + 1)$	0		
$V_{75}(t + 1)$	12,926		
$V_{85}(t + 1)$	25,099	Total Change in Zone 5 = 77,906 Families and Employees	
$V_{95}(t + 1)$	8,100		

*For a definition of each variable, see
Table 10-1.

terms of interzonal travel time and no particulars are given as to how travel-time improvements can or should be made. In fact, there are many ways to reduce travel time — new highway construction, improved signal systems, ramp metering, directional controls, and so forth. The choice among these possible improvements must be left for future iterations in the systemic planning process.

11   A New-Town Housing Model

Increased urbanization — accentuated by population growth, the movement of population away from rural areas, and rapid industrialization — has generated increasingly serious economic, social, and health problems in most parts of the world. In an effort to relieve the build-up of population masses, minimize congestion, and reduce other problems beseting major urban areas, many countries have undertaken the formulation of a national policy regarding the establishment of new towns. There is little general agreement on what characteristics a development must possess to be called a "new town." To most purists, a new town must have an optimum size, population, and spacing; local employment; greenbelts; land-value recapture; and a rather inflexible plan. To many others, all that is required is that the development be large scale and constructed on undeveloped land according to some plan for its overall development. The examples used in this chapter fall more properly into the first category; however, the conclusions reached have application for any type of large-scale planned development. As we have observed: "If these recent trends . . . are viewed in totality, we see the emergence of the New Towns Alternative as the favored and popular approach to regional development. The popularity of new towns caused by the mass media; the generally unanimous recommendation by regional planning agencies that seek to change existing trends; the interest and investment by private organizations; and the elements of a national policy for new towns all give credence to this observation."[1]

Goals of New-Town Planning

The primary goal of new town planning should be the creation of the most favorable conditions of life for all the population. New-town planning, therefore, must be founded upon sound principles of economics and social development, as well as upon principles of good design. As a recent United Nations report points out, the development of new towns must serve as an instrument of national policy for urban and regional planning and not merely as an isolated exercise in physical planning.[2]

While the concept of the new town presents the planner with a unique situation — the opportunity to plan an entire urban complex without having to integrate the new system with previously fixed facilities — the uniqueness of the new town also presents the planner with a serious set of challenges. There is growing evidence to suggest that a series of social, economic, psychological, and ecological problems can arise with the development of new towns. Many of these problems stem from the basic approach of using a physical entity to attain nonphysical goals. Among the new towns developed to date, it is difficult to show that a conscious effort has been made to develop a comprehensive set of interrelationships between the design approach and the nonphysical problems within the ecosystem.

There appears to be substantial agreement among new-town planners that housing and local facilities must be provided simultaneously. To achieve this objective, town planners have turned to the concept of neighborhood planning, which provides a convenient framework for the distribution of essential local services, such as shopping, primary schools, health, social, and community needs. Properly applied, neighborhood planning also offers the best starting point for community development. It is, therefore, a social concept as well as a planning concept.

The Problem of Population Balance

Notwithstanding these efforts to promote orderly development through neighborhood planning, one of the foremost problems confronting the planners of new towns is that of achieving *population balance.* As Lesley White has observed, a progressive housing program is essential to match changing household structure and to meet the needs of differing income and social groups.[3] As Lloyd Rodwin has suggested, imbalances in population can cause harrowing difficulties.[4]

Despite such admonitions, many new towns have been faced with major problems stemming from imbalances in their population. As the London County Council states in their report on the planning of a new town at Hook,[5] many of the original new towns in Great Britain have been faced with sizable fluctuations in the demand for various kinds of physical facilities, such as housing, schools, hospitals, and the like. These problems can be attributed to an imbalance among different classes of population. For example, the type of family most likely to move to a new town is headed by early-middle-age parents who have small children. The principal housing demand, therefore, is for apartments and small homes. With the growth of children and the general rise in income and decrease in mobility of the parents, however, most of the original families can be expected to demand larger and higher quality housing. Moreover, as these families age, they leave behind their initial, smaller housing which, after the usual fifteen-year migration period for new towns, can be expected to remain vacant for a time as part of a housing surplus until a new generation comes along and the cycle repeats itself.

Such imbalances in population can have significant social as well as economic implications. Wyndham Thomas, Director of the Town and Country Planning Association of England, has observed, "For a few brief years it was widely believed in Britain that anyone going to live in a new town stood an even chance of ending his days in a mental hospital. For women the chances were better (or worse?) than even."[6] As Thomas points out, the origin of the notion of "new town blues" was an unconnected group of medical and sociological studies. Similar sociological studies in the United States point to a high incidence of neuroses among suburban housewives living in large-scale, homogeneous developments. One principal cause of these symptoms of anxiety, depression, and unresolved mental conflicts, it has been concluded, is the homogeneity of these communities. The suburban housewife — living among others of similar age and socioeconomic status — has no one to turn to who is "older and wiser" to seek solace and advice; her neighbor's problems are the same as her problems. In short, there are no "elders of the tribe" to turn to for comfort.

The duty of the planner, in seeking to organize the widest possible choice of homes, leisure, job opportunities, and social activities in an environment that is efficient, pleasing, and convenient, must be to achieve a population balance which included families and individuals representative of all stages of the family cycle. One important way to achieve this objective is through the supply of housing types made available through large-scale, planned developments. To date, however, research to provide planners and developers of new towns and other similar large-scale developments with useful guidelines has been lacking in this area. As a consequence, the economic and social problems of population imbalances continue to emerge.

The Purpose of the Housing Models

Optimization techniques have been developed and applied to a number of problems confronting the planner in his efforts to deal with the complexities of urban development. These techniques, in the main, have been utilized in the field of transportation planning. However, these techniques — emerging largely from the field of operations research — are not limited to studies of the movements of peoples and goods. Their general application to other problem areas in the field of planning is just beginning to be explored.

The object of the present study is to formulate optimization models of four housing-use situations in new towns in order to assist in the determination of (1) the number of each type of family which, if attracted to a new town, would minimize the number of vacancies in and unfulfilled demands for a fixed supply of housing of various types; and (2) the number of each type of family which, if attracted to a new town, would minimize the number of housing units needed when (a) there is no constraint on the number of families of each type; (b) the probability of a family being of a given type is equated to a respective value in a representative *existing* population; and (c) the probability of a family being of a given type is equated to a respective value in a representative population of *mobile* families.

The results of this study should give some indication of whether the "balancing" of population — that is, the balancing in numbers of families of various types — has realizable potential. Conversely, these results should reveal whether the desired balance of population diverges radically from the usual composition so as to make its attainment impractical. This latter finding, if substantiated, would imply that there are certain diseconomies and inefficiencies in the housing market of new towns which must be accepted if the concept of new towns is to be promoted.

Formulation of the Models

For the purpose of modeling four typical new-town housing situations, families were classified by size (the assumption was made that family size can be correlated roughly with stages within the family cycle[7]), and the factors of birth, death, marriage, and divorce were used in the simulation of family change over time. It was also necessary to derive probability distributions of family sizes for "existing" and "mobile" families to meet the objectives of the model.

Quantities of six basic types of housing, differentiated by cost, comprise the supply side of the model. The demand for this housing is replicated by associating with each family type a probability of requiring each of the six kinds of housing. In addition, a constraint limiting the total population of the new town after a given number of time periods was identified and incorporated into the models.

Before discussing the full model, some mathematical notations must be established. We can begin by letting

$$x_i^\alpha = \text{number of families of type } i \text{ immigrating to a}$$
new town in time period $\alpha (i = 1, \ldots, n)$
$(\alpha = 1, \ldots, p)$.

In addition, a vector, representing the complete set of families immigrating during the time period, is

$$\mathbf{X}^\alpha = [x_1^\alpha, x_2^\alpha, \ldots, x_i^\alpha, \ldots, x_n^\alpha].$$

As a help in determining the number of *persons* immigrating during the time period, we let

$$p_i = \text{number of persons per family type (size) } i;$$
where
$$\mathbf{P} = [p_1, p_2, \ldots, p_i, \ldots, p_n].$$

The number of houses of type j built in time period α can be represented by b_j^α (where $j = 1, \ldots, m$) and the full range of houses in that period by

$$\mathbf{B}^\alpha = [b_1^\alpha, b_2^\alpha, \ldots, b_j^\alpha, \ldots, b_m^\alpha].$$

The next step is to ascertain the number of families of a given type k which will change in size to some other type i during the period α. For the simulation of family size changes, equations similar to that for $i = 1$ ($n = 7$) shown below can be constructed:

$$p_1 x_1^{\alpha+1} = p_1 x_1^\alpha - 2M^\alpha p_1 x_1^\alpha - \Delta^\alpha p_1 x_1^\alpha + p_1 \Delta^\alpha p_2 x_2^\alpha + D^\alpha \left(\sum_{i=2}^{7} x_i^\alpha \right)$$

$$+ p_1 D^\alpha x_2^\alpha + 2M^\alpha p_2 x_2^\alpha \ ,$$

where

M^α = number of marriages per *person* in period α;

D^α = number of divorces per *family* in period α;

β^α = number of births per *family* in period α; and

Δ^α = number of deaths per *person* in period α.

These equations are summarized in matrix form in Table 11.1. This matrix is designated $\mathbf{F}^\alpha$ and can be expressed in the general form as follows:

$$
\begin{bmatrix}
f_{11}^\alpha \cdots f_{1k}^\alpha \cdots f_{1n}^\alpha \\
\vdots \qquad \vdots \qquad \vdots \\
f_{i1}^\alpha \cdots f_{ik}^\alpha \cdots f_{in}^\alpha \\
\vdots \qquad \vdots \qquad \vdots \\
f_{n1}^\alpha \cdots f_{nk}^\alpha \cdots f_{nn}^\alpha
\end{bmatrix}
$$

Demand Synthesis

The next step in the formulation of the basic model is to determine the relationship between family types and housing types. It is not possible to determine in a simple manner exactly which house each type of family would require upon moving to a new town. Consequently, a probabilistic approach was deemed necessary (i.e., where a_{ij} = the probability of family type i requiring a house of type j). The probabilities used in this determination were derived using the prices of the house types, joint family size-income distributions, and a constant annual house price to annual income ratio (0.14). The resulting family housing demand matrix is designated by **A**, and can be represented in the general form as follows:

$$
\mathbf{A} = \begin{bmatrix}
a_{11} \cdots a_{1j} \cdots a_{1m} \\
\vdots \quad\quad \vdots \quad\quad \vdots \\
a_{i1} \cdots a_{ij} \cdots a_{im} \\
\vdots \quad\quad \vdots \quad\quad \vdots \\
a_{n1} \cdots a_{nj} \cdots a_{nm}
\end{bmatrix}
$$

Other notations used in the subsequent development of the models are as follows:

s_j^{α} = the excess (if any) in period α of the supply over the demand for houses of type j;

$\mathbf{S}^{\alpha}$ = $[s_1^{\alpha}, s_2^{\alpha}, \ldots, s_j^{\alpha}, \ldots, s_m^{\alpha}]$;

e_j^{α} = the excess (if any) in period α of the demand over the supply of houses of type j;

$\mathbf{E}^{\alpha}$ = $[e_1^{\alpha}, e_2^{\alpha}, \ldots, e_j^{\alpha}, \ldots, e_m^{\alpha}]$;

c_i = probability that a family in an *existing* population is of type (size) i;

g_i = probability that a family in a *mobile* population is of type (size) i; and

Φ = desired total population of a new town after a certain number of time periods have elapsed.

Table 11-1

Family Change Matrix, F^{α}

	Family Size in Period $\alpha + 1$						
	1	2	3	4	5	6	7
1	$1 - 2M - D$	$4M + 2D + 2\triangle$	$\triangle$	$\triangle$	$\triangle$	$\triangle$	$\triangle$
2	M	$1 - 2D - \triangle - M$	$3M + 3D + \triangle$	$4M$	$5M$	$6M$	$7M$
3	0	β	$1 - 6M - 3D - \triangle - \beta$	$8M + 4D + \triangle$	0	0	0
4	0	0	β	$1 - 8M - 4D - \triangle - \beta$	$10M + 5D + \beta$	0	0
5	0	0	0	β	$1 - 10M - 5D - \triangle - \beta$	$12M + 6D + \beta$	0
6	0	0	0	0	β	$1 - 12M - 6D - \triangle - \beta$	$14M + 7D + \triangle$
7	0	0	0	0	0	β	$1 - 14M - 7D - \triangle - \beta/7$

Note: (The α superscript for each letter not shown in table)

Determination of Immigrating Families

With these notations, it is possible to determine the number of families of each family type in each period of development. For example, the number of families of each type at the beginning of the second period growing from families immigrating in the first period is F^1X^1, in the third period, $F^2F^1X^1$, and, generally speaking, for the αth period, $F^{\alpha-1} F^{\alpha-2} \ldots F^1X^1$, or,

$$\prod_{\sigma=1}^{\alpha-1} F^\alpha X^1 ,$$

where σ is another subscript designating a period of time. For families immigrating in the second period, the corresponding terms are X^2, F^2X^2, and $F^{\alpha-1} F^{\alpha-2} \ldots F^2X^2$, or,

$$\prod_{\sigma=2}^{\alpha-1} F^\sigma X^2 .$$

The Basic Model

The objective of the first of the four analyses proposed in this study, as stated previously, is to find those types of families which, if attracted to a new town, would minimize the difference between the supply of and demand for housing. Restated, this objective is to minimize the slack or surplus in housing which results at each period of time. The demand for housing in the first period by families immigrating in that period is AX^1, whereas the supply is B° (these houses are built in period o). The difference between these two items, depending on whether it is positive or negative, is S^1 or E^1, and it is this difference that is to be minimized. This type of criterion function is found in the particular linear programming procedure known as goal programming.

The full model would then contain the aforementioned criterion function along with supply and demand equality constraints for each period and the total population constraint for the new town at the final time period under consideration:

$$\min Z = \sum_{j=1}^m \sum_{\alpha=1}^\rho \left(s_j^\alpha \ te_j^\alpha \right)$$

Subject to:
$$\sum_{\lambda=1}^{\alpha} A \prod_{\sigma=\lambda}^{\sigma-1} F^{\sigma} x^{\lambda} + S^{\alpha} - E^{\alpha} = \sum_{\lambda=0}^{\alpha-1} B^{\lambda} \quad (\alpha = 1, \ldots, \rho),$$

$$\sum_{\lambda=1}^{\rho} P \prod_{\sigma=\lambda}^{\rho} F^{\sigma} x^{\lambda} = \Phi$$

$$x^{\lambda} \geq 0 \quad (\lambda = 1, \ldots, \rho),$$

where:
$$\prod_{\sigma=\alpha}^{\alpha-1} F^{\sigma} \equiv 1, \quad \prod_{\sigma=\lambda}^{\lambda} F^{\sigma} \equiv F^{\lambda},$$

and α, λ, and σ are all indices designating various time periods.

Data Used in Models

Having synthesized one model of a housing situation in a new town, the next step is to present the data which will be used in this and subsequent models.

The **F** matrix for each period can be composed as in Table 11.1 by using the birth, death, marriage, and divorce rates shown in Table 11.2. Table 11.3 shows the empirical probability demand matrix **A**, which provides a major input to the constraints of the basic model.

In Table 11.4, three sets of trial data to be used for the right-hand side housing supply constraint are presented. As may be seen from this table, in each successive trial the numbers for each housing type to be built in each period are multiples of the corresponding numbers in the first trial. By creating the right-hand figures in this manner, it is possible to make some interesting comparisons from the resulting output of the model.

The figures for the probability distributions of both family sizes and moving family size characteristics were taken from the *Statistical Abstract of the United States* and are presented in Tables 11.5 and 11.6 below. Other inputs to the model include:

$m = 6$ (costs range from $9.000 for type 1 to $35,000 for type 6),

$p = 5$ (5 year periods),

Table 11-2

Predicted Birth, Death, Marriage, and Divorce Rates for Various Periods of Time, Based on data from Statistical Abstracts of the United States, 1963. F

Period (α)	1965-69	1970-74	1975-79	1980-84	1985-90
β^α	0.3820	0.3725	0.3630	0.3535	0.3440
Δ^α	0.0472	0.0469	0.0466	0.0463	0.0460
M^α	0.0433	0.0441	0.0449	0.0457	0.0465
D^α	0.0390	0.0397	0.040	0.0411	0.0418

Table 11-3

Housing Demand Probabilities A.

	Family Type (Size)						
	1	2	3	4	5	6	7
1	.1700	.1880	.1560	.1410	.1400	.1490	.1710
2	.2000	.1820	.1740	.1780	.1760	.1780	.1810
3	.2100	.1490	.1530	.1600	.1600	.1570	.1500
4	.2500	.2790	.2860	.2990	.2970	.2870	.2700
5	.1200	.1370	.1520	.1560	.1570	.1570	.1550
6	.0500	.0650	.0600	.0590	.0700	.0720	.0730

Table 11-4

Right Hand Side Elements: Total Numbers of Houses of Various Types Constructed Within or Before Each Specific Time Period.

Time Period	House Type	Trial 1		Trial 2		Trial 3	
		Number built in time period	Total number built	Number built in time period	Total number built	Number built in time period	Total number built
0	1	1020	1020	1610	1610	2700	2700
	2	1160	1160	1820	1820	3050	3050
	3	1020	1020	1610	1610	2700	2700
	4	1780	1780	2820	2820	4710	4710
	5	900	900	1410	1410	2370	2370
	6	400	400	620	620	1040	1040
	Total	6280	6280	9890	9890	16570	16570
1	1	640	1660	1150	2760	2030	4730
	2	720	1880	1300	3120	2290	5340
	3	640	1660	1150	2760	2030	4730
	4	1120	2900	2010	4830	3520	8230
	5	560	1460	1010	2420	1780	4150
	6	250	650	440	1060	780	1820
	Total	3930	10210	7060	16950	12430	29000
2	1	510	2170	690	3450	1350	6080
	2	580	2460	780	3900	1520	6860
	3	510	2170	690	3450	1350	6080

Table 11-4 *(continued)*

Time Period	House Type	Trial 1		Trial 2		Trial 3	
		Number built in time period	Total number built	Number built in time period	Total number built	Number built in time period	Total number built
	4	890	3790	1200	6030	2360	10590
	5	450	1910	610	3030	1180	5330
	6	200	850	270	1330	520	2340
	Total	3140	13350	4240	21190	8280	37280
3	1	250	2420	690	4140	340	6420
	2	290	2750	780	4680	380	7240
	3	250	2420	690	4140	340	6420
	4	450	4240	1200	7230	580	11170
	5	220	2130	610	3640	300	5630
	6	100	950	270	1600	130	2470
	Total	1560	14910	4240	25430	2070	39350
4	1	130	2550	460	4600	340	6760
	2	150	2900	520	5200	380	7620
	3	130	2550	460	4600	340	6760
	4	220	4460	810	8040	580	11750
	5	110	2240	400	4040	300	5930
	6	50	1000	180	1780	130	2600
	Total	790	15700	2830	28260	2070	41420

Table 11-5

Empirically Derived Probability That a
Family Is of a Given Size. U.S. Population Data.

Family Type (Size) (i)	1	2	3	4	5	6	7 and above
Probability (c_i)	.059	.299	.198	.190	.122	.068	.064

Table 11-6

Empirically Derived Probability That a
Family Which Moves Is of a Given Size.
U.S. Population Data.

Family Type (Size) (i)	1	2	3	4	5	6	7 and above
Probability (g_i)	.090	.229	.184	.206	.138	.078	.073

Φ = 50,000 people, and

X^4, $X^5 \doteq 0$ (no immigration after first 15 years).

Results

Table 11.7 illustrates the results derived from the three trials of the basic model. In this connection, the concept of *slack* refers to the dearth of houses for families, that is, those housing units for which there is no match with the demand arising from the migrating family types; the concept of *surplus* represents an unfulfilled demand, that is, families waiting for homes (either inmigrating families or resident families with differing housing needs). It also should be noted that after the third period, no new families were "permitted" to migrate into the new town. This constraint is in keeping with the objective of many new-town programs to achieve maximum population levels in the initial fifteen-year period of development. Therefore, shifts in housing demand beyond this period are the result of changes in family composition (i.e., increased family size, marriages and divorces, etc.)

Looking at Trial 1, it may be noted that in Period 1 there is relatively little slack, and the surplus exists only in the single-individual type of units. In the second period, a substantial unfulfilled demand (surplus) is generated at the Family Type 6 level (husband, wife, and four children). This demand continues to build over the remaining periods such that over 87 percent of the cumulative surplus of demand is accounted for by this category. A similar pattern is generated in each of the other trials: 86.5 percent of the surplus in Trial 2 and 73.5 percent of the surplus in Trial 3. It should be noted that the slack in demand (houses in surplus) increases significantly from Trial 1 through Trial 3 in all periods, while the surplus in demand holds fairly steady among trials after the first period (the rather erratic pattern among trials in the third period is a result of the zero slack in Trials 1 and 2).

Direct comparison between Tables 11.4 and 11.7 may be somewhat misleading. The difference between the total number of houses constructed in each trial and the number of families migrating appears much more striking than is indicated by the slack; the reduction in this gap is accounted for by the "new" demands generated by families from within the new town after the first period as a result of changes in housing needs owing to changes in family types.

One other characteristic of the results of these three initial trials should be noted. In each of the trials, there are significant "voids" in the family types accommodated in the new-town development, i.e., Family Type 4 in Trial 1, Types 6 and 7 in Trial 2, and Types 2, 5, and 7 in Trial 3. Thus, the fundamental social objective of population balance is not fully met by any of these trials. The predominance of Family Types 1 and 2, accounting for nearly 50 percent of the household units in Trial 1, over 65 percent in Trial 2, and nearly 75 percent in Trial 3, suggests that this objective of population balance will not be achieved under the constraints of the basic model.

Minimum Housing Requirements Analyses

The objective utilized in the previous analysis — that of minimizing the slack or surplus of housing — may not be a realistic one in practice. Unless there are other major reasons for building exact quantities of each housing type, it is likely that most new-town planners would strive to reduce the total number of houses which must be constructed, while still accommodating the desired levels of growth. It is possible to determine the number of families of each size to be attracted to a new town in order to minimize the number of houses needed, while at the same time equating the supply with the demand. This problem can be symbolized as follows:

$$\min Z = \sum_{\alpha=0}^{\rho-1} \sum_{j=1}^{m} b_j^{\alpha}$$

subject to:
$$\sum_{\lambda=1}^{\rho} A \prod_{\sigma=\lambda}^{\alpha-1} F^{\sigma} x^{\lambda} - \sum_{\lambda=0}^{\alpha-1} B^{\lambda} = 0 \ (\alpha=1), \ldots, \rho),$$

$$\sum_{\lambda=1}^{\rho} P \prod_{\sigma=\lambda}^{\rho} F^{\sigma} x^{\lambda} = \Phi$$

$$x^{\lambda}, B^{\lambda} \geqslant 0,$$

where the vector B^{λ} is now a vector of housing type variables.

Results

The results of the analysis using the above formulation are presented in Table 11.8. The minimum total number of houses is 9422.

Looking back at Table 11.7, it can be estimated that by fixing the supply of housing (at values which were anticipated to be "good"), the planner can foresee 300 to 400 vacancies and a much larger number of unfulfilled demands. Therefore, by remaining flexible in setting housing type supplies, it is possible to achieve substantial increases in revenues from rent and "goodwill."

Other difficulties arise in scanning these results, however. Under this form of the model, only families of Sizes 6 and 7 should immigrate, a situation which is most improbable. Additional constraints are needed further to modify the model to achieve more realistic results.

Table 11-7

Number of Families, by Type, Required to Migrate in Each Period in Order to Minimize Total Slack and Surplus in Housing.

Family Type	Period I total	slack	surplus	Period 2 total	slack	surplus	Period 3 total	slack	surplus
				Trial 1					
1	1,048	- - -	84	192	- - -	27	- - -	- - -	110
2	3,766	- - -	- - -	459	163	- - -	361	- - -	- - -
3	410	- - -	- - -	428	- - -	- - -	- - -	- - -	173
4	- - -	23	- - -	- - -	- - -	- - -	- - -	- - -	36
5	1,098	23	- - -	1,000	- - -	- - -	- - -	- - -	- - -
6	- - -	1	- - -	142	- - -	699	- - -	- - -	1,138
7	- - -	- - -	- - -	697	- - -	- - -	2,219	- - -	- - -
Total	6,322	47	84	2,918	163	726	2,580	- - -	1,457
				Trial 2					
1	4,392	- - -	23	1,848	87	- - -	888	- - -	75
2	2,938	- - -	- - -	312	- - -	- - -	2,964	- - -	417
3	592	- - -	116	1,663	- - -	- - -	64	- - -	197
4	- - -	220	- - -	1,940	- - -	- - -	- - -	- - -	184
5	1,725	119	- - -	381	- - -	- - -	- - -	- - -	- - -
6	- - -	53	- - -	- - -	- - -	721	- - -	- - -	1,434
7	- - -	- - -	- - -	- - -	- - -	- - -	- - -	- - -	- - -
Total	9,647	392	139	6,144	87	721	3,916	- - -	2,307

Period 4			Period 5			Totals		
total	slack	surplus	total	slack	surplus	total	slack	surplus

Trial 1

---	---	---	---	67	---	1,240	67	221
---	---	---	---	---	122	4,586	163	122
---	---	365	---	---	---	838	---	538
---	205°	---	---	---	---	---	228	36
---	131	---	---	---	---	2,098	154	---
---	---	1,635	---	---	1,907	142	1	5,379
---	---	---	---	---	---	2,916	---	---
---	336	2,000	---	67	2,029	11,820	613	6,296

Trial 2

---	436	---	---	750	---	7,128	1,273	98
---	---	---	---	68	---	6,214	68	417
---	---	---	---	---	--°-	2,319	---	313
---	32	---	---	---	---	1,940	252	184
---	64	---	---	---	---	2,106	183	---
---	---	1,938	---	---	2,057	---	53	6,150
---	---	---	---	---	---	---	---	---
---	532	1,938	---	818	2,057	19,707	1,829	7,162

(continued)

Table 11-7 *(continued)*

Family	Period I			Period 2			Period 3		
Type	total	slack	surplus	total	slack	surplus	total	slack	surplus
					Trial 3				
1	11,697	- - -	- - -	9,593	468	- - -	227	1,522	- - -
2	- - -	- - -	97	- - -	- - -	329	- - -	149	- - -
3	3,914	- - -	469	- - -	- - -	- - -	- - -	897	- - -
4	714	452	- - -	458	- - -	- - -	2,777	- - -	- - -
5	- - -	259	- - -	- - -	417	- - -	- - -	95	- - -
6	- - -	178	- - -	282	- - -	470	- - -	- - -	874
7	- - -	- - -	- - -	- - -	- - -	- - -	- - -	- - -	- - -
Total	16,325	889	566	10,333	885	799	3,004	2,663	874

	Period 4			Period 5			Totals	
total	slack	surplus	total	slack	surplus	total	slack	surplus
				Trial 3				
---	1,850	---	---	2,228	---	21,517	6,068	---
---	---	---	---	---	132	---	149	558
---	473	---	---	2	---	3,914	1,372	469
---	---	---	---	---	466	3,949	452	466
---	---	---	---	---	273	---	771	273
---	---	1,616	---	---	1,949	282	178	4,909
---	---	---	---	---	---	---	---	---
---	2,323	1,616	---	2,230	2,820	29,662	8,990	6,675

Table 11-8

Number of Immigrating Families and Number of Houses To Be Built in New Towns To Minimize Total Number of Houses.

Family Type	Period 1	2	3	Housing Type	Period 0	1	2	3	4
1				1	568	462	151	0	0
2				2	608	518	240	71	39
3				3	506	768	528	234	126
4				4	913	365	13	0	105
5				5	522	129	0	0	80
6	301	440	404	6	245	680	644	481	412
7	3064	2044	419						

$z = 9422$ houses

Table 11-9

Number of Families Desired and Number of Houses To Be Built: Existing and Moving Family Size Distribution Analyses.

Existing Family Distribution

Family Type	Period 1	Period 2	Period 3	Housing Type	Period 0	Period 1	Period 2	Period 3	Period 4
1	0	516	263	1	0	1418	929	275	235
2	0	2612	1333	2	0	1572	997	367	372
3	0	1740	888	3	0	1377	1174	497	394
4	0	1662	848	4	0	2491	1108	305	509
5	0	1063	543	5	0	1291	329	0	220
6	0	593	303	6	0	556	1347	764	324
7	0	562	287				$z = 18,861$ houses		

Moving Family Distribution

Family Type	Period 1	Period 2	Period 3	Housing Type	Period 0	Period 1	Period 2	Period 3	Period 4
1	0	824	334	1	0	1462	810	274	238
2	0	2101	852	2	0	1647	904	377	365
3	0	1689	685	3	0	1461	1076	463	370
4	0	1887	765	4	0	2600	777	240	443
5	0	1261	511	5	0	1352	158	0	187
6	0	717	290	6	0	579	1317	691	345
7	0	667	270				$z = 18,147$ houses		

Constraints on Numbers of
Families of Each Type

Two sets of constraints might be used to alleviate the problem mentioned above. In both sets, the probabilities of immigrating families being of given sizes are fixed; however, in the first set, this probability distribution is made equivalent to the family size distribution found in a "normal" population of *existing* families, whereas in the second set, the distribution is made equivalent to that in a "normal" population of *moving* or *mobile* families. The choice of the proper set of constraints must be made in the context of the individual situation.

The two sets of constraints can be represented as follows:

$$\text{Set 1:} \quad (c_i\, x_1^{\alpha}) - (c_1\, x_i^{\alpha}) = 0 \quad (i = 2, \ldots, n)$$

and

$$\text{Set 2:} \quad (g_i\, x_1^{\alpha}) - (g_1\, x_i^{\alpha}) = 0 \quad (i = 2, \ldots, n).$$

The definitions and values of c_i and g_i can be found in Tables 11.5 and 11.6, respectively.

Results and Conclusions

Using each of the sets of constraints listed above in turn, a third and fourth analysis were made, the results of which are presented in Table 11.9. These results show that, in order to obtain a balance of families similar to that which exists in the United States population, 18,861 housing units must be constructed during the first five periods. Seven hundred fewer houses are needed to attract those families "most likely to move," that is, to accommodate a distribution equivalent to that in a "normal" population of mobile families. On the other hand, both figures are almost double the 9422 housing units which constitute the minimum number that must be built.

It can be concluded from these analyses that an endeavor to attract certain sizes of families may lead to substantial savings in housing construction costs. These savings, at the extreme, may be as much as 50 percent of the pre-endeavor costs.

Equally important, however, is the fact that the use of either of the additional constraints permits a closer approximation of the social objective of a balanced population in the new town, not only at the stage of full development, but in the earlier periods as well. Clearly, the first set of constraints, that is, approximating a distribution equivalent to the family size distribution in a "normal" population of *existing* families, achieves the social objective more completely. It should be further noted that this approach could be used to determine the housing supply requirements to accommodate any *desirable* population distribution. That is to say, the probability constraints could be set according to some predetermined population (family size) distribution, and the model output would then provide the planners of the new town with information concerning the most suitable housing supply conditions required to attract and serve this population distribution.

Part Four
Environment for Planning

Part Four consists of four chapters dealing with the environment in which planning must function in this country. Chapter 12 presents the results of empirical research into the structure and context of planning as related to governmental commitment to planning in American cities. Chapter 13 extends this research into the functional and situational elements of the environment for planning. Chapter 14 presents research findings and interpretations of the role of communications in planning. Chapter 15 is a summary of the research on the environment for planning and the development of a general empirical theory as well as suggestions for improving the environment for the advent of systemic planning.

12 Governmental Commitment to the Planning Process

Studies of decision-making enjoy great currency in the social sciences. However, planners who have dealt with the role of planning in the decision-making process, for the most part, have been content to discuss what this role ought to be, giving relatively little attention to an analysis of what it is. Planners are interested in influencing the public decision-making process in a positive way so that it may assume some approach that will "maximize" or "optimize" public policies. Before this goal can be achieved, however, it is first necessary to understand more clearly the process itself.

Efforts to define the role of planning in the structure and processes of government have given rise to important questions concerning governmental commitment to the planning process. Planning can be an effective instrument in the public decision-making process only if there is a relatively high level of commitment to the planning process on the part of elected officials and the general public.

In the growing literature of the planning profession, however, it is difficult to find explicit references to conditions which are likely to produce a significant level of planning commitment. Various demographic, economic, political, organizational, and structural factors frequently are cited as "contributors." To date, there has been little empirical evidence to verify these assumptions, or, finding them lacking, research to identify conditions which in fact do provide the basis for such achievement.

The following chapters undertake to identify a number of these basic assumptions; translate them into measurable structural and contextual variables, situational and functional variables ("inputs" and "outputs" of the planning process), and process variables (principally communication characteristics in local government); and analyze the relationship of these variables to the level of planning commitment and the decision-making process in middle-sized cities.

Planning Is An Eclectic Profession

The field of planning has been criticized for its lack of original techniques and concepts for dealing with urban problems. However, as Dr. Seward Hiltner has observed, "The professional use of technical means . . . does not necessarily lie in unique ownership of individual and discrete tools and means. It lies rather in the perspective brought to this data."[1] Therefore the ability of the planner to mobilize concepts and techniques which he has "borrowed" from other disciplines and to focus them on the problems of urban development may be viewed as a strength rather than a weakness of the profession.

There are, however a number of conceptual gaps which the planning profession must itself fill if it is to carry out its assigned responsibilities. These "gaps" center on areas which are of prime concern to the practice of planning but which are not adequately dealt with by other disciplines. To date, relatively little research has been conducted in these more fundamental areas.

One such area concerns the factors which contribute to a high level of governmental commitment to the planning process. It is generally recognized that cities vary along a number of dimensions as to their acceptance and continuing active support of the planning process. Throughout the country, urban planning has achieved varying degrees of success in carrying out its functional responsibilities within the framework of local government. The extent to which these efforts have been successful cannot be measured by the sheer size of the professional planning staffs or budget appropriations for planning. Nor is it possible to directly measure the tangible results of these planning efforts in all cases. In the words of the late Hugh Pomeroy, "Planning, to be realistic and effective (and it must be both to be either), must be regarded as a continuing process in public administration, consisting of (1) the establishment of policies with respect to the desirable physical form and character of the community and (2) the use of these policies as a guide (a) for public activities and (b) for various regulations applying to private development."[2] Thus it may be suggested that one important measure of the success of planning programs is the degree to which local governments are committed to the planning process on a continuing basis.

Various demographic, economic, political, and structural factors are frequently cited as "contributors" to a high level of planning commitment. To date, however, there has been little empirical evidence to verify these assumptions. The purpose of this chapter, therefore, will be identify these basic assumptions, to translate them into a number of measurable socioeconomic and structural factors, and to analyze their relationship to the level of planning commitment and the decision-making process in middle-sized cities.

Some Implicit Assumptions
Concerning Planning Commitment

In the growing literature of the planning profession, there are a number of implicit assumptions as to the conditions which are likely to produce a high degree of governmental commitment to the planning process. For the purposes of the following analysis, ten such assumptions have been ferreted out of the literature.

1. Cities with high population densities and those with rapid growth will be more acutely aware of the need for planning due to the service demands that are generated by these conditions.
2. Cities with a greater sense of community will manifest a greater commitment

to planning to protect and perserve the positive attributes of the environment and to alleviate the negative ones.

3. Cities with a high level of governmental expenditures will turn to planning and capital improvements programming as a means of more effectively allocating their fiscal resources.
4. Cities which are highly industrialized, i.e., which have an economic base that is dependent upon an export base in manufacturing, will evince a greater support for planning than nonindustrial cities, since the conflict between industry and other aspects of the urban environment will heighten an awareness of the need for planning.
5. Cities with a relatively high percentage of nonwhite population will exhibit a greater reliance on planning and renewal programs to alleviate conditions of poor housing and other blighting factors of the environment.
6. Older cities will have more critical problems of atrophy, blight, and decay and therefore will be more likely actively to seek solutions to these problems through planning and urban renewal.
7. Cities in which the planning function is directly responsible to the principal decision-makers of government are more likely to have successful planning programs.
8. Cities in which government is regarded as an instrument of community growth will assume that the most important ends to be served are population expansion, industrial development, etc. and will actively seek to foster such growth through planning.
9. Cities with a high degree of professionalism in government are more likely to have an active planning program.
10. Cities with a high level of citizen participation in civic affairs are more likely to have an active planning program.

The data used to test these assumptions were originally gathered as part of a much larger research project conducted jointly by members of the faculty of the University of Wisconsin and the University of California at Berkeley. The original study, known as the Governmental Units Analysis, was concerned with all "central cities" with populations of between 50,000 and 250,000 according to the 1960 Census.

Situational and Functional Factors

A second major domain of variables was examined through analyses of data obtained from a detailed questionnaire which was sent to planning directors and chief executives in the 95 cities under study. This category of variables included a number of situational and functional factors which were considered in terms of the "inputs" and "outputs" of the planning process. Inputs include such elements as the size of the planning staff, the degree of professionalism, the length of service of the planning director, and the extent to which consultants were used in preparing a plan. Output factors relate to the level of performance of the agency, its effectiveness in influencing the decision process, degree of satisfaction among participants, sources of difficulties and frustrations (real and assumed), and other related factors.

The Role of Communication

A third domain of variables also was derived from the questionnaire data. The questionnaire contained sections designed to (1) examine a number of decision situations which could be assumed to be common to all of the cities under study, and (2) ascertain the flow of communications involved in the formulation of public decisions. As Daland and Parker have observed, "In order to improve systems of urban planning still further, it is paramount to learn precisely what are the functions or roles that "planners" are now performing within the complex of roles which guide and control the location and character of private and public urban development. Where governmental planning departments have been established, they operate near the center of a communication system consisting of the governmental organization which is designed to create and effectuate public policies. Because of the crucial importance of governmental policy in every aspect of urban life, non-governmental decision makers form a part of this communication network."[3]

Thus, Daland and Parker have made the assumption that planning departments operate near the center of a communication system which is designed to create and effectuate public policies. This assumption is not self-evident, however, but must be framed as a testable hypothesis, capable of empirical analysis. If this assumption is correct, then planning agencies in cities with high planning commitment might be expected to evince certain communication characteristics which differ from those agencies in cities with lower levels of planning commitment. This hypothesis, then, will be of primary consideration in the final phases of the present empirical investigation.

Developing the Dependent Variable

The selection of middle-sized cities for study by the authors of the Governmental Units Analysis was based on the fact that many of the case studies of community power and urban social structure are based on cities within this population range. From this universe of over 300 central cities, 95 in the New England, Middle Atlantic, East North Central, West North Central, and Mountain Census Regions were selected for further analysis. Each of these cities was classified as a "central city" of a Standard Metropolitan Statistical Area in the 1960 Census. Cities of over 50,000 population which fall within the metropolitan area dominated by a larger city were excluded from consideration. Therefore, the resultant sample of 95 cities has been "controlled" for size and for the exogenous influences of larger metropolitan centers. By selecting cities from a number of census regions, it is also possible to test for variations arising from regional influences.

To test the basic assumptions, it was necessary to construct an "index of planning commitment." Thirty measures of planning activities were compiled and analyzed in the development of this index. The selection of these items was based, in part, on the eligibility requirements of a typical "Schedule A" which is developed in conjunction with the local planning assistance program, as provided for under Section 701 of the Housing Act of 1954, as amended.[a] In addition, several elements were added to this list to reflect the importance of plan implementation.

After these elements were compiled for all 95 cities for which information was available,[4] they were divided into three categories: (1) elements relating to the formulation of a comprehensive plan; (2) elements concerned with the status of urban renewal programs; and (3) elements dealing with plan implementation. This latter grouping was further divided into three subcategories: (a) zoning; (b) official map status; and (c) capital improvements budgeting and programming. Two additional indices also were included: (4) planning staff and expenditures; and (5) participation in regional planning activities. The next step was to assign overall cumulative point scores to each of the basic categories. A base score of fifteen points was assigned to the category concerned with the comprehensive plan. The other categories were then "scaled" in relation to their relative importance to the planning process (see Table 12.1). The final step in the formulation of the planning commitment index involved the assignment of weights to each of the elements within the individual categories. While this weighting involved some subjective judgment, it was felt that such a system would be a refinement over a simple cumulative scoring system. A relative emphasis was placed on the implementation devices, since it was felt that the presence of these elements was indicative of a continuous commitment to the planning process.

Based on the assigned weights, an index score was then computed for each of the 95 cities. The cities were grouped according to their index scores into three categories: (1) cities in which there appeared to be a relatively high level of commitment to the planning process in the deliberations of public officials;

[a]Under the administration procedures established by the Urban Renewal Administration of the Department of Housing and Urban Development (formerly the Housing and Home Finance Agency), the administration of the 701 program for local planning assistance is the responsibility of designated state agencies. Among the administrative responsibilities of these state agencies is the formulation of a basic checklist of elements to be included in local planning programs in order to be eligible for participation in the 701 program. This checklist, known as a "Schedule A," is approved by the Urban Renewal Administration, but the actual review procedures are the responsibility of the state agency. The elements of a "Schedule A" vary from state to state, depending on the particular needs of the communities within the state and the particular elements emphasized by the state agency. There are, however, a number of elements common to all "Schedule A" formats. These common elements were applied in the above analysis.

(2) cities in which a more satisfactory level of planning commitment was emerging, although it had not achieved the status of the first category; and (3) cities in which there appeared to be a relatively low level of commitment to planning. A summary of the distribution of the 95 cities on the basis of their index scores is shown in Table 12.1.

Basic Domaines of Variables

As previously noted, the independent variables analyzed can be grouped under three basic headings. For the purposes of this presentation, the *structural and contextual factors* have been grouped as follows: (1) assumptions relating to demographic factors; (2) assumptions concerning social and economic factors; (3) assumptions concerning environmental factors; (4) assumptions relating to governmental organization, public expenditures, and political characteristics; and (5) assumptions relating to the structure of planning organizations.

The various *functional and situational factors* have been grouped according to the following categories: (1) input factors relating to the planning agency; (2) factors concerning the performance of the planning agency; (3) factors relating to the functional role of the planning agency; (4) factors contributing to difficulties encountered in achieving implementation of planning recommendations; and (5) sources of influence in public policy-making.

The principal factors analyzed under the third domain of variables — the role of communication — include (1) access to the communication network; and (2) frequency of communication.

Summary of Findings:
Structural and Contextual Factors

As shown in the accompanying tables, many of the basic assumptions to be found in the literature on planning and urban development are not supported by the empirical data of this study. For example, cities with relatively higher population densities do not exhibit a greater frequency of commitment to the planning process. With regard to population growth, not only is the assumption not supported, but the analysis would suggest that there is no apparent relationship between the level of planning commitment and the population trends experienced by the cities under study.

A partial explanation of these findings lies in two factors. First, cities which are experiencing rapid growth are frequently only partially developed and are riding a crest of prosperity. Under such circumstances, the concept of the "highest and best use" frequently prevails, that is, the private market mechanisms which act upon the patterns of land-use development provide a quasiplanning control over the location of activities with the most suitable uses made of the available sites. However, in cities which have reached a peak in their

Table 12-1

**Distribution of Index of Planning
Commitment Scores.**

Degree of Commitment	Index Scores	Number of Cities	Percent of Total
High commitment	25 to 50*	33	34.7%
Medium commitment	15 to 24	34	35.8
Low commitment	0 to 14	28	29.5
Total		95	100.0%

*Highest score recorded was 41.

development and are experiencing a redistribution of activities (as evidenced by shifts in population), the natural process of land-use succession, as provided by the private sector of the economy, does not operate as efficiently. Therefore, it is necessary to introduce greater public control and planning to achieve the desired ends.

A second partial explanation lies in the fact that it is not population growth (or decline) per se which is the "causal" factor, but the character and composition of the population shifts (see Table 12.2). Thus a city experiencing a major increase in relatively unskilled workers and their families or in minority groups may also be experiencing a parallel outmigration of middle-class families, moving to nearby suburban areas. These shifts may balance one another, with the result that the city's total population shows only slight changes. However, where the exodus of persons with higher socioeconomic status has exceeded in significant proportions, the inmigration of lower-class persons, the problems of the city are multiplied, since the incoming migrants are frequently unable to "pay their way" in terms of taxes and may require greater governmental expenditures for public services. These conditions, in part, may contribute to a city's recognitions of the need for planning.

Examining another measure of population change which more closely approximates this question of population composition, the data reveal that cities with a high percentage of "migrants" in their 1960 population (i.e., persons five years old and over who moved into the city between 1955 and 1960) score in the "high" category of planning commitment with greater frequency than cities with lower percentages of "newcomers." However, there is no apparent relationship between the percentage of nonwhite persons in the population of 95 cities and the level of "high" planning commitment.

These findings concerning the various demographic variables prompt other

Table 12-2

Relationship Between Demographic Factors and Level of Planning Commitment.

	Level of Planning Commitment			
Demographic Factors	Low	Medium	High	Number
a. Population Density				
High (over 6,000)	27%	38	35	(34)
Low (5,999 or less)	32%	34	34	(61)
Difference	−5	+4	+1	
b. Population Trends, 50–60				
Population Declines	27%	35	38	(34)
Population Increases	31%	36	33	(61)
Difference	−4	−1	+5	
c. Percent of Persons Five Years and Older Who Are Recent Migrants				
15% and over	23%	35	42	(26)
0 to 14%	32%	36	32	
Difference	−9	−1	+10	
d. Percent of Population Nonwhite				
5% or more	24%	40	36	(47)
0 to 5%	36%	31	33	(48)
Difference	−12	+9	+3	

questions about the relationship among these variables themselves. It is generally assumed that population change and number of "migrants" in the population are related in some causal way (i.e., a large population increase will result in a large number of "migrants" in the population), and further, that in recent years, a large number of migrants in the population was related to an increase in the percentage of nonwhites. As shown in Table 12.3, while the first relationship holds to some degree, the level of correlation is not as high as might be anticipated. There appears to be no relationship between population change and percentage of nonwhite population, and a negative correlation in terms of nonwhite population and percent of "migrants." Applying the chi-square test through multiple correlation reveals that only about 40 percent of the variation in either population change or percentage of migrants in the population can be accounted for in terms of the other two variables, and less than 5 percent of the variation in terms of the level of nonwhite population.

The assumptions regarding the influence of the economic base on the level of planning commitment exhibits a somewhat higher level of relationship (see Table 12.4), although there are some problems associated with the available measures for testing these assumptions. The manufacturing ratio shows a negative relationship to the index scores of high commitment, that is, nonindustrial cities score "high" in terms of planning commitment with a relatively greater frequency. The employment-residence ratio, on the other hand, shows a positive relationship.[b] Since these two "independent" variables have a product moment coefficient of only .20, it may be assumed that these findings are not contradictory.

In the case of cities with medium planning commitment scores, the manufacturing ratio shows a more positive relationship (i.e., such cities have a greater tendency toward high percentages of their labor forces in manufacturing activities), and these cities more frequently are industrial employment centers with lower medium family incomes. It would seem, therefore, that the important economic variable is not the character of the economic structure, that is, whether the economic base of the community is industrial or nonindustrial, so much as it is the composition of the labor force. Further evidence of this may be derived from the relatively strong relationship between cities with high planning commitment scores and those with high percentages of white-collar workers in their labor force. It might be anticipated that there would be a close

[b]The manufacturing ratio represents workers employed in manufacturing as a percentage of aggregate employment. Due to Census selectivity, the manufacturing ratio is much larger than the actual percentage of total local employment engaged in manufacturing. In an average city, the actual proportion of the labor force engaged in manufacturing would be just over half the manufacturing ratio.

The employment-residence ratio represents the ratio of aggregate employment to the corresponding categories of resident labor force. When these two figures are equal, the E-R ratio is 100. This ratio is a *rough measure* of net commuting for economic activities involved. A city's E-R ratio can rise for either of two reasons — increase in local employment more rapid than increase in population, or decentralization of population more rapid than that of employment.

Table 12-3

**Relationships among Population
Change, Level of Nonwhite Population,
and Percentage of Migrants for 95
Middle–Sized Cities.**

		(2) Nonwhite Population	(3) Percentage of Migrants
(1)	Population Change	$r = .0145$	$r = .6204$
(2)	Nonwhite Population		$r = .1619$

$$r_{1.23} = .631$$

$$r_{2.13} = .218$$

$$r_{3.12} = .643$$

Table 12-4

Relationship between Social and Economic Factors and Level of Planning Commitment.

Social and Economic Factors		Level of Planning Commitment			
		Low	Medium	High	Number
a.	Economic Base				
	Nonindustrial	26%	33	41	(34)
	Industrial	31%	38	31	(61)
	Difference	−5	−5	+10	
b.	Percent of Labor Force in Manufacturing				
	Over 60%	33%	43	24	(37)
	12 to 59%	28%	31	41	(58)
	Difference	+5	+12	−17	
c.	Metropolitan Status				
	Employing Centers	21%	44	35	(62)
	Balanced or Dormitory	46%	21	33	(33)
	Difference	−25	+23	+2	
d.	Employment/Residence Ratio				
	125 and over	22%	37	41	(46)
	58 to 124	37%	35	28	(49)
	Difference	−15	+2	+13	
e.	Percent of White−Collar Workers in Labor Force				
	43 to 69%	19%	36	45	(47)
	20 to 42%	40%	35	25	(48)

(continued)

Table 12-4 *(continued)*

Social and Economic Factors		Level of Planning Commitment			
		Low	Medium	High	Number
	Difference	−21	+1	+20	
f.	Percent of Establishments with 20 or More Employees				
	40% or more	31%	39	30	(46)
	0 to 39%	28%	33	39	(49)
	Difference	+3	+6	−9	
g;	Medium Family Income				
	$5950 and over	32%	30	38	(47)
	$4000 to $5949	27%	42	31	(48)
	Difference	+5	−12	+7	
h.	Percent of Families with Income Under $3000				
	16% and over	24%	42	34	(41)
	0 to 15%	33%	32	35	(54)
	Difference	−9	+10	−1	
i.	Percent of Families with Income Over $10000				
	15% and over	26%	32	42	(47)
	0 to 15%	33%	40	27	(48)
	Difference	−7	−8	+15	
j.	Percentage of Persons 25 Years and Older Having Completed High School				
	40% or more	37	28	35	(51)
	20 to 39%	20	46	34	(44)
	Difference	+17	−18	+1	

relationship between the E-R ratio and the percentage of white-collar workers in the labor force. A high E-R ratio signifies a high level of in-commutation, and it is generally assumed that white-collar workers make up the bulk of commuters. Analysis of the data reveals, however, that these two factors are not highly correlated and, in fact, show a slight negative correlation ($r = .088$).

Cities with medium planning commitment scores exhibit a greater tendency to be Employing Centers (cities with at least 16 percent more jobs in manufacturing trade, or selected services, than resident workers in those activities), while those cities with low planning scores are more frequently found in the Balanced or Dormitory Community categories.

Another measure concerning the impact of the economic base on the level of planning commitment relates to the percentage of establishments within a city with twenty or more employees. The data in this analysis would suggest that cities with relatively few large employment establishments are more likely to have a higher level of planning commitment. It might be argued that this is a spurious relationship, more attributable to the likelihood that small firms are located in nonindustrial cities. However, additional analysis reveals that this relationship holds regardless of the economic base; that is, cities with smaller percentages of establishments with twenty or more employees have higher planning commitments both in the industrial and nonindustrial categories. While the question of support of civic activities by major companies that sell on a regional or national market is still open to debate in the literature,[5] these data would suggest that in cities where there is a predominance of relatively large firms, less support for long-term commitments to the planning process can be engendered from the economic community.

Turning next to a series of social variables which relate either directly or indirectly to the level of economic activity within a community, there is a tendency for cities with lower median family incomes to score in the medium range of planning commitment. This same relationship holds when the percentage of families having incomes of less than $3,000 is examined. However, quite different results are obtained when upper income levels are examined. Here, there is a clear tendency for cities with 15 percent or more of their families with incomes in excess of $10,000 to achieve high planning commitment scores. Another revealing relationship is obtained when the percentage of persons twenty-five years of age and older having completed high school is analyzed. Cities with lower percentages evince a greater tendency toward medium planning commitment scores, while those with low planning scores exhibit the opposite tendency.

The assumption that cities in which the prevailing view is that the function of local government is to provide "life's amenities" will have a greater commitment to planning is more difficult to quantify than the previous assumptions (see Table 12.5). Edward Banfield and James Wilson have suggested the following characteristics of such cities: "Outsiders and transients will be excluded, the labor force kept low, neighborhoods defended by rigid zoning laws and building codes, open space jealously guarded, noise and smoke curtailed, and traffic

Table 12-5

Relationship between Environmental
Factors and Level of Planning Commitment.

		Level of Planning Commitment			
Environmental Factors		Low	Medium	High	Number
a.	Percent of Housing Units Owner–Occupied				
	60% or more	24%	40	36	(45)
	0 to 59%	34%	32	34	(50)
	Difference	−10	+8	+2	
b.	Goodness of City Scores				
	High Scores	20%	39	41	(43)
	Low Scores	37%	35	28	(44)
	Difference	−17	+4	+13	
c.	Williams' Typology for Comparative Local Government				
	Instrument of Community Growth	5	7	10	(22)
	Provider of Life's Amenities	2	8	9	(19)
	Caretaker	5	4	4	(13)
	Arbiter of Conflicting Interests	1	2	3	(6)
d.	Age of City: Census Year in Which City First Reached 50,000 Population				
	1910–1960	31%	42	27	(51)
	1800–1900	27%	30	43	(44)
	Difference	+4	+12	−16	

Table 12-5 *(continued)*

Environmental Factors		Low	Medium	High	Number

Environmental Factors	Low	Medium	High	Number
e. Census Divisions				
New England and Middle Atlantic States	32%	33	35	(46)
East North Central, West North Central, and Mountain States	26%	39	35	(49)
Difference	+6	–6	0	

Level of Planning Commitment

routed around the city. The cost of such measures may be high, but they will be borne. Such communities are likely to consist largely of upper-middle-class families, including wealthy, elderly retired people and young couples who are anxious for the 'right kind of town' for their children."[6]

From this description, it may be suggested that cities with a greater sense of community will have a high percentage of owner-occupied housing. Therefore, as a test of this assumption, the percentage of owner-occupied housing in each of the 95 cities was measured against the level of planning commitment. On this basis, the assumption receives little support from the data.

In recent years, two concepts have been added to the planner's vocabulary which also are related to such cities. Planners speak of the practice of zoning residential areas for large-lot development (over one acre) as "fiscal zoning" in that such practices are frequently applied to keep out certain "undesirable" groups which would raise the costs of providing municipal services (particularly education). A second somewhat broader term, "snobbery planning," has been applied to the planning practices suggested in the description by Banfield and Wilson. Such planning is not necessarily good planning, since the motives of those who favor such practices are not always framed in the interest of the broader community. Based on some analysis of communities which have pursued this approach, it may be suggested that their commitment to planning is not a long-term one, but rather one which selectively calls planning techniques into play to achieve these somewhat questionable objectives.

In lieu of a more definitive measure, E. L. Thorndike's "Goodness of City score" was used as a test of the general attitudes of a community toward growth and development.[7] The assumption is that cities in which government is regarded as an instrument of community growth will actively seek to foster such growth through public planning. Thorndike's index would seem to provide a *rough measure* of such community attitudes, for it does incorporate various dimensions which would characterize cities in which this attitude toward community expansion prevails.

Analysis of the data reveal that there is a positive relationship between cities with high "goodness" scores and those with high planning commitment scores. Since these two variables both represent composite indices, it would be difficult to attribute any clear causal relationship to this finding. One could assume, for example, that if Thorndike were to reconstruct his index today, he would include some measure of planning achievement in the formulation of his scoring system.

The mailed questionnaire sent to both the planning director and the chief executive in each of the 95 cities in the survey sample included a question concerning the typology formulated by Oliver Williams as to what citizens and officials in middle-sized cities expect of their city governments.[8] The respondents were asked to select from among the four characteristic "attitudes" embodied in this typology. The four categories and the distribution of responses received from planning directors are shown in Tables 12.6 and 12.7. The responses from chief executives, although somewhat fewer in number, showed a remarkably close correspondence to the views of their corresponding planning directors. In general, their selections were more "positive," i.e., the first and second categories.

By combining the two more negative attitudes (the third and fourth categories), it is possible to develop an interesting set of relationships. Taking these "attitude" categories in pairs, it may be observed that cities with more positive "attitudes" (the first and second categories) have a tendency to score higher in terms of planning commitment. Cities with medium-level planning commitment scores appear to have a greater tendency toward the view that local government should serve as the "provider of life's amenities," while cities with high commitment scores are fairly evenly distributed between the two more positive viewpoints.

The assumption that older cities will actively seek solutions through planning and urban renewal to their more critical problems of atrophy, blight, and decay, which come with age, receives considerable support from the data (see Tables 12.8, and 12.9). Older cities (i.e., cities which first reached the 50,000 level of population prior to 1900) show a tendency toward higher planning commitment scores. Further, this relationship is even more apparent when older cities with high population densities and/or with major decreases in population are considered. "Younger" cities, having high population densities and/or experiencing population declines, are more likely to fall in the medium range of planning commitment.

These findings concerning the fundamental differences between cities with high and medium planning commitment scores lend support to the notion of "step functions," or critical states, a phenomenon first identified by Ashby in his discussion of stochastic systems.[9] Under this notion, it might be postulated that cities pass through several critical states in terms of their level of commitment to the planning process. In each of these critical states, different sets of factors influence the level of planning commitment achieved at that point in time. These critical states, in part, are a reflection of the structural and

Table 12-6

**Distribution of Responses concerning
Williams' Typology for Comparative
Local Government by Level of Planning
Commitment.**

	Level of Planning Commitment			
Attitude	High	Medium	Low	Total
Instrument of community growth	10	7	5	22
Provider of life's amenities	9	8	2	19
Caretaker	4	4	5	13
Arbiter of conflicting interests	3	2	1	6
Number of cases	26	21	13	60

Table 12-7

**Relationship between Williams'
Typology of Community Attitudes and
Level of Planning Commitment.**

	Community Attitudes		
Planning Commitment	Instrument of community growth	Provider of life's amenities	Caretaker or arbiter
High	45%	47%	37%
Medium	32	42	32
Low	23	11	32
Total	100%	100%	100%
Number of cases	(22)	(19)	(19) $N = 60$

225

Table 12-8

Relationship between Population Density, Age of City, and Level of Planning Commitment.

Population Density	Level of Planning Commitment			
	Low	Medium	High	Number
a. 5,999 persons per square mile or less				
Age of City				
1910–1960	31%	36	33	(22)
1800–1900	28%	36	36	(22)
Difference	+3	0	−3	
b. 6,000 persons per square mile or more				
Age of City				
1910–1960	42%	50	8	(12)
1800–1900	23%	27	50	(39)
Difference	+19	+23	−42	

Table 12-9

**Relationship between Population
Change, Age of City, and Level of
Planning Commitment.**

Population Change	Level of Planning Commitment			
	Low	Medium	High	Number
a. Population Increase				
Age of City				
1910–1960	33%	36	31	(42)
1800–1900	26%	37	37	(19)
Difference	+7	–1	–6	
b. Population Decline				
Age of City				
1910–1960	33%	56	11	(9)
1800–1900	24%	28	48	(25)
Difference	+9	+28	–37	

contextual factors which characterize the city. A change in these factors or a shift in their configuration may cause the city to move to a different level in terms of its planning commitment; that is, commitment to the planning process may not be a continuum, but it may manifest itself in terms of discrete steps.

Pressures on local governments to accept planning as a public responsibility emerged at about the same time and from the same sources as the broader municipal reform movement in the early decades of this century. The goals of the early advocates of planning were part of the larger whole which has been described by various writers as the Anglo-Saxon Protestant middle-class ethos of increased efficiency, the elimination of corruption in government, and the making of local government more responsible to public needs.[10] It might be anticipated, therefore, that in cities where the general programs of municipal reform have been accepted, a higher level of planning commitment will be evidenced. Two elements of municipal reform which do appear to have an impact on the level of planning commitment are nonpartisan elections and at-large elections (see Table 12.10).

While the relationship between nonpartisan elections and the level of planning commitment is relatively strong, it would not seem to follow that this relationship is a direct causal one; some other variables associated with nonpartisanship may intervene and, in part, contribute to this relationship. One such variable relates to the number of councilmen in local governments. At-large elections, of course, generally have resulted in fewer councilmen, thereby reducing the number of "decision-makers" in local government. Analysis of the data reveals that there is a correspondence between smaller councils and the level of planning commitment in the 95 cities under study.

Another important organizational variable concerns the term of office of major elected officials. An implicit assumption is often made that, to be effective, planning must have relative continuity among those officials to whom it must be responsive. If major officials must stand for election every two years, their viewpoint is apt to be more favorable to programs which show results in the short run, rather than to the longer-term programs of planning. The analysis of terms of office as they relate to planning commitment reveals a very interesting pattern. Cities with medium planning commitments tend to have a greater frequency of four-year office terms, while those cities with low planning commitment scores have a clear tendency toward two-year office terms. This relationship, however, may be accounted for, in part, by the correspondence between nonpartisan elections and two-year office terms. Cities favoring nonpartisanship in their elections also have a tendency toward shorter terms of office for their major elected officials.

The relationship between form of government and level of planning commitment shows that cities with a city-manager form of government evinced a significant tendency to score high in terms of planning commitment (a 29 percentage-point difference), while cities with medium and low planning commitment scores exhibit nearly parallel tendencies toward mayor-council or commission forms of government. Since a city-manager form of government

Table 12-10

Relationship between Governmental Organization, Public Expenditures, and Political Characteristics and Level of Planning Commitment.

Organizational and Structural Factors	Level of Planning Commitment			
	Low	Medium	High	Number
a. Type of Election				
Nonpartisan	19%	36	45	(47)
Partisan	40%	35	25	(48)
Difference	−21	+1	+20	
b. Number of Councilmen				
9 or more	38%	35	27	(52)
3 to 8	19%	39	42	(41)
Difference	+19	−4	−15	
c. Term of Office of Chief Executive				
Four Years	20%	49	31	(45)
Two Years	39%	23	38	(47)
Difference	−19	+26	−7	
d. Form of Government				
City Manager	18%	26	56	(27)
Mayor–Council or Commission	34%	40	26	(68)
Difference	−16	−14	+30	
e. Form of Government and Per Capita Employment City Manager Per Capita Employment				
11 or more	10%	40	50	(10)

Table 12-10 *(continued)*

Organizational and Structural Factors	Level of Planning Commitment			
	Low	Medium	High	Number
0 to 10	23%	18	59	(17)
Difference	−13	+22	−9	
Mayor–Council or Commission Per Capita Employment 11 or more	29%	35	36	(31)
0 to 10	38%	43	19	(37)
Difference	−9	−8	+17	
f. Balance of Governmental Revenues and Expenditures Expenditures Exceed Revenues	30%	35	35	(49)
Revenues Exceed Expenditurees or are Balanced	28%	37	35	(46)
Difference	+2	−2	0	
g. Per Capital General Expenditures $80 or more	31%	33	37	(52)
0 to $79	28%	40	33	(43)
Difference	+3	−7	+4	
h. Percent of Revenues from Property Taxes 63% or more	34%	30	36	(47)
30 to 62%	25%	42	33	(48)
Difference	+9	−12	+3	

(continued)

Table 12-10 (*continued*)

Organizational and Structural Factors	Level of Planning Commitment			
	Low	Medium	High	Number
i. Percent of Revenue from Intergovernmental Sources				
15% or more	23%	43	34	(47)
0 to 15%	35%	29	36	(48)
Difference	−12	+14	−2	
j. Percent of Adult Population Voting				
44 to 81%	22%	32	46	(37)
0 to 43%	12%	42	46	(24)
Difference	+10	−10	0	

generally connotes a higher level of professionalism in government, this measure may provide a reasonably good test of the assumption that a higher level of professionalism leads to a greater degree of planning commitment. The hypothesis to be drawn from these findings is that the presence of a city manager provides a more direct line of communication between the planning agency and the decision-making process. This communication link is most important to achieving a high level of commitment to the planning process on the part of public officials.

It might also be assumed that cities with a city-manager form of government would have a higher per capita number of full-time employees in government (assuming this to be a parallel measure of professionalism). However, as shown in Table 12.11, this relationship is not a significantly strong one.

An interesting pattern results from a comparison of form of government, per capita number of governmental employees, and level of planning commitment. It would appear that cities with a city-manager form of government have a higher planning commitment regardless of the size of full-time governmental employment, and in fact, have a slightly lower frequency of high planning commitment when the relative size of full-time staffs is increased. Cities with a mayor-council or commission form of government, on the other hand, appear to increase their planning commitment as the relative size of governmental staff increases. This would suggest that the per capita number of full-time employees in city government may be taken as a relative measure of the level of professionalism in mayor-council and commission forms of government.

Table 12-11

**Relationship between City Manager
Form of Government and Per Capital
Governmental Employment.**

Per Capita Number of Full–Time employees in City Government (in x/1000)	City Manager Form of Government		Difference
	Yes	No	
0 to 10	63%	54%	
			± 9
11 or more	37	46	
Total	100%	100%	
Number of Cases	(27)	(68)	$N = 95$

*Public Expenditures and
Planning Commitment*

There are a number of measures available to test the assumption that cities with relatively high levels of governmental expenditures will turn to planning and capital improvements programming as a means of more effectively allocating their fiscal resources. However, none of these measures conclusively prove this assumption, although they provide some interesting contrasts between cities with high planning commitment scores and those with medium scores. For example, the data reveal that there is relatively little difference in the level of planning commitment between those cities in which revenues exceeded expenditures (cities with a fiscal surplus) and those cities with a fiscal deficit. When general expenditures of government are examined on a per capita basis and related to levels of planning commitment, there would appear to be a fairly close parallel between the "highs" and the "lows."

Implicit in the assumption that fiscal management problems will evoke a greater awareness of the need for and benefits to be derived from planning is the notion that with a high level of commitment to planning and programming techniques, cities can reduce the burden of property tax levies, while at the same time increase the percentage of total revenues received from intergovernmental sources. This assumption is derived from the fact that cities with on-going planning programs are in a better position to take advantage of programs of intergovernmental assistance, which often include evidence of a commitment to planning as a prerequisite for such programs. However, as shown in Table 12.10, these relationships seem to hold best for cities with medium planning commitment scores rather than those with high scores.

Only a partial and admittedly somewhat superficial "explanation" can be suggested for these relationships. Many intergovernmental assistance programs are designed to initiate programs and projects. The continuation of these programs then becomes a responsibility of the local unit of government. Thus, cities with high commitment scores have had to assume a greater share of the financial burden and therefore have had to rely more completely on property taxes, whereas cities with middle level commitments are still receiving "seed money" from intergovernmental sources. The above data provide some evidence to support the notion that cities must have some reasonable commitment to planning to take advantage of many of the intergovernmental assistance programs, as witnessed by the relatively low percentage of cities with low commitment scores receiving more than 15 percent of their revenues from intergovernmental sources.

Citizen Participation in Civic Affairs

The final assumption to be discussed in this section is that cities with a high degree of citizen participation in civic affairs are likely to have an active planning program. Examining this question first in terms of electorate participation through voting, it was seen that the percentage of the adult population voting in local elections does not seem to have any bearing on cities attaining a high score. Further, the opposite effect from what is anticipated by the assumption appears evident when the voting patterns in cities with medium and low planning commitment scores are examined.[c]

As has been noted, the writings of political scientists and sociologists suggest that persons with high socioeconomic status are more likely to participate in civic activities when those of lower status. The difficulties in attempting to generalize as to the socioeconomic status of a city from the available data have been discussed. For example, when a measure such as median family income is related to the level of planning commitment, the results are rather inconclusive. Only when these cities having relatively high percentages of families with incomes over $10,000 are compared with the rest of the sample does any significant relationship appear. It may be something of an overgeneralization, however, to suggest that this relationship stems directly from the higher level of family income, especially in light of the low coefficient of correlation obtained through product-moment analysis of these two variables ($r = .058$). In fact, examining both the low and the high extremes of income levels yields a multiple correlation coefficient of .173 when the variation in planning commitment is measured against both of these independent variables. This means that just over 3 percent of the variation in the dependent variable can be attributed to the effects of the independent variables.

As discussed in the introductory comments to this analysis, the measure

[c]Perhaps equally revealing is the distribution of responses from among the 95 cities to the original questionnaire sent out by the staff of the *Municipal Year Book*. Eighty-five percent of those cities with high commitment scores responded, 65 percent of the cities with medium scores, and only 40 percent of the cities with low scores.

selected to test for socioeconomic status (and therefore to test indirectly the assumption concerning citizen participation) is the percentage of white-collar workers in the labor forces of the various cities under study. The relationship between these variables is a comparatively strong one. Thus, cities with a relatively high percentage of white-collar workers in their labor force are likely to have a significantly higher commitment to the planning process.

Assumptions Relating To The
Structure of Planning Organizations

The most appropriate structure for city planning agencies has been a recurring issue among those concerned with achieving a more effective role for the planning function in municipal affairs. As has been discussed previously, the prescription of the Standard Planning Enabling Act of 1928 — the "independent" planning agency — was based on the theory that the mechanism for preparing and implementing city plans should be insulated and protected from the day-to-day considerations of politics. In 1941, Robert Walker produced evidence which made a strong case for the organization of planning as a municipal department responsible to the chief executive.[11]

While the debate as to the more effective approach continues to occupy the attention of many writers, until recently, empirical evidence on this question has been almost totally lacking. One of the first efforts to explore this question more fully is found in a recent study by Rabinovitz and Pottinger.[12] They conclude, on the basis of a survey of 201 planning directors throughout the United States, that ". . . there is no single kind of planning organization which can best meet the needs of every city. It was found that organizations responsible for effective planning seem to vary greatly with differing local circumstances."

The findings of the present study tend to support those of Rabinovitz and Pottinger insofar as the question of organizational status is concerned. Thus, as shown in Table 12.12, there is relatively little difference in the level of planning commitment attained by cities with "independent" planning agencies as compared to those with other organizational forms, such as planning and zoning agencies, departments of development, planning and housing agencies, or planning and budgeting agencies.

There is some evidence, however, that cities are more likely to have a firmer commitment to the planning process if the planning function is directly responsible to the principal decision-makers. As shown in Table 12.12, nearly half of the cities in which the planning agency is directly responsible to the mayor, city manager, or city council have high index scores as compared to 37 percent of the cities in which the planning agency is responsible to a planning commission or board. This again would suggest the importance of direct communication links between planning and the decision-making processes.

This does not answer the more complex question, however, as to which element in the decision-making process the planning function should be

Table 12-12

**Relationship between Structure of
Planning Organizations and Level of
Planning Commitment.**

Factors Relating to Structure of Planning Organization	Level of Planning Commitment			
	Low	Medium	High	Number
a. Organizational Status				
Independent agency	18%	40	42	(33)
Other	24%	37	39	(41)
Difference	−6	+3	+3	
b. Authority to Which Planning Agency is Responsible				
Chief Executive or City Council	19%	33	48	(27)
Planning Board or Commission	22%	41	37	(46)
Difference	−3	−8	+11	
c. Authority to Which Planning Agency or Planning Commission is Responsible				
Chief executive	14%	36	50	(36)
City council	27%	41	32	(37)
Difference	−13	−5	+18	
d. Agency Responsible for the Capital Budget				
Planning agency	4%	29	67	(21)
Other than planning agency	25%	47	28	(47)
Difference	−21	−18	+39	

Table 12-12 (*continued*)

Factors Relating to Structure of Planning Organization	Level of Planning Commitment			
	Low	Medium	High	Number
e. Formal Organization Chart of City Government				
Chart available	10%	27	63	(30)
No chart	31%	49	20	(35)
Difference	−21	−22	+43	

responsible, the executive or the legislative. As has been noted, T. J. Kent is a strong advocate of the notion that the planning function should be responsible to the city council. In his recent book, *The Urban General Plan,* Kent has carefully documented his theory. This issue cannot be fully explored in this present study, since among the 95 cities, in only 5 cases is the planning agency directly responsible to the city council, and of these 5 cities, only one has a high level of planning commitment. This, of course, is an unfair test of Kent's theory, since the number of cases is so low. It should be noted that this proportion is about the same for all planning agencies, that is, less than 5 percent of all local planning agencies are responsible directly to city councils.

Among the 46 cities in which the planning agency is responsible to a planning board or commission, 32 of these boards or commissions, in turn, are responsible to the city council, while 14 are directly responsible to the chief executive. By adding this link in the chain of authority, it is possible to test the question more fully.

From the data in Table 12.12, it may be suggested that Kent's contention that a stronger planning program can be fostered by making the planning function responsible to the city council does not hold true for the 95 cities under study. Of course, in fairness to Kent's theory, it must be noted that he objects to the concept of the citizen planning board or commission as an intervening body in the chain of authority. On the other side of the coin, however, it would seem evident from the data that high planning commitment scores occur with greater frequency in those instances in which the planning agency is responsible to the chief executive, either directly or acting through a planning board or commission.

One further measure to be analyzed in terms of planning organization concerns the implementation of planning proposals through public expenditures for capital facilities. During the 1930s, local governments began to recognize that planning for the physical plant of the city was closely tied to its ability and willingness to pay for public facilities and services. Therefore, capital expenditure budgets were initiated by many local governments to provide the basis for a more orderly program of public investment. Very often, however, the responsibility for the development and maintenance of capital budgets was delegated to other than the planning agency.

More recently, however, many communities have come to recognize the need for a closer tie between the planning and the budgeting functions, and thus the responsibility for the preparation and supervision of the capital budget has been given over to the planning agency. The assumption might be advanced that those cities which have seen the need for this closer relationship are likely to score higher in terms of planning commitment.

One of the most surprising relationships was obtained from an analysis of the question as to whether a formal organization chart had been prepared for the city government. Of those cities with formal organization charts, 63 percent scored high in terms of planning commitment. It should be noted, while many respondents indicated that the formal organization chart frequently was superceded by informal relationships, it would seem apparent that the availability of an organization chart does provide some indication of a more "progressive" attitude on the part of public officials and therefore offers some indication of the likelihood of a strong commitment to planning.

*Characteristics of Medium Commitment Cities and
the Concept of "Step Functions"*

Cities with medium planning commitment scores might be broadly characterized as "younger," manufacturing employment centers, with larger firms, higher percentages of nonwhites, and having populations with relatively lower income levels and lower levels of educational attainment. The type of elections in these cities may be either partisan or nonpartisan, but there is a strong tendency toward mayor-council or commission forms of government, with the chief executive being elected for a four-year term. Cities with medium commitment also experience relatively lower levels of citizen participation, as measured by the percentage of the adult population voting. The predominate attitude toward government in such communities is that it should serve as a "provider of life's amenities." Governmental employment in these communities may be relatively high on a per capita basis, but there frequently is no formal organization chart to identify the relationships among agencies and their responsibilities.

Thus it may be suggested that the initial recognition of the need for a stronger planning commitment emerges from the basic environmental conditions and problems evident in the city. However, with limited public support, the level of commitment is a modest one. As a community achieves a greater mix of economic activities, it experiences an increase in white-collar job opportunities. This shift, in turn, leads to higher median family incomes and a greater level of citizen participation. The general attitudes toward government change, and pressures are exerted to effect improvements in efficiency and effectiveness. Often this leads to a high degree of professionalism in government and a clearer definition of agency responsibilities. As a part of this general trend toward a more progressive attitude concerning governmental responsibilities, the level of planning commitment is increased.

The Relationship Among Verified Assumptions

If the indices which have been selected are assumed to be valid measures of the phenomena under study, there seems to be a strong relationship between a city's level of planning commitment and (1) the level of professionalism in city government; (2) the form of government and type of elections (mayor-council or commission versus city manager, and partisan versus nonpartisan); (3) the level of citizen participation; (4) Goodness of City scores (assumed to be a general indicator of a more progressive attitude toward the responsibilities of government); and (5) the authority to which the planning agency is responsible. Before the implications of these findings can be fully discussed, however, the relationship between these validated assumptions must be examined.

The extent to which the form of city government, the type of elections, and the percent of white-collar workers in the total resident labor force influences a city's "goodness score" is the first obvious set of relationships to be tested. As shown in Table 12.13, there is relatively little difference between cities with city manager form of government and those with mayor-council or commission forms insofar as Goodness of City scores are concerned.

Although the manager form of government was first recommended for general adoption in 1911 by the National Short Ballot Organization,[d] it might be argued that the city manager form of government did not come into vogue until after World War II, and therefore, it is not adequately reflected in Thorndike's Goodness of City score. This is somewhat circular logic, however, and although proponents of the city manager form of government maintain that it produces a better city (i.e., a high "goodness" city), this assumption, like many of the planning assumptions discussed in this analysis, has not been tested empirically.

There is a relationship between nonpartisanship and cities receiving high "goodness" scores (see Table 12.14). However, since only 57 percent of the cities with nonpartisan elections received high Goodness of City scores, this evidence does not seem too conclusive.

[d]In 1908, the city of Staunton, Virginia passed an ordinance creating the office of general manager, and making him responsible for a number of municipal activities. In 1912, Sumter, South Carolina appointed a manager and gave him complete control over the municipal administration. It was not until 1914 that a sizable city (Dayton, Ohio) adopted the city manager form of government. Following World War II, the concept came into its own, with about seventy-five cities a year adopting the city manager form of government for a fifteen-year period. More recently, however, its spread seems to have lost momentum except in relatively small communities.[13]

Table 12-13

Relationship between Form of Government and Goodness of City Scores.

Goodness of City Score	Form of Government Mayor–Council or commission	City Manager	Difference
High	49%	54%	
			+ 5
Low	51	46	
Total	100%	100%	
Number of Cases	(63)	(24)	$N = 87$

Table 12-14

Relationship between Type of Elections and Goodness of City Scores.

Goodness of City Score	Type of Election Nonpartisan	Partisan	Difference
High	57%	44%	
			+ 13
Low	43	56	
Total	100%	100%	$C = .126$
Number of Cases	(42)	(45)	$N = 87$

Table 12-15

**Relationship between Percent of Labor
Force in White–Collar Occupations and
Goodness of City Scores.**

Goodness of City Score	Percent of Employed Persons in White–Collar Occupations		Difference
	20 to 42%	43 to 69%	
High	26%	78%	
			± 52
Low	74	22	
Total	100%	100%	C = .473
Number of Cases	(46)	(41)	N = 87

Table 12-16

**Relationship between Form of
Government and Age of City.**

Census Year in Which City First Reached 50,000 Population	Form of Government		Difference
	Mayor–council or commission	Manager	
1800–1900	48%	44%	
			± 4
1910–1960	52	56	
Total	100%	100%	
Number of Cases	(68)	(27)	N = 95

Table 12-17

**Relationship between Percent of Labor
Force in White–Collar Occupations and
Form of Government.**

Form of Government	Percent of Employed Persons in White–Collar Occupations		Difference
	20 to 42%	43 to 69%	
Mayor–Council or Commission	85%	57%	
			+ 28
City Manager	15	43	
Total	100%	100%	
Number of Cases	(48)	(47)	N = 95

Finally, from Table 12.15, it would seem quite evident that the Goodness of City score is highly influenced by the percentage of the labor force in white-collar occupations. This again may relate to the earlier finding that highly industrial cities have relatively lower proportions of white-collar workers (and also lower "goodness" scores), although as was noted in the earlier discussion, this is not a one-to-one relationship.

The extent to which the form of government in the 95 cities is influenced by these other "independent" variables is also important to note. As has been pointed out, there is a strong relationship between form of government and type of elections (see Table 12.16). It is frequently assumed that "younger" cities have a greater tendency to adopt the city manager form of government. However, as shown in Table 12.17, this relationship is practically nonexistent.

As with the case of Goodness of City scores, there is a strong relationship between percent of resident labor force in white-collar occupations and the form of government in that city. Cities with a high percentage of white-collar workers appear to have a greater propensity to adopt the city manager form of government than so-called blue-collar cities.

13

Functional and Situational Factors

In this chapter a number of functional and situational factors will be examined as they relate to the various levels of planning commitment. These factors might be considered in terms of the "inputs" and "outputs" of the planning agency. The inputs include such things as the size of the planning staff, the degree of professionalism (the percentage of staff with professional qualifications), length of service of the planning director, and the extent to which consultants were used in preparing the plan. The output factors relate to the level of performance of the planning agency, its effectiveness, the degree of satisfaction among the participants, sources of difficulties and frustrations (real and assumed), and other factors.

Although a full-blown attitude survey was not undertaken in connection with the Governmental Units Analysis study, some indication of performance can be obtained from the responses to the questionnaire and subsequent follow-up interviews and discussions. While the number of responses from chief executives was somewhat more limited than in the case of planning directors, the additional perspective afforded by this information provides an important contribution to an understanding of these situational and functional factors. To the extent possible, the responses from chief executives have been matched with those of their planning-director counterparts, and an analysis has been made of the correspondence or divergence of attitudes.

Continuity of the Planning Function

The first question to be examined relates to the continuity of the planning function (see Table 13.1). As was pointed out in the conclusion of the previous section, planning is a very mobile profession. The current supply-demand situation is such that there is an estimated three jobs for every qualified applicant. In such a seller's market, the planner can achieve fairly rapid advancement by moving frequently from job to job. The planning process, however, is highly dependent on a relatively long-term continuity of concepts and personnel. A plan that does not have built-in programs of implementation and effectuation is likely to have little impact on the public decision-making process. A planner who is unwilling to make a relatively long-term commitment to the planning process in a given community is likely to pass on the frustrations of "constituency building" to his successors.

Analyzing the questionnaire data, it would appear that the length of time that a planning director has spent in the community serves as an important input

Table 13-1

**Relationship between Input Factors
Relating to the Planning Agency and
Level of Planning Commitment.**

| | Level of Planning Commitment | | | |
Input Factors	Low	Medium	High	Number
a. Length of Service of Planning Director				
Four years or more	14%	38	48	(21)
One to four years	26%	38	36	(42)
Difference	−12	0	+12	
b. Continuity of Service and Completion Date of Comprehensive Plan				
Present planning director:				
Was in office when plan was completed	12%	48	40	(25)
Was not in office when plan was completed	27%	33	40	(30)
Difference	−15	+15	0	
c. Year in Which Comprehensive Plan Was Completed				
1960 to 1967	11%	51	38	(37)
1959 or before	31%	27	42	(26)
Difference	−20	+24	−4	

(continued)

244

Table 13-1 (*continued*)

Input Factors	Low	Medium	High	Number
		Level of Planning Commitment		
d. Plan Adoption by City Council				
Plan and subsequent revisions were adopted	18%	36	46	(22)
Plan and subsequent revisions were not adopted	33%	38	29	(21)
Difference	−15	−2	+17	
e. Size of Planning Staff				
Seven or more	2%	39	58	(38)
0 to six	38%	38	24	(34)
Difference	−36	+1	+34	
f. Percent of Planning Staff Full–Time Professional				
Over 40%	12%	45	43	(42)
Less than 40%	36%	32	32	(22)
Difference	−24	+13	+11	
g. Stability of Planning Staff				
Fairly stable	24%	40	36	(47)
Unstable—undergoing change	14%	33	53	(15)
Difference	+10	+7	−17	
h. Degree to Which Consultants Were Used in Plan Preparation				
No use of consultants	15%	15	69	(13)
Portions of plan prepared by consultants	9%	50	41	(34)
Entire plan prepared by consultants	42%	32	26	(19)

245

Table 13-1 *(continued)*

Input Factors	Level of Planning Commitment			Number
	Low	Medium	High	
i. Frequency of Attendance of Planning Director at Meetings of City Council				
As a general rule	28%	41	31	(29)
Less frequently	16%	36	48	(44)
Difference	+12	+5	−17	
j. Response as to Frequency of Attendance offered by Planning Director and Chief Executive				
Same response	20%	45	35	(14)
Different response	7%	29	64	(20)
Difference	+13	+16	−29	
k. General Categories of Suggested Changes				
Organizational changes	12%	35	53	(17)
Procedural changes	22%	45	33	(27)
Difference	−10	−10	+20	

contributing to the level of planning commitment. Twenty-nine of the planning directors responding to the questionnaire have been in their positions for less than two years, which means that in most cases, they were not involved in the preparation of their cities' comprehensive plans. Among those responses available for comparison, 55 percent of the planning directors were not in their present positions when their cities' comprehensive plans were completed.

While the fact that the directorship of the planning agency has changed hands since the completion of the comprehensive plan does not seem to have any significant bearing on cities with high planning commitment scores, it does seem to have an effect on the distinction between medium and low commitment scores. This may not be a direct causal relationship, but it may be a function of the currency of plans in cities with medium levels of planning commitment. Cities with lower commitment scores exhibit a strong tendency to have plans which were prepared in the early years of the federal program for local planning assistance (the 701 program). Most plans in cities with medium levels of planning commitment, on the other hand, are of more recent origin.

Although the "age" of the plan served as a criterion in the establishment of the index of planning commitment in developing this measure, provision was made for a distinction between older plans which have been updated significantly in the past five years, and those plans which are five years old or more and have not undergone major changes and revisions. All but seven of the older plans (those prepared prior to 1960) have undergone major revisions and updating. Therefore, age per se was not a determining factor in measuring the level of commitment to the planning process.

Official Adoption of the Plan

Even though a plan may be updated and revised significantly following its initial preparation, these changes often are internal to the planning operation, and they may not receive the same level of recognition afforded the initial plan such as public hearings and adoption by the city council. Analysis of available data suggests that the currency of officially adopted elements of the plan, including subsequent revisions, is as important as is the "age" of the original plan insofar as it has a bearing on the level of planning commitment. However, these data are limited somewhat due to the fact that state enabling legislation for local planning frequently does not make provision for the official adoption of the comprehensive plan by the city council. The plan and subsequent revisions have an impact on the public decision-making process only to the extent that they have been adopted, either formally or informally, as policy statements of the decision-making bodies of government.

Building on the previous premise, it may be suggested that a more current general or comprehensive plan has a certain amount of "sustaining power" which can hold the level of planning at a fairly high level. Unless provision is made for official adoption of not only the plan but also subsequent major revisions, this "sustaining power" soon wanes as the plan grows older. At the same time, the continuity of a planning director may serve to postpone or slow down, at least temporarily, the decline of this sustaining power. The mere fact that a city has a plan, however, provides no assurances of a high commitment to planning as a process, as is evidenced by the fact that all but one of the cities included in this survey had a comprehensive or general plan.

Size of Planning Staff

As might be anticipated, the size of the planning staff has an important bearing on the level of planning commitment. This factor served the Governmental Units Analysis study as one of the criteria used in determining individual planning commitment scores. However, the relatively high contingency coefficient ($C = .435$) — the highest reported thus far — would suggest that this input measure has "independent" influence on the achievements of the planning agency. It is interesting to note that this measure differentiates between cities with high and with low commitments, but it appears to have relatively little bearing on cities with medium commitment scores. This pattern might again be related to the currency of the comprehensive plan. Planning agencies frequently experience a reduction in staff within a few years after the comprehensive plan has been completed. An analysis of the relationship between size of staff and age of plan reveals that 67 percent of the cities with staffs of over seven persons have completed their plans since 1960, while 52 percent of the cities with staffs of six persons or less completed their plans prior to 1960.

The absolute size of the planning staff may be somewhat misleading, however, since nonprofessionals, such as draftsmen, clerical workers, and secretaries, are often included in these numbers. Therefore, each respondent was asked to indicate the percentage of his total staff which could be considered "full-time professional." No attempt was made to define the term "professional" in the questionnaire; however, it was assumed that the respondent's interpretation would be governed by education, training, and experience. Many of the respondents indicated that they were members of the American Institute of Planners and that many of their professional staff also held membership in the Institute. While nearly two-thirds of the respondents indicated that over 40 percent of their staffs were full-time professionals, the distribution is clearly skewed in favor of cities with medium and high levels of planning commitment.

The relative stability of the planning staff may be considered as a rough measure of both satisfaction and achievement. While over 75 percent of the respondents indicated a general stability in their staff, the highest percentage of unstability occurred in cities with high planning commitment scores. This turnover cannot be directly attributed to a lack of satisfaction, however. Many of the respondents indicated that most ex-staff members moved on to jobs of greater responsibility. Their association with a successful planning program serves as an important springboard to securing a higher position elsewhere. As has been noted, this is a major characteristic of the planning profession.

Use of Planning Consultants in
Plan Preparation

The use of private consultants in the preparation of the comprehensive plan provides another indication of available "inputs" from the planning agency staff. While only 20 percent of the respondents indicated that their cities' comprehensive plans were prepared without the use of consultants, 32 percent of the cities with high planning commitments fell into this category. The majority of the cities, however, used some consultant services to prepare parts of the plan (particularly economic analyses and transportation studies), while 62 percent of the respondents from cities with low planning commitment scores indicated that the plan was prepared entirely by consultants. The distribution of these various categories clearly suggests that a higher level of commitment is likely to result when the plan is prepared by the agency staff. Cities with medium commitment scores exhibit a greater reliance on consultants to undertake portions of the plan. This again may be related to the relatively smaller size of the planning staffs in these communities. Over 90 percent of medium-level cities with planning staffs of six or less used consultants in some major capacity in the preparation of the comprehensive plan, and an equal percentage of medium-level cities with staffs of from seven to twelve persons used consultants to undertake special studies in conjunction with the plan. Two-thirds of the cities with low commitment scores and small staffs, on the other hand, had their plans prepared entirely by consultants.

Frequency of Involvement in
Policy Discussions

The frequency with which the planning agency is brought in on policy discussions serves as another measure of its potential input to the decision-making of government. It is difficult to measure this participation, however, except in a formal sense, for example, by the frequency with which the planner is invited to attend meetings of the city council. Each respondent was asked to indicate the frequency of attendance at such meetings, making his selection from among the following choices: (1) never; (2) rarely, only if invited; (3) whenever a planning proposal is before the council; and (4) as a general rule, with or without an accompanying proposal.

The study's assumption was that, if the planning function is to be an integral part of the decision-making process, the planning director, at the minimum, would be expected to be in attendance at meetings of the city council whenever planning proposals are under consideration. The data support this assumption in that 87 percent of the respondents indicated that they attended council meetings at least on these occasions. Further, 40 percent indicated that they attended as a general rule, with or without accompanying proposals. However, it might be assumed that greater frequency of attendance would be a characteristic of cities with higher commitment scores, when in fact the data indicate just the opposite. The planning director in cities with high levels of planning commitment exhibits a tendency to attend council meetings with less frequency than his counterpart in cities with medium or low commitment scores.

There is, of course, some danger in drawing hard and fast conclusions from data in which the respondent is evaluating his own status or performance. However, in analyzing the responses of chief executives on this same question, there seems to be a close agreement at the medium and lower levels and a divergence of opinions at the high levels of planning commitment. Here again, however, the respondents may be expressing attitudes or opinions that will make their programs "look good." In the case of cities with high commitment scores, for example, in almost all instances of divergence, the responses of the chief executive indicated a greater frequency of attendance than the corresponding responses of the planning director. Among medium-level and lower-level cities, the reverse was generally the rule.

Procedural and Organizational Changes

Each respondent was asked to indicate the changes in procedural steps or organizational structure which he felt would be necessary to increase or improve the opportunity for effecting the proposals and recommendations of his planning agency. Since this was an open-ended question, there was a great diversity of responses. Two suggested changes which predominated, however, were (1) improvements in general public relations and information programs; and (2) the establishment of a "department of development." Together, these accounted for over half of the suggested changes.

Further, it is possible to group the suggested changes according to the general categories of procedural changes and organizational changes. By so doing, an interesting pattern emerges. Responses from planning directors in cities with high commitment scores predominated in the area of organizational change, while there was a tendency for directors from cities with medium and low commitment levels to favor procedural changes. Thus it might be postulated that, when the critical stage of high planning commitment is achieved, procedural aspects of planning, to a large extent, have become integrated into the day-to-day activities of local government. In part, this may account for the lower frequency of attendance of meetings of the city council by planning directors from cities with high planning commitment scores. Therefore, agency heads express greater interest in changes which will provide further recognition and status (such as the creation of a "department of development") and which will broaden the scope of their agency's responsibilities.

Summary of Findings Regarding Input Factors

In summary, these data suggest that the age of the comprehensive plan has relatively little bearing on the level of planning commitment. Of greater importance is the continuity of service of the planning director (regardless of whether or not he was in office when the plan was completed) and the extent to which the plan and subsequent revisions are officially adopted by the city council. A larger planning staff, with a relatively high degree of professionalism, contributes to a higher level of planning commitment in two ways: (1) by increasing the likelihood that the plan and subsequent revisions will be prepared within the framework of local "expectations"; and (2) by increasing the points of contact between the planning agency and other public officials and agencies, thereby giving the planning function greater visibility. A critical stage is achieved when the procedural aspects of planning have been accepted in the day-to-day operations of government. Beyond this point, attention can be focused on achieving greater hierarchical status, responsibility, and authority.

Factors Concerning the Performance of the Planning Agency

A number of writers have suggested that the type of plan produced, whether by consultants or by the planning agency staff, will have an important bearing on the general acceptance and overall effectiveness of the planning process. If the plan is largely a technical document, with relatively few policy recommendations, it is assumed that its use and the subsequent performance of the planning agency will be somewhat different from that which might be anticipated if the plan were to embody broad social goals and objectives and programs designed to achieve these aims.

The Character of the Comprehensive Plan

Each of the respondents in the planning commitment study was asked to describe the contents of his city's comprehensive plan. While some guidelines were provided, as indicated below, an opportunity for individual responses was also afforded. The following descriptive choices were adopted, in part, from an earlier survey conducted by Rabinovitz and Pottinger; the numbers in parentheses following each description indicating the distribution of responses: (1) an illustrated set of proposals with partial documentation (9); (2) an explicit set of objectives documented by a proposed land use map and a timetable for accomplishing these objectives (13); (3) a "general" plan with more specific proposals for various plan elements (facilities, transportation, open space, etc.) (38); (4) a more general statement of policy objectives and an illustrated exploration of the available types of alternatives for achieving these objectives (7); and (5) other (5).

It may be seen that the "general" plan approach was highly favored by the respondents. The more specific "land-use plan" approach ran a poor second. It is interesting to note that the approach which comes closest to the so-called "policies plan" was selected by relatively few respondents, even though this approach, of late, has received considerable discussion in the literature.

From an analysis of the distribution of these approaches, it may be concluded that the conceptual character of the comprehensive plan — that is, the way in which its content and purpose are envisioned by those responsible for its preparation — has relatively little bearing on the performance of the planning agency or on the level of planning commitment (see Table 13.2). It should be noted, however, that there was not always a consensus within a city government as to what the comprehensive plan is or should be. Although the relatively limited number of responses from chief executives prohibits a more definitive analysis, it would appear that there is some difference of opinion as to the contents of the plan, particularly in cities with medium and low planning commitment scores. One might assume that the chief executive would view the plan more as a technical document, while the planner would see it as embodying policy recommendations. A careful comparison reveals just the opposite. In the overwhelming majority of cases where a difference of opinion was expressed, the less technically oriented interpretation was given by the chief executive.

The extent to which the comprehensive plan has been implemented through changes in the city's zoning ordinance provides another important measure of the planning agency's performance. In most cities, zoning predates comprehensive planning by several decades. In terms of the purposes that they were designed to serve, these early zoning ordinances proved to be remarkably successful, especially in the stabilization of property value. However, the prohibitory and regulatory character of these early zoning ordinances frequently are no longer appropriate to deal with the more critical aspects of contemporary urbanization. Thus, new approaches to guide and control land use are required. Many such approaches have been incorporated into the more advanced planning programs.

Examining the available data, it is possible to effect three related measures of planning achievement in terms of changes in the zoning ordinance. The first of these examines the extent to which the comprehensive planning efforts of the planning staff have resulted in the preparation of a new zoning ordinance for the city. It may be seen that there is a strong tendency for cities with high planning commitment scores to prepare new zoning ordinances as a part of or following the preparation of the city's comprehensive plan. Cities with medium and low commitment scores, on the other hand, show a tendency toward making revision of existing ordinances.

It must be recognized, however, that the character of zoning revisions may fall anywhere along a continuum from minor changes to major modifications in the purpose and intent of the basic ordinance. Therefore, a second measure of planning achievement through zoning relates to a further breakdown of the distribution along this continuum. Here again, cities with high planning

Table 13-2

**Relationship between Performance
Factors and Level of Planning
Commitment.**

Performance Factors	Level of Planning Commitment			
	Low	Medium	High	Number
a. Description of Comprehensive Plan				
"General" Plan	24%	34	42	(38)
Other description used	21%	41	38	(34)
Difference	+3	−7	+4	
b. Status of Zoning				
New ordinance prepared within past five years	14%	24	62	(21)
Revisions made of existing ordinance	23%	44	33	(48)
Difference	−9	−20	+29	
c. Character of Zoning Ordinance Revisions				
Major revisions	19%	37	44	(27)
Minor changes only	29%	52	19	(21)
Difference	−10	−15	+25	
d. Changes in Zoning in the Past Five Years				
New ordinance or major revisions	17%	31	52	(48)
Only minor changes	29%	52	19	(21)
Difference	−12	−21	+33	
e. Degree of Participation of Planning Agency in				

Table 13-2 (*continued*)

Performance Factors	Level of Planning Commitment			
	Low	Medium	High	Number
Capital Improvements Programming Activities				
Direct Participation	7%	38	55	(40)
Indirect or no participation	46%	42	12	(24)
Difference	−39	−4	+43	
f. **Degree of Participation of Planning Agency in Capital Budgeting**				
Direct participation	0%	30	70	(23)
Indirect or no participation	34%	44	22	(41)
Difference	−34	−14	+48	

commitment scores exhibit the higher level of positive achievement (greater incidence of major revisions) while cities with medium commitment do not fare as well as cities with low commitment scores.

Combining the results of these two analyses provides a third measure, which relates more positive levels of change in zoning to relatively minor changes. The results of this analysis reveal an even more distinctive pattern, favoring cities with high commitment scores.

There seems to be no ready explanation as to why cities with medium commitment scores appear to have a less favorable climate for major zoning changes than is the case in cities with low commitment scores. Unfortunately, information concerning the age of existing ordinances is unavailable on a comparable basis, and a question concerning this point was not included in the mailed questionnaire. Therefore, these data cannot be controlled in terms of the intervening influence of the age of the existing ordinance.

In the previous discussion of the organizational status of planning, it was noted that recognition of the need for a closer tie between the planning and budgeting functions of government has resulted in the delegation of responsibilities for the preparation and supervision of the capital budget to the planning agency. The data presented in the previous chapter clearly show a strong relationship between the level of planning commitment and the extent to which the planning agency has been given this budgeting responsibility. This relationship is even more pronounced when the question of agency responsibility for the preparation of the capital improvements program is examined.[a] In cities with high commitment scores, the planning agency shows a strong tendency toward direct participation in the capital improvements programming activities of local government. The contingency coefficient for these data is the highest achieved in this analysis.

While the planning agency may not be given the responsibility for formulating the capital budget, it frequently is called upon to make major contributions to these deliberations. Such direct participation most frequently characterizes the relationship of the planning agency in cities with high commitment scores. It is of significance to note that, among the respondents to the questionnaire, there was no indication of direct participation in capital budgeting activities among planning agencies in cities with low planning commitment scores.

[a]The distinction made here between the capital budget and the capital improvements program has become fairly widely accepted in the planning profession, although finance men tend to use the terms "capital budget" and "capital budgeting" for the whole process. A capital improvements program is a relatively comprehensive document which undertakes to establish priorities for capital facilities over a five-year to six-year period. the capital budget represents the most immediate segment of the capital improvements program (usually paralleling the operating budget) and provides more exacting and definitive scheduling and cost figures for capital outlays.

Two additional measures of planning-agency involvement in the financial planning activities of local government can be derived from the questionnaire data. The first of these relates to the extent of agency participation in studies concerning the community's tax structure. While only five respondents indicated that their agencies participated directly in tax structure studies (three from cities with high planning commitments and two from cities with medium commitments), over one-third of the respondents indicated that their agencies have been called upon to supply basic data, projections, or other information relating to such studies (defined as indirect participation in the questionnaire).

Degree of Participation of the
Planning Agency in
Various Public Studies

There is a strong tendency for planning agencies in cities with high commitment scores to participate in studies of the community's tax structure. Such studies, of course, have an important bearing on the ability of local government to anticipate needed changes in tax policies in order to meet growing demands for new services and facilities. Comparing the responses of the chief executives with those of the planning directors in cities where this information is available, it would seem apparent that a greater degree of involvement on the part of the planning agency is anticipated by the chief executives than is recognized by the planning directors. This is particularly true in those cities with high commitment scores, where over 75 percent of the chief executives indicated a more direct involvement in tax studies as compared to 60 percent of the planning directors, and in cities with medium commitment scores, where the figures were 43 percent and 33 percent, respectively.

A second measure of planning-agency involvement in the financial planning activities of local government relates to the preparation of the operating budget. Here again, the data shows a relatively strong tendency toward a greater involvement of the planning agencies in cities with high commitment to planning (see Table 13.3). As with the previous measure, the expectations of the chief executives regarding their planning agencies' participation is significantly higher than that of the corresponding planning directors. Of the responding chief executives, 70 percent indicated a direct or indirect involvement, while only 50 percent of the corresponding planning directors saw their agencies' involvement to this degree.

On the basis of these findings, it might be suggested that participation in the fiscal management activities of local government is one of the most significant indicators of planning achievement. Entrance into these activities is not easily gained, for traditionally these responsibilities have been delegated wholly to other agencies and officials in the governmental hierarchy. However, the translation of planning recommendations into fiscal commitments is fundamental to a successful planning process. Such conversions, it would seem, come

Table 13-3

**Relationship between Degree of Partici-
pation of Planning Agency in Various
Public Studies and Level of Planning
Commitment.**

Degree of Participation in Public Studies	Level of Planning Commitment			
	Low	Medium	High	Number
a. Studies of Tax Structure				
Direct or indirect participation	7%	37	56	(27)
No participation	33%	39	28	(36)
Difference	−26	−2	+28	
b. Preparation of Operating Budget				
Direct or indirect participation	12%	41	47	(34)
No participation	32%	36	32	(31)
Difference	−20	+5	+15	
c. Traffic and Transportation Studies				
Direct participation	14%	43	43	(20)
Indirect or no participation	40%	30	30	(44)
Difference	−26	+13	+13	
d. Parking Problem Studies				
Direct participation	12%	43	45	(21)
Indirect or no participation	38%	33	29	(42)
Difference	−26	+10	+16	
e. Renewal and Redevelopment Studies				

Table 13-3 (*continued*)

Degree of Participation in Public Studies	Level of Planning Commitment			
	Low	Medium	High	Number
Direct participation	20%	32	48	(44)
Indirect or no participation	25%	50	25	(20)
Difference	−5	−18	+23	
f. Housing and Relocation Studies				
Direct participation	7%	43	50	(30)
Indirect or no participation	33%	35	32	(34)
Difference	−26	+8	+18	
g. Review of Proposed Zoning Changes				
Direct participation	20%	42	38	(55)
Indirect or no participation	30%	20	50	(10)
Difference	−10	+22	−12	
h. Site Selection Studies for New School Facilities				
Direct participation	22%	30	48	(27)
Indirect or no participation	21%	45	34	(38)
Difference	+1	−15	+14	
i. Site Selection Studies for New Park Facilities				
Direct participation	20%	37	43	(51)
Indirect or no participation	28%	43	29	(14)
Difference	−8	−6	+14	

(*continued*)

Table 13-3 (*continued*)

Degree of Participation in Public Studies	Level of Planning Commitment			
	Low	Medium	High	Number
j. Relocation Studies for Major Public Facilities				
Direct participation	19%	36	45	(42)
Indirect or no participation	27%	46	27	(22)
Difference	−8	−10	+18	
k. Metropolitan and Regional Planning Studies				
Direct Participation	14%	38	48	(42)
Indirect or no participation	32%	41	27	(22)
Difference	−18	−3	+21	

about only after the planning function has become an integral part of governmental operations, with a high level of commitment to the planning process on the part of public officials. Once this commitment has been achieved, the opportunity for even greater participation is often apparent, as evidenced by the expectations of chief executives as to the planning agency's role in these matters.[b]

As the planning function becomes more widely accepted within the operations of local government, the planning agency is frequently called upon to undertake many other types of studies only indirectly related to the preparation of a comprehensive plan. In instances where the planning agency has not achieved the confidence of elected officials and heads of operating departments, these studies are generally undertaken by other agencies. For example, studies of traffic and transportation, while a vital input to the development of a comprehensive plan, are often undertaken by the city engineer's office or the public works department with little or no reference to the possible contributions of the planning agency. This is not to suggest that the planner should be given sole responsibility for such studies; however, he should be included as a member of the "task force" whose job it is to deal with such problems of urban development.

It may be concluded, therefore, that a rough measure of a planning agency's level of achievement can be obtained by an examination of the extent to which the agency has become involved in such studies. As shown in Table 13.3, there is a clear tendency for planning agencies in cities with high and medium levels of planning commitment to directly participate in studies of traffic and transportation and studies of parking problems in the central business district.

It is frequently the practice in local government to make a functional distinction between planning and urban renewal activities and to assign the responsibility for each of these areas to separate agencies. Here again, however, the need for a closer integration of these two important aspects of urban development becomes more evident as the planning function achieves fuller involvement in the public decision-making process. There is a clear tendency for planning agencies in cities with high planning commitment scores to become directly involved in studies of urban renewal and redevelopment needs and studies relating to housing and relocation problems.

[b]The reluctance on the part of some planning directors to avail themselves of these opportunities may stem from several factors. Acceptance of planning by officials charged with fiscal management responsibilities is often more in the form of a tolerance rather than an outright acceptance. Finance officers frequently consider the planner to be an idealist whose utopian recommendations have little basis in fiscal reality. Recognizing the "cold war" balance which often exists, a planning director may be willing to forego a more direct involvement in these areas in exchange for the financial officer's acquiesence toward a fuller involvement by the planning agency in other activities. Another factor stems from the training received by many professional planners, both in a conceptual and technical sense. For many years, plan implementation through programs of public finance was considered outside the domain of the city planner. Only recently have planning curricula been expanded to include courses in financial planning and capital improvements programming.

While the distribution of responses among chief executives and planning directors was similar on the question of agency participation in studies of traffic, transportation, and parking problems, the level of expectation is much higher for chief executives regarding participation in studies of renewal and housing. Over 80 percent of the chief executives saw the planning agency in a direct participation role in renewal and redevelopment studies (as compared to 66 percent of the planning directors) and 60 percent of the chief executives saw a similar role in housing and relation studies (as compared to only 45 percent of the corresponding planners).

In a number of other areas in which the planning agency is often called upon to conduct special studies, the data reveals that cities with medium planning commitment scores exhibit the strongest tendency toward more direct participation. These areas include (1) utility franchise studies; (2) air and water pollution studies; (3) studies concerning the need for new social welfare programs; (4) drafting of architectural control ordinances; and (5) review of proposed zoning changes. In each instance, cities with medium commitment scores show a strong positive difference in the distribution of responses, while cities with high or low commitment scores show either a low positive or a negative difference. This is not to suggest that planning agencies in cities with high commitment scores do not participate in such studies, however; it often is merely a matter of a slightly greater frequency of participation on the part of agencies in cities with medium commitments.

Partial explanations might be suggested concerning these findings. With the exception of the review of zoning, in which nearly all respondents indicated a high level of participation, the studies undertaken are often exploratory in character and, as a result, they may not have a direct impact on the decision-making process. In terms of the previously described model of public decision-making, the "demands" which give rise to such studies may be "unexpressed demands" in that, at the moment, they do not represent public issues concerning some generally recognized dysfunctional condition. In other words, the planning agency may undertake such studies on their own initiative or as a result of some internal "felt need." Second, these studies fall within the realm of "brush fire" activities which may occupy considerable amounts of staff time and effort as an agency attempts to build confidence among elected officials and heads of operating departments in its abilities.[c]

[c]The concept of "brush fires" is frequently alluded to in planning literature. This concept relates to the need for a planning agency to become involved in a great number of activities which, on the surface, may seem to have little bearing on the main purpose of planning – the development of a comprehensive plan. This involvement in more immediate matters, however, helps to establish the service function of the planning agency and to build a broader constituency for the planning process. Therefore, it is of particular importance that planning agencies take on these assignments as they try to become entrenched in government.

When these special studies become a more direct input in the decision-making process, the pattern of participation changes somewhat. Thus, examining such questions as the degree of involvement of the planning agency in the decision regarding the selection of a new school site, the site for a new park facility, or the relocation of a major public facility reveals that agencies in cities with high commitment scores have a greater tendency for direct participation.

One final measure of planning-agency performance relates to the degree of participation in studies and programs which deal with the broader problems of the metropolitan area. This participation has a dual dimension. First, there is the question of recognition on the part of elected officials of the need for metropolitan planning — for an involvement with problems that go beyond the city's jurisdictional boundaries. Second, there is the question of the city planning agency's direct participation in such metropolitan planning activities. In the first instance, there is a stronger tendency for chief executives in cities with high commitment scores to recognize the need for a more direct participation on the part of their planning agency in metropolitan planning activities than is evident in cities with medium or low commitment scores. It would seem to follow, therefore, that there would be a greater involvement on the part of planning agencies in cities with high commitment scores in metropolitan or regional studies. This assumption is supported by the data given in the last entry in Table 13.3.

Factors Relating to the
Role of the Planning Agency

Perhaps the single most significant question raised in the questionnaire concerned the planning agency's role in advising the chief executive and city council on matters relating to the planning process. A similar question was posed by Rabinovitz and Pottinger in their national survey of 201 planning directors. Their findings were summarized as follows: "Seventy-one percent of the respondents stated that they purposely integrated policy advice and value judgments with their technical recommendations. The percentage is similar for those in independent and in executive agencies. Moreover, many planning directors oppose insulation from politics through the protection of jobs by tenure or civil service status."[1]

The respondents to the planning commitment survey were asked to make a similar statement concerning their role in the public decision-making process. Three choices were given: (1) strictly a technical activity of applying the tools of the profession to a given project or problem in seeking a satisfactory solution; (2) recommendations are largely of a technical nature, but some policy judgments are inherent in advisory role; (3) policy advice purposely integrated with technical advice and recommendations based on value judgments as well as technical expertise. Provision was also made for particularized definitions by individual respondents.

The overall results tend to coincide with the findings of the Rabinovitz-Pottinger study in that 68 percent of the respondents indicated that they saw their agency's role as one of providing policy advice mixed with value judgments. The manner in which these responses were distributed among the three levels of planning commitment is very revealing, however. As shown in Table 13.4, planning directors from cities with high commitment scores showed a stronger tendency toward the more technically oriented definitions than is evident at the other two levels. However, none of the respondents saw their agencies' role as being "strictly technical."

The conclusions that may be drawn from these findings are not completely clear. They suggest, however, that many planning directors may have expectations as to the role of their agencies, which they can never hope fully to achieve. With limited commitment on the part of elected officials, policy recommendations emerging from the planning process are likely to have only modest effect on public decisions. Regardless of the sender's intent, it may be that the advice and recommendations of the planning agency are most often "received" by the city council and chief executive on the basis of their technical content, that is, as informative communication rather than influential communication.

Thus, while some planning directors may assume that their agencies have achieved the status of a "prerogative participant" in decision situations, planners are brought into the decision-making system because of their technical competence — the special skills and information which they possess. As a higher level of commitment to the planning process is achieved, planning directors may come to recognize that the most significant contribution their agency can make is in providing the technical basis for more rational decisions. They are more aware that their recommendations and proposals must be modified in light of political considerations, and that this modification falls properly to those officials who are directly responsible to the community's electorate.

Unless the planner exhibits an ability to generate innovative approaches to the problems confronting the community (a quality which, in turn, is likely to increase the planning agency's acceptance and the level of commitment to the planning process), his aspirations are likely to go unfulfilled. At the same time, the planner must seek the position of a communication intermediary serving as a vital link between the decision-making bodies and the operating agencies of government. To achieve this status, the planner must gain the confidence of these agencies as well as the decision-makers. These points will be discussed further in subsequent sections of this analysis.

It also is important to examine the views of the chief executives as to the role ascribed to the planning agency. While the relatively limited response level prohibits a more definitive analysis, from the available data it is clear that the attitudes of chief executives frequently stand in direct contrast to those of the planning directors. There is a stronger tendency among chief executives from high commitment cities to see their planning agencies in a policy advisory role, while those from cities with medium commitment scores tend to favor the more technically oriented definitions.

Table 13-4

Relationship between Factors Concerning the Role of the Planning Agency and Level of Planning Commitment.

Factors Concerning Role of Planning Agency	Level of Planning Commitment			
	Low	Medium	High	Number
a. Planning Director's Definition of Agency's Role				
Policy oriented	21%	44	35	(48)
Largely technical	17%	26	57	(23)
Difference	+4	+18	−22	
b. Chief Executive's Definition of Agency's Role				
Policy oriented	15%	30	55	(20)
Largely technical	18%	41	41	(17)
Difference	−3	−11	+14	
c. Role of Planning Agency as an Identifier of Problems				
Role identified	23%	33	44	(48)
No role	8%	69	23	(13)
Difference	+15	−36	+21	
d. Role of Planning Agency in Determination of Boundary Conditions				
Role identified	22%	36	42	(22)
No role	18%	43	29	(39)

(continued)

Table 13-4 (*continued*)

Factors Concerning Role of Planning Agency	Level of Planning Commitment			
	Low	Medium	High	Number
Difference	+4	−7	+3	
e. Role in Exploration of Alternatives				
Role identified	20%	34	46	(35)
No role	19%	50	31	(26)
Difference	+1	−16	+15	
f. Role in Alternative Selection				
Role identified	19%	33	48	(27)
No role	21%	47	32	(34)
Difference	−2	−14	+16	
g. Role of Planning Agency in Seeking Politically Acceptable Decisions				
Role identified	18%	35	47	(17)
No role	21%	43	36	(44)
Difference	−3	−8	+11	
h. Role of Planning Agency in Determining Action Programs				
Role identified	22%	26	52	(27)
No role	35%	35	30	(34)
Difference	−13	−9	+22	

In an effort to probe more deeply into the matter of the role of the planning agency in the decision-making process, a second question was asked at the conclusion of the questionnaire. It was pointed out that various writers have suggested that public decision-making can be viewed as a multistage process. A seven-stage decision-making process, corresponding to the theoretical stages enumerated in the previous discussion of the public decision-making model, was then presented, and the respondents were asked to indicate the points in this process at which their agency is most active and effective. The seven stages presented in the questionnaire are as follows (the percentages in parentheses indicate the frequency of positive response for each stage): (1) the identification and definition of the problem (79 percent); (2) the determination of the conditions which the solution to the problem must satisfy (36 percent); (3) the exploration of alternative solutions which fit these conditions (57 percent); (4) the selection of an alternative which most closely approximates a "right" decision (44 percent); (5) the modification of this decision through compromise, adaptation, and concessions to make it generally (politically) acceptable (27 percent); (6) the determination of the action programs necessary to carry out the decision (44 percent); and (7) the monitoring of the feedback to test the validity and effectiveness of the decision against the actual course of events (13 percent).

Several aspects of the overall distribution of responses are somewhat surprising. The first is the relatively low percentage of respondents identifying a role for their agencies in monitoring feedback. There has been considerable discussion of late in the periodical literature of planning concerning this aspect of the planning process, that is, the need for a continuous review of programs to determine their effectiveness in meeting overall goals and objectives. The currency of this concept, however, was not reflected in the responses to this question to the extent one might have anticipated.

Although a substantial majority of the respondents indicated that their agency served to identify problems, just over half included "the exploration of alternative solutions" as a major responsibility of the planning agency in the decision-making process. Here again, this is somewhat surprising in light of the current emphasis in the literature on this aspect of the planning process. In general, these responses do not approximate the levels that might have been anticipated in light of the higher level of response to the more fundamental question concerning the planning agency's contributions as a policy adviser.

It is of interest to compare the responses to the chief executives to this question with those of their planning directors. Such a comparison is provided in Table 13.5 for those cities in which dual returns were obtained. In all but one case, the frequency of response of the chief executives was higher than that of the planning directors. (Although no readily apparent explanation is available, it is also interesting to note that the frequency of responses of this more limited group of planning directors is lower in all cases than that of the total number of available responses.) This difference would seem to be of particular significance in terms of the exploration of alternatives and in the determination of the

Table 13-5

Comparison of Responses between
Planning Directors and Chief Execu-
tives concerning the Role of the
Planning Agency in the Multistage
Decision–Making Process

Stage in Decision Process	Frequency of Response	
	Chief Executives	Planning Directors
1 Problem identification and definition	61%	78%
2 Determination of conditions which solution must satisfy	53%	34%
3 Exploration of alternatives	61%	50%
4 Selection of alternative	45%	41%
5 Development of politically acceptable solution	21%	19%
6 Determination of action programs	37%	34%
7 Monitoring feedback	18%	6%

conditions which the solution to the problem must satisfy. Thus it would seem, on the basis of this somewhat limited sample, that chief executives have a higher level of expectation as to the contributions to be made by the planning agency in the decision-making process than is manifested by the planning directors.

An examination of these data in terms of the various levels of planning commitment reveals several trends. In terms of the questionnaire's seven stages, there is a strong tendency for directors from cities with high and low planning commitment scores to see their agency's role as one of (1) problem identification and definition. The preponderance of cities with low commitment scores might be explained, in part, by the fact that this more limited role constitutes the extent of participation by many of these planning agencies. As for the second stage, there is (2) relatively little significance in the distribution of responses on the question of "determination of boundary conditions." It may be that relatively few planners have come to recognize this important function in the decision-making process or their role in making this determination. However, failure to take cognizance of these boundary conditions may result in the formulation of plausible but unrealistic solutions to the problems.

Also noted was a clear tendency for planning agencies in cities with high commitment scores to play a more positive and direct role in (3) the exploration of alternatives and (4) the selection of an alternative which most closely approximates a "right" decision. While over 50 percent of the chief executives in middle-level cities suggested that the planning agency should perform these two important functions in the decision-making process, only 30 percent of the planning directors in these cities were in accord with this definition of the planning agency's responsibilities.

There was general acceptance of the concept that (5) the responsibility for modifying optimal solutions — through compromise, adaptation, and concession — in order to achieve programs which are politically acceptable falls to the elected official in the decision-making process; however, the differentiation was clear between cities with high and with medium planning commitments on the basis of attitudes toward the role of planning agencies in (6) determining the action programs necessary to carry out decisions. The data would seem to indicate that a greater responsibility for the implementation of decisions accompanies a higher commitment on the part of elected officials to the planning process; or conversely, that planning agencies in cities with medium commitment scores have yet to achieve the status in the organizational structure of government where they are called upon to develop the programs necessary to carry out public decisions. Finally, relatively few respondents saw any role for the planning agency in (7) the monitoring of feedback to test the validity and effectiveness f public decisions.

There wou l seem to be added evidence in these findings to support the notion of critical stages, or step functions, suggested at the conclusion of the previous chap r. Planning agencies in cities with high commitment scores show a significant ten ency toward greater involvement in the decision-making process at all stages except in the identification of boundary conditions. This greater degree of involvement would suggest that these agencies have achieved three important roles in the public decision-making process: (1) in the identification of problems; (2) in the innovation of alternative solutions; and (3) in the design and implementation of programs to carry out public decisions.

Thus it would appear that the initial efforts to establish planning as an integral part of the on-going operations of local government should focus on the agency's "sensory" role — serving to identify and define problems. Further agency involvement generally takes the form of problem-solving activities, relating to more immediate action programs. Paralleling this increased involvement is a further opportunity for building a constituency — a clientele group — which is receptive to the longer-range aspects of the planning process.

The next step is an involvement in program design and program implementation, working in close cooperation with various operating agencies within the hierarchy of local government. Here again these activities frequently relate to the handling of "brush fires," or at best, they are likely to be less than the "comprehensive" approach envisioned by most neophyte planners. If the planner is unable to move out of this critical stage to the next level, he may have to be satisfied with being a planning administrator, concerned with the day-to-day aspects of zoning, subdivision regulations, and so forth. Some planners, of course, have accepted this role and are not interested in any further involvement in the decision-making process.

Finally, after the planner has proved himself and the value of the trade which he plys, he can engage in more innovative activities, such as the formulation of long-range development alternatives, with some expectations that his recommendations will find a receptive audience among the decision-makers. The planner who is unwilling to engage in the time-consuming process of constituency building is likely to encounter personal and professional frustrations. His plans may be accepted "with thanks" by the chief executive and members of the city council, but his expectations of assuming a major policy advisory role are likely to go unfulfilled. In some instances, of course, the planner may be fortunate enough to step into a situation where much of this groundwork has been accomplished by his predecessor.

There is impressive evidence in the literature of public administration to suggest that with relatively new, insecure programs, more effort must be devoted in institutional and educational activities. With more established, stable programs, on the other hand, greater attention can be given to professionally and politically innovative activities. Planning education and planning literature have tended to stress long-range planning as the primary goal of the planning program. Thus the planning director is often faced with a dilemma. If his agency is not making tangible progress toward the completion of a comprehensive plan, he may find it necessary to apologize to other professionals, including his own staff. At the same time, there is evidence to suggest the serious consequences of concentration on technical work and political innovation before an acceptable climate of opinion and an institutional base in government has been established.

Factors Contributing to Difficulties Encountered in
Achieving Implementation of Planning Recommendations

To determine some of the fundamental difficulties confronting planning agencies in their efforts to achieve fuller implementation of planning recommendations, each respondent was asked to check off from a list of twelve "factors" as many as he felt appropriately described situations which he had encountered. These factors cover such problems as (1) a lack of understanding on the part of the public or elected officials of the proposals; (2) a lack of public or political concern for long-range planning; (3) insufficient time and effort spent by planning commissioners to secure the passage of recommendations; (4) a lack of influence and prestige on the part of planning commissioners; (5) an emphasis on political expediences; (6) policy conflicts between chief executive and city council; (7) policy disagreements between chief executive and planning agency; and (8) lack of support because planning proposals allegedly cost too much. In general, these factors can be grouped under four headings: (1) public difficulties; (2) commission difficulties; (3) council difficulties; and (4) difficulties with chief executive.

Nearly all of the respondents checked off more than one factor; some checked all of the factors and even added others. A dual analysis of each of the major categories is possible, first in terms of whether or not a problem was identified, and second in terms of the nature of the problem. A comparison can also be made with the responses of the chief executives to a similar questionnaire (slight modifications were made to shift the character of the questions so as to be more appropriate for chief executive responses).

Lack of public support and/or public concern for longrange planning proposals constituted a major difficulty encountered by most planning agencies in achieving plan implementation (78 percent of the respondents). Although there is a slight tendency in the direction of cities with high commitment scores, analysis of this data would suggest that public difficulties in the implementation of planning recommendation are a universal condition. The same conclusions hold true for the type of difficulties encountered. As shown in Table 13.6, the frequency distribution between "lack of understanding of planning proposals" and "lack of concern for long-range planning" is similar for all three levels of planning commitment.

In comparison to the previous set of factors, a relatively small percentage of the planning directors expressed any difficulties emerging from their dealings with the planning commission or board (37 percent). Here again, the relatively uniform distribution of responses would suggest that no significant relationship exists between these factors and the level of planning commitment. However, 73 percent of the respondents indicated that they had

Table 13-6

Relationship between Factors Contributing to Difficulties in Achieving Plan Implementation and Level of Planning Commitment.

Problem Areas	Level of Planning Commitment			
	Low	Medium	High	Number
a. Extent of Problems Stemming from Lack of Public Support or Concern				
No apparent problems	21%	43	36	(14)
Problems identified	22%	34	44	(50)
Difference	−1	+9	−8	
b. Type of Public Difficulties Encountered				
Lack of public understanding	23%	32	45	(22)
Lack of public concern	21%	36	43	(28)
Difference	+2	−4	+2	
c. Type of Difficulties Encountered by Planning Director in Dealing with City Council				
Political expediencies	25%	36	39	(36)
Lack of understanding	18%	36	46	(11)
Difference	+7	0	−7	
d. Type of Difficulties Encountered by Chief Executive in Dealing with City Council				
Political expediencies	13%	40	47	(15)

Table 13-6 (*continued*)

Problem Areas	Level of Planning Commitment			
	Low	Medium	High	Number
Lack of understanding	20%	40	40	(5)
Difference	−7	0	+7	

e. **Existence of Difficulties in Dealing with Chief Executive**

Problem Areas	Low	Medium	High	Number
No difficulties	0%	50	50	(18)
Difficulties encountered	32%	29	39	(44)
Difference	−32	+21	+11	

f. **Type of Difficulties Encountered in Dealing with Chief Executive**

Problem Areas	Low	Medium	High	Number
Policy issues	36%	32	32	(25)
Fiscal issues	26%	26	48	(19)
Difference	+10	+6	−16	

encountered difficulties in the city council. Further, nearly 80 percent of these "difficulties" were associated with "political expediencies." A similar distribution was found when the more limited number of responses from chief executives were examined. Here, 60 percent of the respondents noted difficulties emerging from their dealings with council on planning matters, and of this number, 75 percent attributed these difficulties to "politics." The frequency distribution, however, shows relatively little relationship to the level of planning commitment; in fact it shows a divergency between the responses of chief executives and those of the planning directors.

Of the four categories of "difficulties," perhaps the most significant is the one which relates to problems encountered in dealings with the chief executive. In this instance, 71 percent of the responding planning directors indicated some level of difficulties in securing implementation of their planning recommendations. There is a strong tendency for such difficulties to be encountered in those cities with low commitment scores. In fact, all of the respondents from such cities indicated some sort of difficulty in dealings with chief executives.

Examining more closely the question of type of difficulties encountered, there is a clear shift from policy issues to fiscal issues (either lack of adequate funding or lack of support because planning proposals allegedly cost too much) as the level of planning commitment increases. Thus, it may be suggested that policy issues are encountered with greater frequency in cities with lower planning commitments, both in terms of conflicts between the chief executive and the city council as well as between the planning agency and the chief executive. As the planning function receives greater acceptance, these issues diminish and financial questions more often serve as points of disagreement.

Sources of Influence in Public Policy-Making

In an effort to obtain some further information as to the major sources of influence in public policy-making in middle-sized communities, two ranking questions were included in the mailed questionnaire. In the first question, the respondents were asked to rank, in the order of their relative influence on the development of public policy, five agencies or officials from a list of twenty-one agencies or officials most frequently found in local government. As might be anticipated, the mayor was selected as "most influential" in the majority of cases (62 percent) (see Table 13.7). In those cities with high commitment scores, however, mayors were selected as "most influential" by just over half of the responding planning directors. This pattern is even more pronounced when the responses of chief executives are examined. While 64 percent of the respondents indicated the mayor as the most influential participant, only 41 percent of the chief executives from high commitment cities expressed this opinion. As noted previously, many of the cities with high commitment scores also have a manager-council form of government. In many cases where this form of government has been adopted, the mayor serves as the ceremonial head of government while the manager provides the executive leadership on policy matters.

Beyond the initial selection of the "most influential" participant, however, there is relatively little discernible pattern to the subsequent responses for the second through the fifth most influential participants. That is to say, no single agency or official predominates at any level of planning commitment or for any ranking of influence beyond the level of "most influential." However, there is a slight tendency for city managers in cities with high planning commitment scores to exercise a more significant influence on public decisions and policies, as indicated by the composite votes casted. City engineers in cities with low commitment scores tend to occupy a similar position of importance in the public policy-making process.

Many studies have suggested that public decisions are influenced to a significant degree by a wide variety of interest groups outside the structure of government. To measure the possible relationships between these patterns of influence and the level of planning commitment, each respondent was asked to select and rank from among the listed thirteen such interest groups those which, in his opinion, were most influential in public policy-making in his community. Provision was also made for "free choices" beyond those in the following list:

Chamber of Commerce
Taxpayers association
Local press
Merchants' organizations
Social and economic elites
Political parties
Reform organizations
Church groups
Neighborhood associations
Union or trade groups
Business leaders
Other citizens' groups
Service clubs

An examination, first, of the group ranked highest reveals some interesting patterns. Four groups received nearly equal numbers of votes: (1) Chamber of Commerce and business leaders; (2) local press; (3) social and economic elite; and (4) political parties. While there is a slight tendency, as shown in Table 13.8 for planning directors in cities with medium commitment scores to select Chambers of Commerce or business leaders as most influential, the contingency coefficient for this data is not particularly significant. Taking each of the remaining groups in turn, however, it would appear that the local press has a greater tendency to exert influence on public decisions in cities with high commitment scores; social and economic elite groups in cities with medium planning commitments; and political parties in cities with low planning commitments. As in the case of public officials and agencies, there is no dominant patterns beyond the level of "most influential" (see Table 13.9).

Two conclusions might be drawn from these findings. The first is that planning directors are unaware of the subtle influence which might be exercised by various interest groups in the community, and therefore are unable, as a group, to identify the source or extent of this influence, regardless of the level of planning commitment. The second, and perhaps more valid, conclusion is that very often there is no discernible pattern of influence on policy issues — that the conclusions of pluralistic theorists are correct in that community power is diffused rather than solidified in any sort of "elite" group.

Table 13-7

Relationship between the Most Influential Public Official or Agency in Policy–Making and Level of Planning Commitment.

Most Influential Public Official or Agency	Level of Planning Commitment			
	Low	Medium	High	Number
a. As Identified by the Planning Director				
Mayor	21%	43	36	(44)
Other official	19%	29	52	(27)
Difference	+2	+14	−16	
b. As Identified by the Chief Executive				
Mayor	14%	53	33	(21)
Other official	19%	19	62	(16)
Difference	−5	+34	−29	

Table 13-8

**Relationship between Groups Outside
of Government Selected as Most Influential in Public Policy–Making and
Level of Planning Commitment.**

Planning Commitment	Groups Outside of Local Government					
	Chambers of Commerce and business leaders	Others	Difference	Local press	Others	Difference
High	47%	40%	–7	55%	40%	–15
Medium	32	38	+6	27	37	+10
Low	21	22	+1	18	23	+ 5
Total	100%	100%	C = .071	100%	100%	C = .117
Number of cases	(19)	(40)	N = 59	(11)	(48)	N = 59

Groups Outside of Local Government

Social and economic elite	Others	Difference	Political parties	Others	Difference
36%	44%	+ 8	31%	46%	+15
46	33	−13	38	35	− 3
18	23	+ 5	31	19	−12
100%	100%	$C = .098$	100%	100%	$C = .138$
(11)	(48)	$N = 59$	(13)	(46)	$N = 59$

Table 13-9

Relationship between Distributions of
Interest Groups Outside of Government Ranked among the Top Five in
Influence on Public Policy and Level
of Planning Commitment.

Planning commitment	Overall distribution of responses	Chambers of Commerce and business leaders	Local press	Social and economic elite
High	41%	42%	40%	43%
Medium	37	36	38	37
Low	22	22	21	20
Total	100%	100%	99%	100%
Number of cases	(274)	(76)	(47)	(30)
Contingency coefficient		.014	.000	.014

Planning commitment	Political parties	Other
High	42%	38%
Medium	33	38
Low	24	23
Total	99%	101%
Number of cases	(33)	(78)
Contingency coefficient	.024	.020

14 Communication as a Measure of Participation

It has been suggested that effective communication is the "warp and woof" of the decision-making process. It is of particular importance, therefore, to examine the role of the planner in the communication network of local government. Of primary concern in this final phase of the empirical investigation is the testing of the hypothesis that planning agencies in cities with high planning commitment scores evince certain communication characteristics which differ from those agencies in cities with lower levels of planning commitment. This hypothesis is a more general statement of the assumption advanced by Daland and Parker that more successful planning departments operate near the center of a communication system which is designed to create and effectuate public policies.[1]

Access to the communication network is a principal factor in determining the degree of participation and, in turn, the extent of potential influence in decision situations. The possession and subsequent transmittal of information are contributing factors in establishing points of access to the communication network. One test of the primary hypothesis concerning the difference in communication characteristics among planning agencies can be made through an examination of certain aspects of access and participation.

Influence in decision situations often emanates from "clusters" of persons or representatives of institutions which are capable of influencing the course of public action. These "decision clusters" in turn are linked through a network of communication maintained by intermediaries who have membership in or access to more than one cluster. That is to say, "decision clusters" often are not linked at the top of the hierarchy of communication but at a point further down this hierarchy where persons can move more readily as envoys between "clusters." It may be postulated that the more effective planners are in serving in this intermediary role, the greater the likelihood of success in their planning endeavors.

In a sense, this is a more specific statement of the primary hypothesis, that among the principal characteristics which differentiates planning agencies in cities with high commitment scores from those agencies at other levels is a greater participation of the planner as a communication intermediary among decision clusters. This, then, is a basic corollary to be examined in the following analysis.

Frequency of Communication

The principal source of data for the following analysis is derived from two questions included in the questionnaire sent by the authors to 95 planning agencies as part of the planning commitment study. It was noted in the questionnaire that the day-to-day operations of government require continual contacts among professional staffs and officials. The respondents then were asked to indicate the extent to which they or members of their staff communicate with one twenty other public officials or agencies in local government. The list of officials and agencies is the same as was discussed at the end of the preceding chapter in connection with the influence exerted by the public sector on the development of public policy. The following alternatives were suggested to facilitate the responses: (1) daily contact; (2) frequent contact — two times a week; (3) occasional contact — three to four times a month; (4) seldom — twice a month or less; and (5) not at all. The respondents were also asked to indicate with which of these agencies or officials they or their staff have the most direct and frequent contacts.

Most Direct and Frequent Contact

Taking these questions in reverse order, there were 112 usable responses concerning direct and frequent contacts from among the 76 questionnaires returned by planning directors. Where more than one agency or official was listed, the additional listings were recorded and included in the analysis. The frequency distribution of these multiple responses corresponds closely with the overall frequency distribution of cities in the three levels of planning commitment. Therefore, the inclusion of multiple responses has no significant effect on the findings. The frequency distribution of the total usable responses is shown in the first column of Table 14.1.

While mayors received the largest percentage for any single category in terms of overall responses (22 percent), city engineers followed closely with 19 percent. A strong tendency to communicate most frequently with the mayor is evident among respondents from cities with medium commitment scores. Respondents from cities with low commitment scores, on the other hand, show a strong proclivity to communicate more directly and frequently with the city engineer. The rather strong tendency for respondents from cities with high commitment scores to identify the public works director is of interest, suggesting a close tie between planning activities and programs of implementation in these cities.

Two combined categories also are shown in Table 14.1. The first, combining the responses for mayor and city manager, illustrates the predominance of the

Table 14-1

Relationship between Direct and Frequent Contact with Various Public Officials and Agencies and Level of Planning Commitment.

Agency or Official	Level of Planning Commitment			
	Low	Medium	High	Number
Total usable responses	22%	37	41	(112)
Mayor	24%	52	24	(25)
City manager or mayor	16%	42	42	(36)
Public works director	8%	23	69	(13)
City engineer	33%	33	33	(21)
Public works director or City Engineer	24%	29	47	(34)
Other Official or Agency	26%	38	36	(42)

city manager form of government among cities with high commitment scores. As a result, the frequency distribution for communication with chief executives in cities with high commitment scores more closely approximates the "normal" distribution for the overall usable responses.

The second combined category groups together the responses for public works directors and city engineers. These two officials might be thought of as the principal agents of the "development" sector of local government. It is interesting to note that the position of public works director is not universal among the 95 cities, but it is found in all cases in cities with high commitment scores. Twenty-seven percent of the respondents from cities with medium commitment scores and 21 percent from cities with low commitment scores indicated that their city *did not* have a public works director. Taken in combination, there appears to be a relatively lower frequency of communication in cities at the medium level of planning commitment between the planning agency and these representatives of the development sector.

The responses received from chief executives to this same question are shown in Table 14.2. The largest percentage in terms of the overall response is represented by the public works directors and city engineers (37). Only four chief executives (two in each of the high and medium cities) indicated that their most direct and frequent contact was with the planning director. The distribution of responses concerning the frequency of contacts with the chief finance officer most closely approximates the overall distribution of usable responses.

Comparing the data in Tables 14.1 and 14.2, it might be suggested that contacts between the planning director and the chief executive at all levels of planning commitment is unidirectional. That is to say, much of the contact is in the form of written communication (reports, memoranda, recommendations, and so forth), which is passed upward from the planning officer to the chief executive and downward from the chief executive to the planners (often through intermediaries). This communication characteristic would seem particularly evident in cities with medium planning commitment scores. The stronger ties with the public works director and/or city engineer on the part of planning agencies in cities with high commitment scores would seem to work to their advantage, since chief executives seem to have a strong proclivity at all levels to communicate frequently with these officials. At the same time, the greater involvement of planning agencies in these cities in fiscal matters, as indicated in the previous analysis, would seem to offer another channel of communication with the policy-making sector, that is, through the chief finance officer. At the lower end of the planning commitment scale, planning agencies seem to communicate with the policy sector through the office of the city engineer.

These findings tend to qualify and expand upon the earlier conclusions suggested by Daland and Parker on the basis of their analysis of communication relationships between planners and other actors in the "political arena" in the cities of the Piedmont Crescent of North Carolina.[2] Daland and Parker assert that in the great majority of cases, communication between the planning

Table 14-2

Relationship between Direct and Frequent Contact between Chief Executive and Various Public Officials and Agencies and Level of Planning Commitment.

Agency or Official with which the Chief Executive
has Most Direct and Frequent Contact

Planning commitment	Total usable responses	Public works director or city engineer	Chief finance officer	Planning director	Other
High	47%	38%	47%	50%	59%
Medium	39	38	40	50	35
Low	14	24	13	0	6
Total	100%	100%	100%	100%	100%
Number of cases	(57)	(21)	(15)	(4)	(17)

director and other actors occurred on a two-way basis. This assertion, in part, would seem to receive support from the present data. However, this communication is not face-to-face contact but more often takes the form of written communication. At the same time, the initiation of the communication often comes from the planner.

Daland and Parker also suggest that the planner's influence on the broader aspects of developmental policy are exerted through other members of the administrative organization of the city, and particularly the city manager.[3] This conclusion receives substantial support from the above data. However, the avenues of influence (points of access to the communication network) vary according to the level of commitment to the planning process. Thus, planning agencies in cities with high commitment scores have a greater range of available channels through which their influence can be exerted.

Frequency of Communication with Officials
in the Policy Formulation Sector of Government

While the preceding analysis begins to suggest some of the different communication characteristics among the various levels of planning commitment, a more complete picture requires an examination of the frequency of communication between the planning agency staff and other officials and agencies in local government. For the purposes of discussion, the various officials and agencies included in the questionnaire have been grouped into four broad categories. The first of these categories, which includes the mayor, city manager, city clerk, chief finance officer, budget director, and city treasurer, might be called the *policy formulation sector* of local government. These administrative offices provide the principal "prerogative" participants in any decision-making situation. The second category has been referred to previously as the *development sector* and includes the public works director, the city engineer, the superintendent of streets, and the water and sewer department. The third category to be examined is the *planning support sector*. This category includes the planning commission or board, the zoning officer, building inspector, parks and recreation director, and the city librarian. These agencies and officials provide more direct inputs into the planning process in the form of information, policy, and programs of implementation. The final category includes a group of *line agencies* which are responsible for a number of important administrative functions of local government. These include the city health department, the personnel director, superintendent of schools, and the city police and fire chiefs and their departments.

Table 14.3 shows that there is a strong tendency for planning directors in cities with high commitment scores to communicate with their chief executive on less than a daily basis. At the lower end of the planning commitment scale, the responses indicate a greater propensity for daily communication. Again the unidirectional character of this communication should be underlined. Although

Table 14-3

Relationship between Frequency of Communication with Officials in the Policy Formulation Sector and Level of Planning Commitment.

Frequency of Communication with Selected Officials	Level of Planning Commitment			
	Low	Medium	High	Number
Chief Executive				
Daily	30%	37	33	(30)
Less Frequently	10%	36	54	(48)
Difference	+20	+1	−21	
City Clerk				
Two times a week	23%	40	37	(35)
Less frequently	21%	36	43	(28)
Difference	+2	+4	−6	
Chief Finance Officer				
Two times a week	22%	39	39	(23)
Less frequently	19%	39	42	(31)
Difference	+3	0	−3	
City Treasurer				
Occasionally: 3 to 4 times a month	16%	37	47	(19)
Less frequently	29%	36	35	(31)
Difference	−13	+1	+12	

usable responses from chief executives in cities with low commitment scores was relatively limited, there is nothing to suggest that this communication is face-to-face or reciprocal in its frequency.

As shown in Table 14.3, there is no strong relationship evident in terms of the frequency of communication between the planner and the city clerk. Although planning directors in cities with medium commitment scores apparently often communicate with the city clerk as frequently as two times a week, the relatively low contingency coefficient would suggest that this has little bearing on the level of planning commitment.

The data on communication between the planning director and his staff and the chief finance officer would suggest that there is relatively little relationship between the frequency of this communication and the level of planning commitment achieved (see Table 14.3). This is somewhat surprising in light of the rather strong relationship which was found in terms of level of participation of the planning agency in fiscal management activities and level of planning commitment. This finding would suggest that the planning agency communicates through an intermediary in these matters. While only twenty-four of the responding planning directors indicated that their city has a budget director as an officially designated officer of local government, over half of this number are in cities with high planning commitment scores. Although it would be somewhat misleading to make any further direct statistical analysis of these responses, it might be suggested that the budget director serves as a principal channel of communication for the planning agency in matters of fiscal management.

Although communication between the planning agency and the office of the city treasurer generally takes place on a less frequent basis than is the case with other officials discussed to this point, it is interesting to note that there is a noticeable tendency for planning agencies in cities with high commitment scores to communicate on a more frequent basis than is evident at other levels (see Table 14.3). According to the governmental data of *The Municipal Year Book*, the position of city treasurer is often an elected office and, in fact, ranks second only to the office of mayor in terms of its frequency as an elected position. Thus in a number of cities the city treasurer is an important political figure. This suggests that the city treasurer offers another channel of communication for the planning director in fiscal matters.

It must be concluded that, with the exception of the chief executive, where the tendency is for planning directors in cities with lower commitment scores to communicate on a more frequent basis, there are no apparent relationships between level of planning commitment and frequency of communication between the planning agency and these administrative officials. In general, however, it may be observed that the reported levels of communication with the prerogative members of the policy formulation sector are less frequent at the higher levels of planning commitment. These responses must be examined in light of the fact that they represent self-evaluations. By the same token, the responses of the chief executives would suggest that a much greater number of contacts take place between their offices and the planning agency in cities with high commitment scores than are indicated by the responses of the planning directors in these cities. Fourteen of the fifteen responding chief executives from cities with high commitment scores indicated that their contact with the planning director was on a "frequent" basis (two times a week).

Frequency of Communication with Officials
in the Development Sector of Government

The pattern of a lower frequency of communication between the planning agency and other officials in cities with high commitment scores carries over to the development sector as well, as indicated by Table 14.4. Although a large percentage of the respondents from these cities indicated that their most direct contacts was with the public works director, there is a tendency for the frequency of communication to be lower than at other levels of planning commitment. This pattern holds for communication with the city engineer, although to a much lesser extent. There is relatively little relationship between patterns of communications with other officials in the development sector and the level of planning commitment.

In general, it may be concluded that while agencies in the development sector of government provide important communication links for planning agencies in cities with high commitment scores, there is a clear tendency for the frequency of this communication to be somewhat lower than is the case in cities with lower commitment scores.

Frequency of Communication with Officials
in the Planning Support Sector of Government

With the exception of the city planning commission or board, there is a clear tendency for planning directors in cities with high planning commitment scores to have a greater frequency of communication with agencies and officials in the planning support sector than is evident at other levels of planning commitment (see Table 14.5). The less frequent communication between the planners and the members of the planning commission in cities with high planning commitment is not surprising. One of the principal functions of the planning commission is to serve as a communication link between the planner as a technical expert and the policy-makers in government. However, in those cases where the planning function has achieved a fairly high degree of acceptance, this communication link is no longer as important. Very often the function of the planning commission changes to one of a sounding board for new ideas and as a vehicle through which formal reports are conveyed to the general public. In this role, communication can be maintained on a less frequent basis.

It might be expected, on the other hand, that the need for a greater frequency of communication with agencies in the planning support sector would

Table 14-4

Relationship between Frequency of Communication with Officials in the Development Sector and Level of Planning Commitment.

Frequency of Communication with Selected Officials	Level of Planning Commitment			
	Low	Medium	High	Number
a. Public Works Director				
Two times a week	21%	38	41	(34)
Less frequently	22%	17	61	(18)
Difference	−1	+21	−20	
b. City Engineer				
Two times a week	24%	38	38	(45)
Less frequently	27%	27	46	(11)
Difference	−3	+11	−8	
c. Superintendent of Streets				
Occasionally: 3 to 4 times a month	22%	37	41	(27)
Less frequently	33%	33	33	(18)
Difference	−11	+4	+8	
d. Sewer and Water Department				
Occasionally: 3 to 4 times a month	22%	39	39	(36)
Less frequently	23%	36	41	(22)
Difference	−1	+3	−2	

Table 14-5

Relationship between Frequency of Communication with Officials in the Planning Support Sector and Level of Planning Commitment.

Frequency of Communication with Officials or Agencies	Low	Medium	High	Number
a. Planning Commission or Board				
Two times a week	25%	42	33	(24)
Less frequently	21%	33	46	(33)
Difference	+4	+9	−13	
b. Zoning Officer				
Two times a week	19%	28	53	(32)
Less frequently	23%	46	31	(13)
Difference	−4	−18	+22	
c. Building Inspector				
Two times a week	20%	38	42	(45)
Less frequently	31%	31	38	(16)
Difference	−11	+7	+4	
d. Parks and Recreation Director				
Occasionally: 3 to 4 times a month	20%	37	43	(44)
Less frequently	28%	39	33	(18)
Difference	−8	−2	+10	

The column header "Level of Planning Commitment" spans Low, Medium, and High.

increase with increased planning commitment, since these agencies provide important avenues for plan implementation. There is a strong tendency for frequent communication between the planners and the zoning officer in cities with high commitment scores. However, this is not the case in cities with medium levels of commitment to the planning process. It is interesting to note that the highest level of "not appropriate" responses occurred at the medium level of planning commitment. Over 37 percent of the respondents indicated that they, in fact, were the zoning officers for their communities. There is a tendency for more frequent communication between the planners and the building inspector in both high and medium cities, while the frequency of communication with the parks and recreation director shows a more even gradiant from high to low.

Frequency of Communication with Line Agencies

Two interesting relationships are encountered when the data concerning communication between the planning agency and various line agencies are examined. These data point up a fairly strong tendency for more frequent communication between the planner and the superintendent of schools in cities with high commitment scores. Based on the somewhat limited response from chief executives, it might be noted that this tendency does not hold up as strongly in terms of their communications with superintendents.

The second significant relationship is in terms of the frequency of communication between the planning director and the personnel director. While only 60 percent of the respondents indicated that their city had a personnel director, the data would suggest a very strong tendency for planning directors in cities with high commitment scores to have more frequent contacts with the personnel officer.

**Overall Patterns of Communication —
Communication Constellations**

In an effort to develop some method by which more fully to examine the overall implications of these patterns of communication, a rather primitive technique of graphic interpretation, called a "communication constellation," was developed in conjunction with this study. The authors acknowledge that this method of analysis has been freely adapted from the field of sociometry, as developed by J. L. Moreno and others, and apologize for any misuse or oversimplification of these techniques.

The diagrams or "communication constellations" illustrated by Figures 14.1—14.10 were constructed on the basis of an average of all responses from planning directors at each level, that is, the five categories corresponding to the frequency of communication were assigned numerical values, added together, and the sum divided by the total number of responses. The results were plotted on a series of concentric rings drawn at three-quarter-inch intervals. The following list identifies the numbered circles.

Key for Figures 14.1 through 14.10

A. Planning Director
1. Chief Executive
2. City Manager
3. City Clerk
4. Chief Finance Officer
5. Budget Director
6. City Treasurer
7. Public Works Director
8. City Engineer
9. Superintendent of Streets
10. Sewer and Water Department

11. Planning Commission
12. Zoning Officer
13. Librarian
14. Building Inspector
15. Parks and Recreation Director
16. City Health Officer
17. Personnel Officer
18. Superintendent of Schools
19. City Police Chief
20. City Fire Chief

The first step in constructing a communication constellation is to plot average levels of communication around some selected central figure — an individual or group in the communication system — at varying distances according to the frequency of contact. In Figure 14.1, the participants in the various sectors examined in the previous discussion are plotted in a clockwise manner around the planning director of a "typical" city with a high level of planning commitment. From this diagram, it may be observed that the principal communication link with the policy formulation sector is the city manager. The frequency of communication with other participants in this sector falls along a gradient ranging from the mayor through the city clerk and chief finance officer to the budget director and finally the city treasurer. Communication with the development sector is principally through the city engineer and public works director, while the zoning officer, building inspector, and parks and recreation director serve as the principal contacts in the planning support sector. Communication with the line agency sector is relatively infrequent, with no predominate point of contact. Figures 14.2 and 14.3 represent similar plots of the data for cities with medium and low planning commitment scores.

A comparison of these three constellations begins to point up some of the differences and similarities in the patterns of communications at the various levels of planning commitment. With the exception of a greater frequency of communication with the mayor's office and the planning commission and a relatively lower frequency of communication with other participants in the planning support sector, there is little difference between the communication patterns in cities with high levels and medium levels of planning commitment. The responses from planning directors in cities with low commitment scores would suggest a greater frequency of communication with all participants in the formulation sector except the city treasurer. Comparable frequencies of communication as those found at other levels of planning commitment are evident for participants in other sectors. If the premise is accepted that this

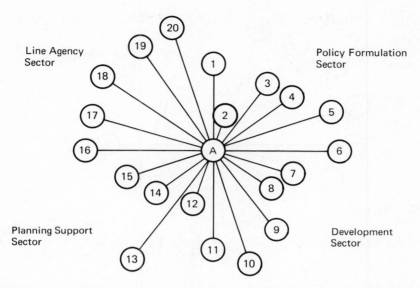

Figure 14-1 Schematic Diagram of Frequency of Communication between Planning Director and Other Officials in Cities with High Planning Commitment Scores.

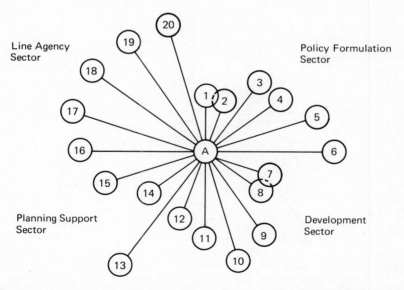

Figure 14-2 Schematic Diagram of Frequency of Communication between Planning Director and Other Officials in Cities with Medium Planning Commitment Scores.

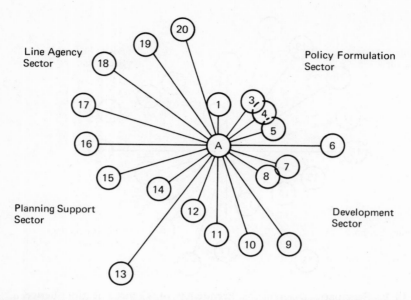

Figure 14-3   Schematic Diagram of Frequency of Communication between Planning Director and Other Officials in Cities with Low Planning Commitment Scores.

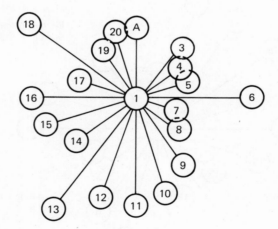

Figure 14-4   Schematic Diagram of Frequency of Communication between Chief Executive and Other Officials in Cities with High Planning Commitment Scores.

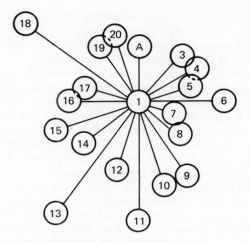

Figure 14-5 Schematic Diagram of Frequency of Communication between Chief Executive and Other Officials in Cities with Medium Planning Commitment Scores.

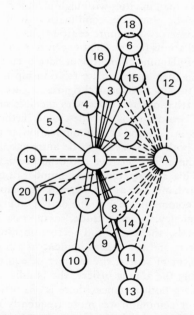

Figure 14-6 Schematic Diagram of Frequency of Communication between Chief Executive and Planning Director and Other Officials in Cities with High Planning Commitment Scores.

communication is largely unidirectional, emanating with the planning director, this greater frequency of communication would be in keeping with the characteristic efforts of planning agencies in cities with low commitment levels to become "established" in the hierarchy of local government.

Similar communication constellations can be plotted for communication between the chief executive (or any other major participant) and other officials or agencies in local government. In Figure 14.4 the communication constellation of the chief executive in cities with high levels of planning commitment has been plotted. Figure 14.5 illustrates the same plot for chief executives in cities with medium commitment scores. However, the relatively low response level for chief executives from cities with low commitment scores made it prohibitively difficult to plot a constellation diagram for those cities. Here again a comparison can be made to reveal similarities and differences in the patterns of communication. In cities with high commitment scores, a greater frequency of communication between the chief executive and chief finance officer is evident, whereas there is a slightly more frequent level of contact between the chief executive and the public works director and a significantly higher level of communication between the chief executive and the zoning officer in cities with medium commitment scores. The city health director and the city treasurer also appear to have more frequent contacts with the chief executive in cities with medium commitment scores than in cities with high planning commitment.

These constellations can be plotted in combination to illustrate common or reciprocal relationships between two or more central figures. Thus in Figure 14.6 the communication constellations for the chief executives and planning directors in cities with high levels of planning commitment have been combined, with the other participants shown in their approximate relationship in terms of reported frequencies of communication by both central figures. Figure 14.7 illustrates the same combination of constellations for cities with medium commitment scores.

A comparison of these two diagrams provides some further insights into the similarities and differences in patterns of communication at these two levels of planning commitment. In both cases, as might be anticipated, the frequency of communication between the chief executive and other participants is far greater than that of the planner. This is illustrated by the number of officials or agencies that are plotted on the left-hand side of the diagram. Participants falling toward the middle of the diagram communicate with the chief executive and the planner with about the same frequency. These include, in the case of cities with high planning commitment scores, the parks and recreation director, the building inspector, the city treasurer, and the superintendent of schools. In the case of cities with medium commitment scores, the number of equitable frequencies is somewhat smaller, including the zoning officer, the building inspector, and the superintendent of schools. In both instances there is one official or agency with whom the planning director communicates more frequently than does the chief executive. In the case of cities with high commitment scores, it is the zoning officer; in cities with medium commitment scores, it is the planning commission.

Perhaps the most important conclusion to be reached from this graphic

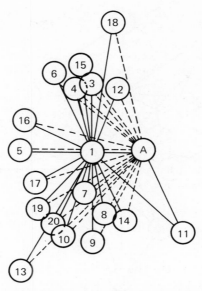

Figure 14-7 Schematic Diagram of Frequency of Communication between Chief Executive and Planning Director and Other Officials in Cities with Medium Planning Commitment Scores.

analysis is that the planner, in fact, does not serve as the central figure of a communication constellation. Rather he serves as an important participant in one or more constellations. This can be illustrated by a further extension of the communication constellation concept, which in turn evolves into a more complete graphic description of the communication network at various levels or planning commitment.

Several cities were selected from each of the three categories of planning commitment, and brief questionnaires were sent to key participants in each of the four sectors discussed previously. These participants were asked to respond to a question similar to the one from which the above data have been drawn. The results yield a surprising correspondence in communication patterns at the three levels of planning commitment. From these data it may be concluded that the city manager serves as a vital communication link among the various sectors of government in cities with high planning commitment. He has daily contact with the mayor's office, and nearly as frequent communication with the public works director. His communication with the chief finance officer, the budget director, and the city engineer places him in a central position insofar as coordinating the day-to-day activities of government is concerned.

The city clerk in cities with high commitment, although serving a somewhat lesser communication role than is evident at the other two levels, provides important linkages with the personnel director and the superintendent of

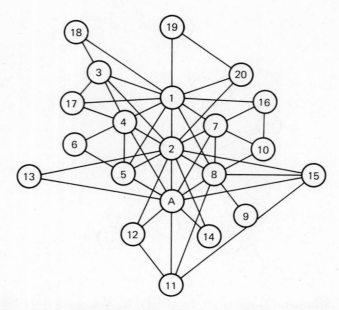

Figure 14-8 Network of Communication for Public Officials in Cities with High Planning Commitment Scores.

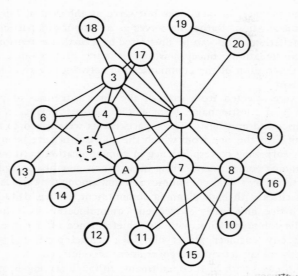

Figure 14-9 Network of Communication for Public Officials with Medium Planning Commitment Scores.

schools, as well as with various line agencies. The chief finance officer serves as the coordinator of activities in the development sector. The data would suggest that the link between the public works director and the superintendent of streets is made through the city engineer.

It is possible to superimpose the various constellations that have been plotted in order to obtain a generalized picture of the network of communication in cities with high planning commitment scores (see Figure 14.8). From this schematic diagram, it may be suggested that the principal figure in the communication network is the city manager rather than the mayor. The city manager serves as the "filter and funnel" through which much of the communication to and from the mayor passes. The chief finance officer and the public works director share in the close contact with the mayor within their own particular sectors of responsibility.

There are multiple channels of contact between the planning director and other major participants in the communication network. For example, the planning director has frequent contact with the budget director as well as fairly regular contact with the chief finance officer. By the same token, the contact with the development sector is made through both the city engineer and the public works director. The planning director, in turn, serves as a communication link for the planning commission, the zoning officer, and the building inspector. It is interesting to note that the data would suggest that the frequency of contact between the planning commission and the zoning officer is about the same as that between the planning commission and the director at this level of planning commitment. This would seem to support the earlier observation that the role of the planning commission changes somewhat as the level of planning commitment increases among officials in local government.

As has been noted, a relatively small percentage of cities at the medium level of planning commitment have a city manager-council form of government (20 percent). As a result, the patterns of communications shift somewhat, with the public works director and the city clerk playing a more important coordinative role among the various participants. The frequency of communication between the city clerk and the mayor is greater at the medium level of commitment than is evident at the high level. At the same time, the chief finance officer appears to play a somewhat lesser role, although still serving as an intermediary for the fiscal operations of government. In several cities with medium commitment, the function of the public works director is carried out by the city engineer. The office of budget director is also characteristic of cities with higher planning commitment scores and frequently is not found at the medium level of commitment.

As shown in Figure 14.9, in which the various communication constellations for cities with medium planning commitment scores are superimposed, the absence of a city manager and the office of budget director has significant implications for the planning director by reducing the channels of communication available between his office and other sectors of local government. Thus the planning director must rely more on direct communication with these

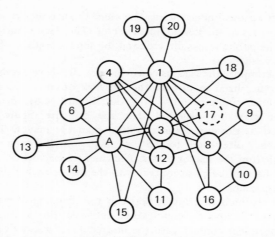

Figure 14-10 Network of Communication for Public Officials in Cities with Low Planning Commitment Scores.

sectors and with the mayor. The planning director retains his role as a communication link for the planning commission, the zoning officer, and the building inspector. There is some evidence to suggest, however, that the public works director and/or the city engineer provide an additional link between the planning commission and the mayor's office.

Cities at the low level of planning commitment are characterized by the frequent absence of the position of public works director. Much of the coordination provided at higher levels by the public works director and/or city manager is now a functional role of the city clerk. The data indicate that frequent communication takes place between the city clerk and the city engineer, the zoning officer, the personnel officer (where this position exists as a separate office), the chief finance officer, the planning director, and the mayor's office. The communication constellation for the city engineer is similar to that found in medium commitment cities when there is no public works director. The city engineer is a principal communicator for the development sector and the planning support sector. At the low level of planning commitment, the zoning officer appears in a much more important communication role and, in fact, might be considered a communication link between the planning sector and the development sector.

Figure 14.10 again represents the superimposition of the various communication constellations, generalized somewhat for illustrative clarity. The more central position of the city clerk is evident in this diagram. Although the frequency of communication between this office and that of the mayor is not quite as great as between the finance officer and the mayor, it would appear that the city clerk serves in the "filter and funnel" position occupied by the city manager and/or public works director at higher levels of planning commitment.

15 The Decision-Making Process

A fundamental assumption in this discourse has been that rational decision-making results from a flow of choices — a sequence of acts which are mutually related to the attainment of some end or collection of affiliated ends. Thus, *rational decisions* must be distinguished from *opportunistic decisions*, that is, decisions which are made as events unfold. Opportunistic decisions may not be mutually related, nor do they have a single overriding design or plan. In short, opportunistic decisions do not entail planning, whereas rational decisions require the orderly, systematic procedures of planning. This statement does not preclude the possibility, however, that opportunistic decisions may have to be made during a planned, rational course of action.

A second distinction must be made between problem-solving and rational decision-making. A good deal of the discussion of decision-making tends to center on problem-solving situations, thereby providing a somewhat distorted picture of the decision-making process.[1] The majority of decisions that can be handled effectively through the use of problem-solving techniques are relatively routine, *tactical decisions.*

One of the major obstacles to the development of a more complete understanding of the processes of decision-making stems from the generic use of the term "decision." Clearly, not all decisions are of the same magnitude. In some instances, decison-making may be a relatively simple task, and decisions may be reached as a matter of routine. In other areas, however, decision-making may require the most demanding exercise of judgment, reasoning, and imagination. In the first instance, a decision is merely the mechanism that activates some precast response — a regulatory device held in readiness for the advent of a decision-demanding situation. In more complex cases, however, a decision becomes a means of outlining a commonly acceptable response where none existed before. Such decision situations arise when (1) unfamiliar demands result in a lack of general agreement as to relevant patterns of response to achieve a particular set of goals; or (2) there is disagreement as to the goals themselves. Such decision situations require innovation rather than the application of some precast response.[2]

The terms *problem-solving* and *decision-making* frequently are used interchangeably. This is an unfortunate semantic generalization, for the process of problem-solving could serve as a useful distinction in discussing patterns of decision-making. If both the conditions of the situation and the requirements that must be satisfied are known, problem-solving is the only approach necessary. In such cases, the task is merely one of choosing from among a few obvious alternatives. The decision criterion is usually one of economy. While many tactical decisions reached through the use of problem-solving techniques may be relatively complicated and important, they invariably are unidimensional in nature.

Decisions with far-reaching implications are generally decisions of *strategy*. In order to arrive at effective (i.e., rational) decisions in such instances, it is necessary (1) to find out what the problem situation is; (2) to determine what alternative courses are open to change the situation; (3) to identify the most effective solution in light of available resources; and (4) to determine what additional resources might be necessary (and feasible) to achieve a more effective solution. It is possible to reach a rational choice as to the course of action to be pursued only after these steps have been taken. The procedures required to arrive at decisions of strategy are the procedures of the systemic planning process.

Adaptive Decisions — Adjustments
Within Established Expectations

It would seem appropriate to insert a third category in the continuum of tactical-strategical decisions to account for decisions which begin with programmed responses but which require considerable reconstruction of program details. Such decision activities might be identified as *adaptive decision-making.*

Adaptive decisions seek to alleviate built-up pressures by removing the more immediate sources of demand or by providing a satisfactory alternative solution to that which is sought.[3] Adaptive decisions provide a means of modifying established patterns of response and thereby reestablish a flow of productive activity on a more or less stable basis. Since such adaptations may not eliminate the root causes of the problem, they are often only temporary solutions. As pressures of displacement continue to mount, adaptive decisions may no longer suffice, and, in some instances, may even contribute to the total stress on the decision system.

Since accommodation is relatively less painful and less disruptive to the status quo, most patterns of activity that become dysfunctional are dealt with through adaptive rather than innovative decisions. Adaptive decisions lead to certain minor revisions in expectations, whereas innovative decisions may lead to new or substitute expectations. The term *expectations* is used in this connection to denote the indigenous criteria against which persons affected by a particular decision gauge its efficacy. The principal test of the efficacy of new patterns produced by a decision is their compliance with the minimal expectations sanctioned by the social system (i.e., an organization, group, community, or society).

When the system's expectations are met through adaptive decisions, fine adjustments are initiated that lead to routinization of the response. The revised pattern gradually is "programmed" as a legitimized pattern of response, that is, as a regulatory device. Even though they may dissipate effectively those stresses which evoked the initial need for adjustment, adaptive decisions may include some ill-conceived steps or unanticipated side effects which, in turn, produce new and unfamiliar stresses. In such cases, further adaptive decisions may be required to produce more satisfactory patterns.

Innovative Decisions —
Accommodation through New Expectations

There are limitations to the malleability of the structure of a decision system, however. Adaptive adjustments must be devised within these limits. When the suggested accommodations call for changes which exceed these limits, a major problem emerges. This might be called the "policy problem" in that such situations require innovative decisions to bring about major modifications in *ends* as well as *means.*

In one sense, an innovative decision differs from an adaptive decision principally in the rate at which change comes about. A series of adaptive decisions eventually may introduce as substantial a change in the structure of the system as would come about from an innovative decision. The two modes differ in intent, however, for the innovative decision is a deliberate attempt to deal with an intolerable situation through a frontal attack rather than through oblique incremental operations. This is not to deny the value of incremental decisions. The highest art of decision-making may be said to lie in knowing when to induce change in genuine increments and when to use the bold stroke of innovation. However, situations requiring innovative decisions usually involve issues that run to the roots of a system, issues so central and compelling that they cannot be disposed of either obliquely or incrementally.

Once the need for innovation is apparent and accepted, an overt appraisal of the identifiable goals and objectives of the system generally follows in an effort to place the innovation in its proper perspective. This appraisal often brings to the surface conflicting motives distributed among several otherwise discontinuous roles within the system's organizational structure. Since decision-making involves an aggregate of people collaborating through some imposed system (a system which they have inherited and continually remake), individual goals frequently diverge and become inconsistent with the overall goals of the system. So long as conflicting goals remain unstated (i.e., as not explicitly held up to the light for examination), these inconsistencies may go unnoticed, even though they may be dysfunctional to the total system. However, when innovation is introduced, and these goals must be made explicit, conflict becomes evident and must be dealt with if the system is to retain its stability.

Decision-Making as a Dynamic System

Many studies of community decision-making have failed to give adequate attention to the dynamic aspects of decision-making. By concentrating on a particular aspect or phase of decision-making, these studies present a "static" picture, even though they often acknowledge the dynamic characteristics of the decision process. For example, by focusing only on issues which have reached the public arena, the pluralists' model ignores the screening activities of the private sector and the decisions made within the structure of government which narrow the range of alternatives (i.e., set the public "agenda") in terms of the issues which emerge in the public arena.

In the present discussion, the process of decision-making is viewed as a complex system involving the gathering, evaluating, recombining, and disseminating of information. It is a dynamic system within which communication both binds the system together and moves if from stage to stage in the process of responding to demands for both tactical and strategic decisions.

A Dynamic, Open, Goal-Directed, Stochastic System

An effective decision-making system does not merely seek equilibrium in the sense of the classic model. The classic equilibrium model assumes that, in the face of change, a system is compelled by some overriding force to reestablish some preexisting state of equilibrium. This concept of equilibrium is incapable of describing an important range of dynamic phenomena. On the basis of empirical observations, it must be concluded that an open system does not merely have static continuity at some fixed level of equilibrium. Rather, in responding to the forces of change, an open system frequently strives to create conditions that, under favorable circumstances, permit it to achieve some new level of stability. At times, positive action may be taken to destroy a previous equilibrium or even to achieve some new point of continuing disequilibrium.

Adaptation to change represents more than simple adjustments to events which impose themselves on a system's structure. It is a primary characteristic of all open systems that they are able to manifest a wide range of actions of a positive, constructive, and innovative sort for warding off or absorbing forces of displacement. In short, an open system need not just react to change by oscillating in the neighborhood of some point of equilibrium or by shifting to a new one. A growing awareness of these "dynamic" qualities of an open system also must lead to a concern for a more thorough examination of the temporal sequences by which the structural configuration of a system shapes its functions, and which in turn is altered by functional change. At the same time, recognition must be given to the fact that an open system interacts continually with its broader environment.

Viewed in cybernetic terms, public decision-making can be considered as an open system which acts through a stochastic search process in seeking relative stability. Even though the decision-making system appears to act through a trial-and-error process, its behavior is teleological or goal-directed. In the search process, the system may pass through a number of critical stages until it eventually settles down in a field where conflicts with its environment are minimized.

Expressed and unexpressed demands, emanating from the broader environment and from within the decision system, continue to act as disturbances to the stability of the system, however. These disturbances force the system to develop and employ regulatory devices to counter these "dysfunctional" aspects.

The Character of Regulation in Decision-Making

Regulation in decision-making situations can take one of three basic forms: (1) it can produce a programmed decision by adopting an approach which has proved successful in other decision-demanding situations; (2) it may lead to adaptive decisions which may not get at the root causes underlying the demand but may satisfice; or (3) it may serve in a more innovative role. "Adaptive planning," which treats the symptoms of a problem without examining underlying causes, and "consensus planning," which seeks to find a least common denominator so as to minimize changes in expectations, serve as examples of satisficing approaches. Programmed and adaptive decisions return the system to the same relative set of states in which it existed prior to the disturbance (i.e., prior to the demand for a decision). Innovative decisions, on the other hand, result in an alternation of the structural configuration of the system or produce new states, i.e., introduce new courses of action not evident prior to the disturbance. In short, while programmed and adaptive decisions produce modifications in the system, innovative decisions often lead to the creation of new systems. Adaptive decisions yield revisions of expectations among the participants within the system. Innovative decisions produce new expectations both within the system and in the broader environment.

The range of adjustments possible under each of these forms of regulation is governed by the relative number of responses available to the system when confronted by decision-demanding situations. This is analogous to the Law of Requisite Variety in cybernetic terms — a set of regulators (R) only can be successful in warding off a set of disturbances (D) if the number of alternatives available to R (R's variety) is equal to or greater than those available to D (D's variety).[4] While it is possible to increase the range of variety available to regulatory devices through coupling, the number of potential couplings is greatest in the case of innovative decisions. In this sense, coupling can be equated to increased access to channels of communication within the decision-making system.

Formulation of a Decision-Making Model

While attempts have been made to analyze decision-making as a universal process, there are considerable differences in the ways in which each of these decision responses — programmed, adaptive, and innovative — are handled in the decision system. It is important, therefore, to recognize these differences and, in formulating decision-making models, to examine systematically the unique attributes of these general classes of regulatory devices and their impact on the decision-making process.

It is also important to be cognizant of those factors which trigger the decision-making process. The elementary components of decision-making are characterized by a good deal of randomness, with considerable arbitrariness in the sequence of steps taken. In the early states of decision-making, demands for decisions are first identified and categorized and the problem is defined. Analysis of these early states requires a systematic approach if meaningful insights are to be derived. As Northrup has so aptly pointed out, "One may have the most rigorous of methods during the later stages of investigation but if a false or superficial beginning has been made, rigor later on will never retrive the situation."[5]

Demands as the Inputs of a Decision System

While a particular system under study often is set apart from its broader environment, it must be recognized that many aspects of this environment have an important impact upon the system. These enter the system in the form of *inputs*. In the case of a decision system, these inputs take the form of *decision demands*. Since the concept of demands is central to the model being developed, it is important at the outset to clarify the meaning to be attributed to this term. A demand has been defined by David Easton as ". . . an expressed opinion that an authoritative allocation with regard to a particular subject matter should or should not be made by those responsible for doing so."[6]

In this definition, *demand* takes on a neutral connotation, in that it is not necessarily associated with some set of value preferences on the part of the demand-maker. A demand, in fact, may be used to conceal true preferences, as when alternative programs are promoted for the purpose of generating support for some other, unexpressed course of action. In the context of the present discussion, however, such *expressed demands* represent only part of the overall demand inputs of the decision-making process. Demands also arise from dysfunctional conditions of a given situation confronting a system which may not take the form of an "expressed opinion." Such conditions may be interpreted from within the system as constituting a "demand," even though they have not been identified or verbalized as such "outside" the system.

A demand may be quite narrow, specific, and relatively simple and direct in nature, or it may be highly general, vague, and complex. Expressed demands may take the form of specific grievances and discontents relevant to a given experience or situation. At the other end of the continuum are such highly generalized demands, for example in the public sector, as broad pleas for better government, more vigorous fiscal policies, victory in war, or the alleviation of poverty. Generalized demands seldom include any specific courses of action. "Causes," stemming from various ideologies, are frequently among the principal sources of such demands, although they embody ill-defined, all-encompassing programs of action.

Expressed demands may be directed to some specific individuals or group within the decision system, or they may be ubiquitous in their orientation. In either case, associated with every expressed demand is some set of expectations concerning the response that should emerge from the system. Unexpressed demands also arise from a variety of sources and assume multifacet characteristics. They share in common with expressed demand the fact that someone within the system must recognize the conditions giving rise to such demands as being "out of phase" with some set of acceptable conditions. In other words, before demands can gain entry into the decision system, they must be "sensed" as demands.

The State of Uncertainty and Doubt

It is this perception of "sensing" of a demand which sets the decision-making process in motion. Very often, this perception is merely a sense of uncertainty or doubt which exists because the constituent elements in some segment of the broader environment are unsettled or are not unified. This concept of uncertainty is a positive one. It does not mean a mere lack, absence, or deprivation in a purely negative sense, as would exist if the doubts were simply subjective states. The uncertainty stems from a particular, objective situation.[7] The objective observations of the situation do not coincide with the definition of what *should be*. The latter set of conditions may be either subjectively or objectively defined.

An individual's conceptual frame of reference, in large measure, governs the way in which he approaches an uncertain situation and, further, will contribute to the identification of a situation as being "out of phase" with the presently acceptable system. Background and training may provide an individual with a well-constructed set of concepts which makes him more sensitive to certain problems that others might pass over unobserved.

Thus the role of the trained technician, as an "initiator" in the decision-making process, can be identified more clearly. He must continually appraise various aspects of the accepted system and identify any elements in the broader environment that may seem to be potential displacements to this system. This role might be likened to the cybernetic regulator which acts as a warning device against displacements which threaten to drive the system out of some desirable set of states. The role of the technician beyond this initial phase may vary considerably, depending on the course of response assumed by the decision system. This phase of the decision-making process is frequently overlooked or deemed to be outside the actual process. Such a view fractionalizes the decision process unduly, however, thereby producing somewhat distorted conclusions as to the nature of the final decision.

It should be noted that the demands for decisions may originate from within the system itself, as well as coming from sources external to the system.[8] It may be suggested, however, that the manner in which these inputs or demands are handled within the system varies only slightly whether the sources of uncertainty are external or internal.

The Screening of Demands to Determine Intakes

Once a situation has been identified as uncertain (or potentially uncertain), there are four possible responses that may be made. Each of these responses involves a further degree of commitment to the decision-making process. The first possible response is to disregard the uncertain situation; that is, to decide to do nothing about it. Such a response is likely when the demand is below some threshold of tolerance. If, for any number of reasons, this response is invoked, then the process is cut short and abandoned. The second response is to further identify the uncertain situation as one which can be handled through programmed decision devices. This suggests that some sort of "memory bank" exists within the decision system in which these programmed decision devices are "stored" and against which uncertain situations are "tested" to determine if an appropriate programmed decision is available. Here again, the process is cut short through the application of a programmed response.

If either of the two remaining possible responses is invoked, the decision-making process moves to the next state — the state of classification and definition. It may be suggested, therefore, that inputs are "screened" to determine the actual *intakes* into the system. This screening filters out those demands for which no further action is to be taken at present and those which can be handled through programmed decision devices.

The Stage of Classification and Definition

"Uncertain situations," as discussed in the preceding section, are not the same as "problematic situations." Although uncertainty is essential to the initiation of the decision-making process, more is required before a problematic situation can be identified. Analysis does not begin with the uncertain or unsettled situation — this is anticipatory to analysis. Under analysis, the problematic situation is made explicit. As Anatol Rapoport has noted, the first step in solving a problem is to state it: "The statement usually involves a description of an existing state and desirable state of affairs where the factors involved in the discrepancy are explicitly pointed out. The success with which any problem is solved depends to a great extent on the clarity with which it is stated. In fact, the solution of the problem is, in a sense, a clarification (or concretization) of the objectives."[9]

The more a given situation is extensionalized, the better the classification, and the greater the promise of a successful solution. Vague statements of the situation lead to vague methods, where success is erratic and questionable. The first question to be asked concerning an uncertain situation is: "Is this a symptom of a fundamental disorder or problem or merely a stray or unique event?" While the generic problem situation can often be dealt with through the application of a programmed response, the truly exceptional event can be handled only as it is encountered.[10]

Strictly speaking, a distinction must be made among four, rather than two, different types of problem sets. First, there is the truly generic event, of which the individual occurrence is only a symptom. Most problems that confront a decision system fall into this class. As a rule, such generic situations require adaptive decisions. Frequently, programmed decision devices are applied to the symptoms of a generic problem. Until the generic problem set, or root cause of the apparent problem, is identified, however, tremendous amounts of time and energy may be spent in the piecemeal application of programmed decisions without ever gaining control of the generic situation.

The second type of occurrence is the situation which, while a unique event for a given decision system, is actually generic. As far as the present decision-makers are concerned, this is a nonrecurrent or unique situation. What is often overlooked is that the problem set is a generic situation which has confronted other decision systems in the past on other occasions. An effective decisions can be formulated through the application of some general rules. For these rules, the decision-makers can look to the experiences of others.

The third possible classification is the truly unique situation. Here, the event itself may be unique or the circumstances in which the event occur may be unique. Truly unique events are rare. Whenever one appears, however, the question must be asked: "Is this a true exception or only the first manifestation of a new generic problem?" This, then, is the fourth and last category of events with which the decision-making process must deal — the early manifestation of a new genus.

General rules, policies, or principles usually can be developed or adopted to deal with generic problem situations. Once the correct policy has been formulated, all manifestations of the same generic situation can be handled fairly pragmatically through the adaptation of the rule or principle to the concrete circumstances of the situation, that is, through adaptive decision-making. The unique problem set require greater innovation to arrive at a successful solution.

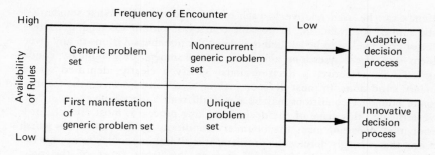

Figure 15-1 Classification and Definition of Basic Problem Sets.

Figure 15.1 illustrates the relations among these four categories and the two fundamental dimensions of *availability of rules and principles* for dealing with these problem situations and the *frequency of encounter* of these situations.

A common mistake in decision-making is to treat a generic problem set as if it were a series of unique events. The other extreme of treating every problem incrementally, through the application of programmed decision devices (i.e., treating a unique event as if it were just another example of an old problem to which the old rules should be applied), can have equally negative repercussions.

A very real danger in this phase of the process is not a wrong definition, but a plausible but incomplete one. Safeguards must be taken against incomplete definitions by checking them against all the observable facts and discarding any definition the moment it fails to encompass any of these facts. If the problem set cannot be stated specifically, then the analysis of the problematic situation has been adequate or of sufficient depth. Emotional bias, habitual or traditional behavior, or the frequent tendency of human beings to seek the path of least resistance may result in a superficial analysis, followed by a statement of the "apparent" problem instead of the "real" problem. An excellent solution to an apparent problem will not work in practice, because it is the solution to a problem that does not exist in fact. Consequently, short-circuiting this phase of the process may actually result in more time being spent later to get at the real problem when it becomes painfully evident that further analysis is required.

The Identification of Constraints,
Boundary Conditions, and
Standards for Evaluation

The next major step in the decision-making process is the establishment of clear specifications as to what the decision must accomplish. In so doing, five basic questions must be answered: (1) What are the existing or potential constraints to an effective solution to the problem set? (2) What objectives must the decision meet and what are the minimum goals to be attained? (3) What measure(s) of efficiency can be used relative to each of the objectives? (4) What standard(s) can be applied for evaluation of possible courses of action? (5) What definition of "most effective" is to be applied in judging the possible solutions to any given problem set? These questions aid in the establishment of "boundary conditions." To be effective, a decision must satisfy a clearly identified set of boundary conditions. In most decision-making situations, however, the identification of boundary conditions may be a most difficult undertaking.

Nevertheless, this stage of the decision-making process is most crucial, for a decision that does not meet the boundary conditions of the problem is worse than one that wrongly defines the problem. It is all but impossible to salvage the decision that starts with the right premise but stops short of the right conclusions. Furthermore, clear thinking about boundary conditions is needed to recognize when a course of action, brought about by a given decision, must be abandoned. A common cause of failure in a decision lies in the inability to recognize a subsequent shift in objectives – in specifications – that makes a prior "right" decision suddenly inappropriate.

Often decisions are made in which the specifications to be satisfied essentially are incompatible. In other words, to achieve goal A through the course of action prescribed by the decision precludes the achievement of some other goal, or at best, makes this achievement highly unlikely. This situation represents a classic case in which the boundary conditions were not fully and clearly identified. For example, decisions are often made which involve a "gamble" or so-called "calculated risk." This is the type of decision that might work if nothing whatever goes wrong. Such decisions often arise from something much less rational than a gamble, however – namely, a hope against hope that two or more clearly incompatible specifications can be fulfilled simultaneously.

As a rule, the articulation of goals and objectives seldom is sufficiently specific to be of any real value in establishing boundary conditions for any particular decision. Therefore, decisions are made with the vague hope that they will implement the overall goals and objectives of the system. What is required is some mechanism whereby these overall goals can be translated into more specific program goals and through which identifiable boundary conditions can be tested against the more general (and remote) goals and objectives. In deterministic decision situations, such mechanisms are generally available. In stochastic situations, it is unlikely that such mechanisms can be readily developed. The best "device" continues to be experience, coupled with a careful delineation of the problem and the objectives associated with the required solution.

The Formulation of Alternatives

Once the boundary conditions of the problem set have been specified, it is possible to pass on to the next phase of the decision-making process – the formulation of alternatives. Several alternatives should be developed for every problem situation; otherwise, there is a danger of falling victim to a false "either-or" proposition. There is a common confusion in human thinking between a true contradiction embracing all possibilities, and a contrast listing only two out of a number of possibilities. This danger is further heightened by a tendency to focus on extremes. A second danger lies in the fact that the formulation of alternatives may take a somewhat different course in adaptive decision-making. Here a standard set of alternative "models" may be selected for analysis, the outcome being limited by the initial set of "givens." This procedure tends to limit the evolutionary nature of alternative formulation and it should be avoided if possible even in adaptive decision-making.

Alternative solutions are the only means of bringing the basic assumptions concerning a given situation up to the conscious level, thereby forcing examination and testing of their validity. Alternative solutions are no guarantee of wisdom or of the right decision. But at least they prevent making what would have been known to be the wrong decision had the problem been thought through.

Alternative approaches relevant to the possible solution of a problem set differ in grade according to the level of reflection reached. At first, they are relatively vague; but as the alternatives operate to direct further observations, they become more suitable in their capacity to resolve the problem set. As alternatives become more appropriate, observations likewise become more acute. Perception and conception continue to work together until the former more fully describes the problem set, while the latter represents a possible method of solution.[11]

The next step is to develop an understanding of the possible consequences, by-products, and side effects associated with each of the suggested alternatives. This examination consists of an identification of the implications of particular courses of action in relation to other alternatives. The relationship so formulated constitutes a proposition — if such and such a relation is accepted, *then* the system is committed to such and such other courses of action because of their membership in the same set.

The examination of suggested alternatives with reference to their operational fitness involves an investigation to determine their capacity to direct further observation to secure additional factual material. This examination may result in the rejection, acceptance, or modification of ideas in an attempt to arrive at more relevant alternatives. Alternatives are a function, in part at least, of the data and concepts at the system's disposal. One possible alternative should always be considered, that of taking no action at all. This alternative seldom is recognized as a "decision," although it is as much a commitment as taking some specific positive action. The consequences that might result from a decision against any action must be clearly spelled out. By carefully considering the alternative of doing nothing, the traditional ways of doing things, which reflect past needs rather than those of the present, can be examined more carefully.

Frequently in the search for alternatives, an impasse will be reached. In such cases, the restructuring of the problem set may provide new or additional insights into the possible alternative solutions. Problem restructuring involves the manipulation of elements of which it is composed; for example, it may involve a change of viewpoint, or a permissible modification of objectives, or a rearrangement of the other elements of the problem set as it is stated. Framing and analyzing alternatives and their consequences in light of the problem set and the relevant facts of the situation is a major part of all rational decision-making. In spite of its primacy to the decision-making process, there are no simple hard-and-fast rules for "hitting upon" the right set of alternatives.

The Search for a Best Solution

Only after a number of alternatives have been considered is it possible to determine the "best" solution. If an adequate job has been done to this point, it will be found that either there are several alternatives to choose from, each of which would resolve the problem set, or there are half a dozen or so which fall short of perfection but which differ among themselves as to the area of shortcoming. It is a rare situation in which there is one and only one solution. In fact, whenever analyses lead to this comforting conclusion, one may reasonably suspect the conclusion of being little more than a plausible argument for a preconceived idea.

There are two basic modes of operation for finding the "best" solution from among several alternatives. The mode selected depends on the general class of decision sought — adaptive or innovative. Since adaptive decisions merely require that the alternative meet the minimal expectations sanctioned by the system, the "best" alternative can be selected on the basis of relatively simple criteria. The selected alternative should be one that provides a "satisfactory" solution to the problem set (thereby alleviating the pressures created by the demand), while creating a minimum disturbance of established expectations. No single alternative may satisfy these conditions, and therefore it may be necessary to combine elements from several alternatives to achieve these objectives. The innovative decision requires a more rigorous analysis and testing, since it ultimately will result in a modification or substitution of expectations. In seeking the "best" solution to a situation requiring innovation, there are four criteria which may provide helpful guidelines.

The terms *risk* and *gains* rather than the more traditional concepts of costs and benefits are used in the discussion of these criteria for several reasons. Efforts to convert the positive and negative aspects of any alternative into dollar-and-cents terms frequently result in too narrow a frame of reference. Assessments of benefits frequently involve double accounting. Direct benefits, for which dollar figures can be derived, often are counted again in terms of the more indirect benefits. Thus in arriving at a "net gains" figure, such indirect benefits must be "discounted" in order to avoid an unrealistic assessment. In developing a cost-benefit matrix, items often are omitted because they represent "intangibles." However, many of these "intangibles" are important "risks" or "gains" which may seriously affect the ultimate outcome of the decisions. Risks and gains must be weighed only after they have been completely listed.

The first criterion for a "best" solution has to do with the risk involved. The *risk* of each course of action must be weighed against the *expected gains.* There is no riskless action, or even riskless nonaction. What matters is neither the expected gains nor the anticipated risk, but the ratio between them. Every alternative, therefore, should contain an appraisal of the "odds" it carries. The value of such an analysis lies not in the end results but in the process which must be pursued in arriving at these end results. If no alternative is found suitable in terms of risks and gains, then it may be necessary to return to the previous phase in an effort to formulate more suitable alternatives. This process may go through a series of iterations before it is possible to pass on to the next phase.

The second criterion involves an assessment of *economy of effort.* The various alternatives must be examined to determine which of the possible courses of action will give the greatest results in terms of net achievement with the least effort, while at the same time attaining the needed change with the least necessary disturbance to the total system. It must be recognized that grandiose schemes may have many hidden risks which, if carefully considered, would reduce the overall economy of effort. By the same token, solutions which fall short of producing optimal results may yield a series of incremental decisions that in the long run will involve a much higher expenditure of effort.

The third criterion is concerned with the *timing* of the possible alternatives. If the situation has great urgency, the preferable course of action may be one that dramatizes the decision and serves notice that something important is happening. If, on the other hand, long and consistent efforts are needed, a slow start that gathers momentum may be preferable. In some situations, the solution must be final and must immediately lift the vision of those involved to new goals. In other cases, what matters most is to get the first step taken — the final goal may be shrouded in obscurity for the time being.

The final criterion deals with the *limitation of resources.* Decisions are often made, procedures developed, and policies formulated without first asking: "Are the means available for carrying these things out?" Perhaps the most important resource to be considered is the personnel required to carry out the decisions. No decision can be any better than those individuals or agencies responsible for its implementation.

A less than optimal decision should never be adopted simply because the resource competence to do what is right is lacking at present. Efforts must be made — and provided for in the decision — to raise the ability, skills, understanding, and standards of those who must carry out the programs associated with the decision. The "best" decision should always lie between genuine alternatives, that is, between courses of action which will adequately solve the problem set.

Modification to Gain an Acceptable Decision

The effective decision-maker must start out with what is "right" or "best" rather than what is acceptable or possible precisely because he will invariably be forced to make compromises in the end.[12] This factor relates back to the specification of boundary conditions, for if it is not clearly known what will satisfy the boundary conditions, the decision-maker cannot distinguish between a right compromise and a wrong one. The decision-maker gains little if the decision-making process starts out with the question: "What is acceptable?" In the process of answering this question, important things are usually overlooked and any chances of coming up with an effective solution — let alone the right answer — may be lost. The things one worries about seldom happen, while objections and difficulties no one thought about may suddenly turn out to be almost insurmountable obstacles.

After the "best" solution has been identified, the first step in seeking an acceptable decision is to make a reconnaissance of the expectations of the system. Unlike the adaptive decision process, innovative decisions nearly always require that expectations be altered and modified. Therefore, a careful appraisal must be made of expectations both internal and external to the decision system. These expectations are the relevant factors which must be accommodated by the decision.

It may be anticipated that, upon matching the proposed solution against the expectations of the system, one of three conditions will be found: (1) the expectations are in accord with the proposed solution, in which case an acceptable decision has been found; (2) the expectations are ambivalent to the proposed solution; or (3) the expectations are hostile to the proposed solution. In the latter two cases, some means must be devised to divert the hostile attitude and to engender support for the proposed solution. If no acceptable means are found, internal demands will be heightened, and a further reconnaissance of the system's expectations will be required.

This process of modification and compromise is somewhat akin to what other decision-making models have identified as "accommodating the power structure." The more neutral notion of *system expectations* has been used to give recognition to the role of the internal structure of the decision-making process, as well as to provide a model which is adaptable to both the "power-structure" and "pluralistic" approaches to decision-making. Thus the term *expectations* can include all factors, both internal and external to the decision system.

Converting the Decision into Action

Although thinking through the boundary conditions may be the most difficult phase in the decision-making process, converting decisions into effective action is usually the most time-consuming phase. Yet a decision will not become effective unless action commitments have been built in from the start. In fact, no decision has been made unless carrying it out in specific steps has become someone's work assignment and responsibility. Until this is achieved, it is only a good intention.

The flaw in many policy statements is that they contain no action commitments — they fail to designate specific areas of responsibility for their effective implementation. Converting a decision into action requires that several distinct questions be answered: (1) Who has to know of the decision? (2) What action has to be taken? (3) Who is to take this action? and (4) What does the action have to be, so that the people who have to do it can do it? The first and last of these questions too often are overlooked — with dire consequences.

Action commitments become doubly important when people have to change their behavior, habits, or attitudes in order for a decision to become effective. Care must be taken to see that responsibility for the action is clearly assigned and that the people are capable of carrying it out. The measurements, standards for accomplishment, and incentives associated with the proposed action must be changed simultaneously with the introduction of the decision.

The Feedback Phase

Provision must be made throughout the decision-making process for "feedback." Feedback occurs, intentionally or unintentionally, at many stages in the decision-making process. Much of this feedback is internal to the process, resulting in a recycling of a particular phase in order to achieve further refinements and modifications. The feedback which has an impact on the entire system generally occurs at two points: (1) after the decision has been made and action programs have been initiated; and (2) whenever internal demands are created within the system. In both cases, new demands (inputs) may be generated, causing the total system to recycle.

Information monitoring and reporting are particularly important after a decision has been reached, in order to provide continuous testing of expectations against actual results. Even the best decision has a high probability of being wrong; even the most effective decision eventually becomes obsolete. Failure to provide for adequate feedback is one of the primary reasons for persisting in a course of action long after it has ceased to be appropriate or rational. The advent of the computer has made it possible to compile and analyze great quantities of "feedback" data in a relatively short time period. It must be recognized, however, that computers can handle only abstractions. Abstractions can be relied upon only if they are constantly checked against concrete results. Unless decision-makers build their feedback around direct exposure to reality, their decisions may result in sterile dogmatism.

A basic aspect of the decision-making process is the development of a predictive capacity within the system to identify changing conditions which might necessitate modifications in the selected courses of action. Controls should be developed for a given solution by (1) defining what constitutes a significant change for each variable and relationship which appears as a

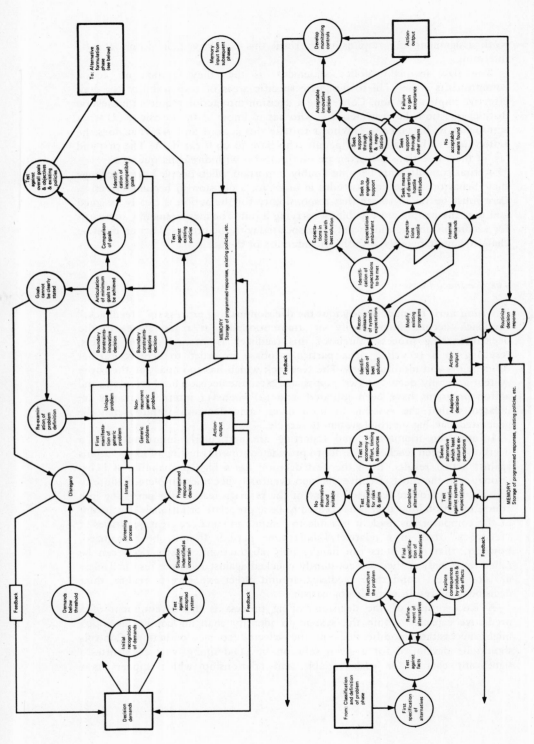

Figure 15-2 A General Cybernetics Model of the Decision-Making Process.

component in the decision; (2) establishing procedures for detecting the occurrence of such significant changes (providing modifications in the screening devices); and (3) specifying the tolerable range within which the solution can be modified if such changes occur and beyond which new solutions must be sought.

A Diagrammatic Representation of the
Decision-Making Model

The various phases of this cybernetics model of the decision system are summarized in Figure 15.2, which illustrates the sequential relationships among these component phases. Although this model of decision-making is presented in nine distinct phases, it would be misleading to assume that, in real life, problems are so obliging as to permit an easy, logical sequence of attention. As Joseph Cooper has observed; "[Problems] conceal their true nature so that halfway down the path of a decision you may find that you must retrace your steps for a new beginning. Or you may have alternatives for decision presented to you which, in your belief, are not the only or the best possible courses. This, too, will send you back to the beginning."[13]

Alternatives usually are not created by moving in an orderly sequence from the first phase to the last phase. It is not uncommon for new alternatives to occur from time to time while data about the problem are still being collected. Moreover, in complex situations, different phases of the process may develop at different rates, or various phases may appear simultaneously in different aspects of the same problem set. For example, the alternative formulation phase may be reached for one aspect or subsidiary problem of a more complex problem set, while other parts of the same problem set are still in the phase of definition and analysis. Nevertheless it is necessary to approach the patterns of decision-making phase by phase, in order to adequately analyze the process. Only in this way is it possible to uncover meaningful and useful insights as to how the process can be improved.

Part Five
Conclusions and Prospects

Part Five consists of one chapter which is both a summary of conclusions and some reflections of the short-range and long-range prospects for systemic planning. An annotated bibliography and literature guide may be useful for the readers who desire more detailed information on the elements of systemic planning that were beyond the scope of the present book.

16 Conclusions and Prospects

As we stated in the beginning of this book, we have attempted to bring together a variegated number of topics which we believe come under the umbrella of *systemic planning*. We propose that systemic planning is valuable both in theory and in application if it does no more than provide this umbrella, which has been missing until now. Theory and application which are generic enough to be of interest to a broad range of planners concerned with many of the topics covered in this book will allow for increased usefulness and relevancy for many of the tools of systemic planning as well as a basic way of thinking about the theory and application of planning.

We may be criticized as being more concerned with "hard" science than with "soft" science. We readily admit that the theory and application of systemic planning is more relevant to physical goals than to nonphysical goals. It may be argued that social science has not yet reached a stage at which systemic planning can be utilized as an effective tool for dealing with elusive, unordered, and nonconsensus goals such as those usually associated with social planning. For the present, systemic planning is applicable to physical planning problems and to problems of public budgeting; someday it may be useful for social planning.

Our major concern in this final chapter is to provide a summary of the conclusions that have been reached for the various topics covered. A few limited prospects for the short term and for the long term also will be offered. We do not want to conclude with sweeping generalizations. We would rather make some rather specific conclusions and prospects, and propose that many applications of all or some of the elements of systemic planning may hold great interest and efficacy for planners.

Theory

The entire first part of this book was devoted to a detailed formulation of the theoretical foundation for systemic planning. This was essential for the comprehension of the way in which the various elements of the theory fit into the system. We have also tried to elaborate on our notion that planning should be a systemic, or "system-like," process rather than a highly quantified and regularized process. This was essential lest we be accused of misleading the unwary by overselling a good product that has just been placed on the market and that has not received the extensive testing and use by consumers to allow for advocates to make extravagant claims. In accord with our compromise perspective of this theory, we prefer to think of its usefulness as being dependent upon the skill and insight with which practitioners make modifications to both the fundamentals and the details.

The Challenge

The process of systemic planning which has been sketched out is obviously general. It is the new generation of planners that must fill in the details and make such a process operational. This is not, however, an area in which this generation should immerse itself without first more fully developing its thinking. It may evolve that the impetus and research money will be found to make an outright transfer of systems analysis to planning. By all that is now known, however, it would seem that such an approach is doomed to failure.

Certain "inputs" must first be developed in order to adequately expand upon the notion of systemic planning. One of the most important of these inputs is the determination of just what the goals and objectives of the people in urban systems really are. This is an extraordinarily complex undertaking in itself, but assuming that it can be accomplished in the near future, then an attempt must be made to find some more appropriate definition of what "should be" in the urban system. If planners are to avoid the imposition of goals and objectives on the people they serve, then a fuller understanding of the actual and desirable goals and objectives must be developed.

Techniques also must be developed to enable a better quantification of the components of urban systems. Specifically, research of the type that has been achieved in connection with the transportation subsystem must now be undertaken for other subsystems. If models can be developed for trip ends, then perhaps these techniques can be applied to housing starts, recidivist identification, school needs, economic infrastructure, and so forth. This is not to say that success with transportation will guarantee success in other areas. However, this research should encourage others to struggle through the frustrating experiences that are likely to be encountered as the further application of these techniques is explored.

Another important methodological development is in the area of prediction. It is almost platitudinous to observe that planners project past trends into the future. Yet it must be recognized that there is no reason why many of these trends should or could continue. A prediction technique is needed which provides an understanding of the future, given varying assumptions as to trends and conditions. The operational problem is that once we leave the area of projecting past trends, we have no tools for predicting new trends — but we may have a fairly clear conception of what these trends could be.

A heavy burden must be borne by the planners of the new generation with respect to the ability to translate the complex process of systemic planning into something that decision-makers and the general public can comprehend. The employment of sophisticated tools of analysis is often criticized because the results are completely esoteric to the people who must use them for decisions. In addition, such tools of analysis often lead to a cleavage between the planners and the public, who view these efforts with great suspicion. These criticisms should not be taken lightly. The use of systems analysis has had its greatest success in areas where technicians prevailed in decision-making roles, and where there was seldom any requirement or need for public approval and understanding. This, obviously, is not the case with urban systems. It is not essential that decision-makers and the concerned public fully understand the procedures of systemic planning. The planner must be able, however, to translate the results of his analysis into terms that can be understood by the public.

Planners must create a rapport with the decision-makers before any attempt is made to apply systemic planning. Since decision-makers will be the major users of the analysis, it is important that they have a great deal of confidence in the people who will be executing the technical work. Thus, a relationship must be developed whereby the decision-maker can accept the results of the analysis with the assurance that it is valid without having to question it in detail.

These, then, are some of the challenges confronting the new generation of planners. They will be asked to apply scientific methods in areas which have been only peripherally scientific. It is clear that an overly zealous application of systems analysis does not hold the answer. But it is also clear that the more traditional approach to the planning process omits many of the benefits that could accrue from a "systems" approach. The kind of middle road that has been described herein would seem to be an adequate compromise which can be modified and reevaluated as further experience is gained in these matters.

Action Programs Model

It can be shown that systemic planning can be explained in terms of a cybernetic model. In essence, the conversion system is now responsible for making the decisions that will enable implementation of the planning. This is a proper sequence, since it is not within the realm of planning but is rather within that of the elected representatives of the public to enable this conversion of objectives into programs that are action oriented. Relating this model to the political system model, it can be seen that the demands of the public have been translated into planning objectives; but the supports for this translation must now come from the public if the conversion mechanism is to be effective and stable. Similarly, as the conversions are made, it is essential that feedback be generated and appropriate revisions made. This is the continuing nature of the systemic planning process. It can also be seen that this is the area in which direct public involvement in the planning process can be attained.

PPBS Systems

The second part of this book was concerned with the most widely known application of the systems approach to planning. Considerable time was spent with this matter because it is often assumed to be an entity of its own and not part of the systemic planning process that has been proposed. PPBS systems should be kept within the proper framework of systemic planning or there is a danger of developing a sophisticated implementation mechanism with little planning to be implemented.

The emphasis of the PPBS system approach is on its ability to provide increased and more valuable information. PPBS is a system for *aiding* decision-makers. The word "aiding" must be underscored to emphasize the very important point that PPBS systems is not a decision-making process, but is an instrument for providing decision-makers with a better basis in information and analysis upon which to make a decision. In the past, legislators, chief executives, and others concerned with budget allocations were forced to make decisions without adequate knowledge of the implications of alternatives. They relied on the traditions of log-rolling, pork-barreling, and incrementalism that resulted in ineffective use of very limited resources. Hopefully, the use of PPBS will permit more light to be shed on the costs and consequences of alternative courses of action, and will provide legislators and the chief executive the opportunity to make more rational decisions in resource allocation choices.

Program Analysis

As has been suggested, public budgeting procedures have undergone a number of significant changes since the twenties. These changes in procedures have been reflected, in part, in the functions and responsibilities assigned to the finance agency in any government jurisdiction. However, since many activities relating to governmental expenditures and revenue programs were delegated prior to the advent of these more comprehensive budgeting and related fiscal matters, many functions have been assigned earlier to other single-purpose agencies which continue to persist in the current structure of government. Thus, revenues may be collected by one agency, local fiscal controls exercised by another, audits conducted by a third, and budget-making assigned to a fourth agency. The budget-making process is further complicated by the various distinctions made between operating budgets and capital budgets, and by the wide range of agencies which may be involved in capital improvements programming.

The responsibilities for developing an effective budget must be shared by a number of individuals and groups within government. The chief executive, the legislative body, the various operating or line agencies, the finance agency and the planning agency — each play an important role in the decision-making process. "Each group attempts to look at the program as a whole and makes decisions about its parts. But, because of its particular function and position, each group sees the problem with a slightly different emphasis."[1]

As might be expected, for example, there is a tendency for operating departments to overemphasize the importance of their own project requests in the assignment of priorities. The finance agency, as the "watchdog" of expenditures, is primarily concerned with maximizing the returns from individual projects and achieving economies in the total program. Very often, this results in an emphasis being placed by the finance agency on the short-run implications of expenditure requests. The planning agency, in turn, must have a greater concern for the longer-range implications and the functional relationships among projects. Frequently, this requires that projections be made beyond the immediate needs in an effort to explore some of the more subtle ramifications of the individual project requests.

Ultimately, the decisions regarding expenditures and allocations of limited fiscal resources must rest with the chief executive and the legislative body. As the elected representatives of the people, these public officials must share a primary concern for the broader interests and welfare of their constituents. Here again, however, their particular functions and positions dictate that they place emphasis on different aspects of the budget. The chief executive must assume a position which emphasizes middle-range objectives, falling somewhere on the continuum between the short-range emphasis of the finance agency and the longer-range viewpoint of the planning agency. The chief executive also must pay particular attention to the political consequences of the decisions which are made concerning expenditures.

The legislative body also must take cognizance of the political implications of its decisions. In general, however, the concern of members of the legislative body tends to gravitate toward the more immediate objectives of the programs, placing particular emphasis on the cost factors involved. "The program is submitted to each of these groups in turn and, in theory, the successive applications of these slightly different points of view result in a program that is "balanced" for the common good of the community."[2] Of course, the drawbacks of this approach, in terms of the time required to carry out this process and in terms of the compromises which often are necessary, are obvious. As one student of government has put it: "Rome wasn't built in a day — but it would have taken a hell of a lot longer if the construction proposals had to go through our modern form of democratic government."

To circumvent the delays which often arise from this pluralistic approach, the budgeting phase of PPBS must be developed in a spirit of close coordination and cooperation among the various groups involved. Unfortunately, all too often these groups view one another as "adversaries" rather than as allies serving complementary functions.

Program Scheduling and Work Programming

We chose to emphasize one approach to program scheduling and work programming over other alternative methods. Our basic reason was that there is considerable experience and success with the critical path method (CPM) approach, which we believe is considerably enhanced and made more relevant to our purposes when used in conjunction with heuristic programming. There is the undeniable simplicity of the techniques which enhances their value even further. Despite what may seem like binding conclusions, the principal advantage of this approach is its flexibility. Once the critical path is determined, it can be altered at any time in order to accommodate operational problems or program changes that may arise during the actual project. Furthermore, in most cases these problems can be anticipated in advance, thereby minimizing the time lost through program adjustments.

With a relatively simple set of analytical devices, it is now possible to program governmental activities in order to minimize costs and thereby maximize the effective and efficient use of scarce resources. The critical path method technique essentially identifies maximum time and float time among sequentiated activities. Heuristic programming provides a convenient set of guidelines for modifying a given network in light of limited resources. These programs, however, are only a starting point for the range of programming techniques and cost analyses that can be undertaken.

Contrary to the often heard argument, there are no real impediments to the use of these techniques for a wide range of governmental activities because of an inability to identify costs and resources required for any given job or event. Nor are these techniques impeded by a lack of an end-product orientation. The critical path method and heuristic programming techniques, like many of the analytical techniques being developed, require a minimum amount of technical knowledge and programming skills. They rely primarily on the sincere efforts of the administrator to develop an accurate description of his agency's activities and objectives. There is no inherent reason why this combined approach cannot be applied to any level in the public or private sectors.

Physical Development Models

Part Three of this book was an examination of three models of physical development, and of the interesting tool of computer graphics for presentation of the output from models as well as other information relevant to systemic planning. One of our major concerns in this part was to demonstrate that some of the heady mathematics and theorems of the theory of systemic planning are practical in real-world situations. Case studies were chosen carefully to show where models had been developed and used for systemic planning purposes. This use was generally directed toward the evaluation of alternatives of planning for the physical environment, and to a certain extent for securing a basic understanding of the physical environment in order better to perform systemic planning.

The chapter on computer graphics may have appeared to some readers to be exotic in the context of the book. We hoped to demonstrate that graphics are an example of a proper use of computers in the systemic planning process and helpful to planners using the tools and methods of science. We did not want, and tried by all means to avoid, a book heavily oriented to information and computer science. There has been much written in these two areas, and we saw no need to expand upon the literature for our purposes. Thus, it can be concluded that computer graphics offer a good example of why the computer is little more than a speedy and efficient tool for systemic planning.

Computer Graphics

The relative merits of the various hardware and software mentioned can best be discussed in terms of three major criteria: applicability, cost, and availability. Graphic devices generally have not been developed with the planner and his needs in mind. Many of those devices which have been developed are still in the experimental stages, and they are relatively expensive. Finally, most of these experimental devices are available only in limited quantities.

Applicability. Devices which produce soft copy, namely, the cathode ray tube (CRT), have only limited applications in planning, except for those planning offices which do a considerable amount of site, location, and highway planning. Frequently, the cathode ray tube may be used very effectively with an information system as an output medium for particular data. In the larger planning offices that are developing an information system, or that have access to an existing system, the cathode ray tube type of graphic display may have considerable merit because of its capacity for instantaneous answers on the screen to computer queries (much like the cathode ray tube equipment used for airline reservations).

Devices that produce hard copy generally have a wider range of uses in a planning office. Those that can be used to produce computer-generated movies or perspective drawings are practical only for those planning offices engaged in a large volume of site planning work or those engaged in transportation planning.

The X-Y and table plotters are also somewhat limited in their usefulness. Planners who have requirements for considerable volumes of graphs and charts may find these devices very useful. However, the authors' experience with these devices indicates that the amount of programming needed to use them is beyond the capabilities of most planners, who have little or no experience with a computer. Further, the amount of programming work can be justified only where voluminous output is needed.

The standard line printer has considerable merit for many of the applications of graphics to planning. It is possible to produce usable graphs on the line printer, as well as maps of great readability. In many planning offices, the real need is to show trends and patterns of development and change. Therefore, the high precision of many of the other devices, such as the table plotter, is unwarranted. The line printer is precise enough to produce a map of sufficient quality for virtually all planning applications. It is completely adequate for use' as a tool in influencing decision-makers.

Cost. A second aspect of computer graphics equipment is their cost. Except for the line printer, all graphic devices involve costs in addition to those for the computer itself. Graphic devices, just like any machine, must be maintained. This may entail training a present employee or hiring a new one. It will involve a maintenance agreement with the vendor of the equipment. Therefore the decision to purchase new graphic equipment should be made only after a thorough investigation of *all* the added costs involved.

Recent years have witnessed the growth of computer software and time-sharing services. These services make it possible to use and program a computer without owning one or hiring programmers. This development has tended to lessen previous cost restraints for computer graphics. The authors have found, however, that there are few services which have the hardware or software facilities to provide computer graphics services. Those that are available, nonetheless, are very good, and they are priced reasonably.

Availability. A planner quite frequently will not have access to the latest and most sophisticated equipment for computer graphics. The usual case will be the situation in which the planning department will have access to the governmental data-processing computer. Therefore the ability to produce readable maps, using only the line printer with which all computers are equipped, may not only be the cheapest but also the only practicable media for the planner to avail himself of the advantages of computer graphics.

Aside from questions of practicality and cost, many of the devices mentioned will work only when supported by a particular machine or model. Therefore, the availability of computer time on a governmental data-processing machine may limit the range of devices available. Therefore the authors feel that unless a particular planning department has the technical expertise and the demonstrated need for sophisticated graphics devices, it should consider using the line printer as the graphic output medium.

The initial experience with computer graphics can be had at a relatively low cost when using the line printer, since the only additional outlay beyond that for computer time is for the programs themselves. In most cases, these costs are a fraction of the costs of the more advanced graphical devices (Symap is available for about $500.00, for example, and a table plotter may easily cost ten times that much). Finally, the quality of output available from the line printer is adequate for most planning agencies.

Urban Form Model

The basic conclusion to be derived from the discussion of the Urban Form Model is that this a priori analytical approach to studying the interrelationships among urban functions, spatial organization, and environmental form has met with a fair degree of success for the first run. If nothing else, it is a way of analytically showing that these interrelationships do exist and that one can begin to make them explicit. It is clear that this is only a beginning, and many aspects of the simulation need improvement.

The simulation must be subjected to a more rigorous testing than has been possible. Data collection and sources need improvement, and several urban areas which fulfill the constraints should be examined. There should also be an index to determine the quality of the environment in a cell, but it should probably be kept distinct from the environmental form index, and accounted for in a different column. Even in an analog model, the quality index, if developed, should be expressed in a manner that distinguished it from the quantitative indices. There is also some value in using smaller parts of the square-mile grid, that is, a sixteenth, which will enable greater detail and understanding. The computer can greatly facilitate a solution to this problem. And finally, research should be directed to improving the relationships that go into the open-space and cultural-form indices — or perhaps an examination of the necessity for including these urban functions as separate elements should be undertaken.

This approach is a beginning that merits further refinement and improvement. It is not a grandiose scheme for improving the urban ills of the world, nor is it an attempt conclusively to automate or make explicit the study of urban functions, organization, and form. It should be viewed solely as a tool that may be useful to planners in dealing with the complex decision problems of urban areas. It is essentially a basis by which a planner can generate environmental form and then analyze it in both an objective and a subjective manner. This leads to some long-range possiblilities for use of this approach in planning.

With the improvements in computer hardware, software, and visual (off-line and on-line) devices, the entire series of interrelationships could be placed in computer storage, allowing for an on-going simulation. This would enable a planner to evaluate environmental form, or any individual form index, for past, present, and future implications. For example, by solely using the projected population of the cells under analysis, the computer could generate the environmental form of each cell, either numerically or through output on visual devices.

This has potential for the evaluation of change in a planning area. For example, by storing the present simulation in memory, problems can be posed to the computer. An example might be: Given the present environmental form simulation, simulate the following X cells after a freeway is routed through cells x_i. Or, analogously, generate the environmental form of x_i cells if a major residential development is created in cell x_i. These problems can be based on the population variable, or on any key variable that is made explicit in the interrelationships. The computer will then generate the effect of the proposed changes and produce output. This output could be a printout of cell indices, or an analog model such as a map, or possibly a block model through the use of cathode ray tubes. The potentials are quite interesting, and they are limited only by the imagination.

Empiric Programming Model

Using such techniques as the Empiric programming model in the systemic planning process, the input of alternative policy decisions can be analyzed, tested, and evaluated in terms of a set of desired goals and objectives, thus enabling the presentation of a series of clear-cut public-policy choices to decision-makers together with the implications of each. The systemic planning process does not apply *strict* optimization techniques, nor does it restrict freedom of choice. Rather, it attempts to make planning a more meaningful procedure by evaluating the likely functional or performance characteristics to be derived from alternative policies, plans, and programs.

New-Town Housing Model

Four models of new-town housing situations have been presented. The determination of which of these models is most appropriate can be made only in the face of a given development objective. The planner may wish to know which types of families should be attracted, to minimize vacancies and overdemand; he may wish to find what types of houses to build for a fixed distribution of incoming population; or he may wish to know the minimum number of houses to build. All of these situations are possible and, perhaps, probable. Therefore, each has been given a separate and detailed analysis. The application of these models will provide the planners, developers, and managers with significant information upon which to base critical decisions regarding the development phasing of large-scale residential areas.

Environment for Planning

The entire fourth part of this book is a confrontation between theory and the real-world commitment, trust, and effectiveness of planning. The perspective is largely focused on how cities behave with respect to their planning functions. This is most valuable research, in our opinion. It not only gives our theory a real-world set of constraints, but it also gives insights on certain matters that must be improved if the environment for planning is to be adequate. By way of an apologia, the results of our findings also point out the major failings of urban and regional planning in American cities in its present form.

Structural and Contextual Factors

A basic conclusion to be drawn from the analysis of structural and contextual factors is that industrial cities frequently lack an adequate base of support for planning either from the general citizenry (which is often predominately blue-collar in composition) or from the business community (which has a higher percentage of large firms relative to nonindustrial cities). Thus, although the problems facing industrial cities may require comprehensive planning in order to reach effective solutions, this lack of public support results in a lower level of planning commitment in many cases.

This lower level of planning commitment among industrial cities is also reflected in the data concerning the commitment to planning among older cities. Although 68 percent of those cities having reached 50,000 population prior to 1900 are in the industrial category, only 40 percent of these older industrial cities have a strong planning commitment. Similarly, industrial cities with relatively high percentages of nonwhite population manifest a lower frequency of commitment to planning than nonindustrial cities.

Finally, it would appear that cities with a city manager form of government and a high percentage of white-collar workers in their population are likely to have a higher level of commitment to more progressive governmental programs (and in this sense have a greater commitment to community growth and expansion), and therefore a higher commitment to the planning process. These findings would seem to follow from the assumption, suggested in much of the literature of political science, that the adoption of a city manager form of government is indicative of a greater reliance on professionals in the operations of local government. In the absence of a city manager form of government, cities with higher per capita number of full-time employees are more likely to have a higher level of commitment to planning. This would seem also to follow from the concept of professionalism in government.

If the notion is accepted that persons with white-collar occupations are more likely to participate in various civic and governmental affairs (as a result of their higher socioeconomic status), it would follow that such cities should manifest a greater awareness of the need for (and therefore, commitment to) planning and other related programs. The combined effects of higher percentage of white-collar occupations and the city manager form of government can be clearly illustrated by the data obtained in our research.

As many of the current writings in the fields of political sociology and public administration have suggested, citizen participation and interest in governmental affairs often decline as governments become more bureaucratic and professional. If this is the case, then these two factors would appear to be countervailing forces, the implications of which will have an important bearing on the success of any governmental program which relies on public participation and support.

In the context of modern public service, surrounded by potential citizen interest and participation, the professional in government is often faced with the problem of making the distinction between the professional's role of establishing goal directives and his role of assisting decision-makers through the rational application of the techniques of his profession. In a survey by Rabinovitz and Pottinger reported upon in the *AIP Journal*,[3] 71 percent of the 201 planning directors responding to a questionnaire stated that they purposely integrate policy advice and value judgements with their technical recommendations, while only 4.5 percent maintained that planning is strictly a technical function with regard to governmental decision-making. Such an overwhelmingly weighted response is in keeping with the training which most professionals receive in preparing for public service.

The neophyte professional, while in the university, is led to respect the traditional independent goals and honorific images of professional life — the ideal of independent public service, ruled only by the practitioner's inner authority or ethics. After he is employed, however, he soon discovers that goals, practices, and everyday demands are established by "nonprofessionals" within an institutional and political framework. As Professor Herbert Gamberg has observed, "The conflict of independent decision and dependent position, of power of knowledge and the authority of those without knowledge, of the ideal of self-sufficiency and the actuality of interdependence is a major source of tension in modern professional life."[4]

Many writers have criticized the public policy-making process, suggesting that its specialized, fragmented, and piecemeal aspects result in a lack of coordination and a neglect of important consequences. It is frequently suggested that as a result, most public decisions are made incrementally, through compromise or "mutual adjustment," and without the benefit of coordination and planning. More recently there has been a growing coterie of writers who, rather than decrying this lack of comprehensiveness as many of their colleagues have done, assert that the current practices serve government and the public fairly well. These writers maintain that those aspects that the critics propose to alter are precisely the devices that make the process work with an acceptable degree of rationality and self-correcting feedback. It may be suggested, however, that these writers, by focusing their analysis at the point where decisions are "legitimated," have overlooked the important role of the professional in governmental decision-making. Such studies tend to ignore the lower portion of the decision-making "iceberg," where much of the coordination and comprehensiveness which they find lacking in the system is actually achieved.

The middle-sized city offers the professional a particularly ambiguous base of operations, however. In most cases, one finds a genuine antagonism and mistrust toward outside experts and "intellects," and a faith only in homegrown officials without "fancy" educations and ideas. Paradoxically, because of frequent citizen apathy to public issues, the middle-sized city also can be quite amenable to the innovations of those professionals who define their roles politically and who are not easily frustrated by the long-term patience and perseverence necessary to prepare a conservative system for change. As Professor Gamberg has suggested, the professional who is content to do relatively little behind a smokescreen of expertise can usually have an easy tenure in middle-sized cities. The conflict in professional ideology between bureaucratic security and political involvement can be easily resolved in favor of the former, and in the absence of vigorous community and political leadership, the professional in such cities can become an entrenched bureaucrat without even the problem of taking orders.

However, city planning is a notoriously mobile profession. Advancement is usually accompanied by a change in location. Under such conditions, it is often difficult for the planner to establish the necessary rapport with other governmental officials, both civil and elected, and with the general public to bring about this change. The problem is further complicated by the fact that city managers, who can serve as important components in the planner's link with other governmental agencies (as the findings of this study have suggested), also are something of a band of "educated gypsies," frequently using their records in smaller communities to secure more lucrative positions in larger municipalities.[5]

The findings of this phase of research may be viewed in terms of a typology of political culture, having as its major dimensions (1) "professionalism" in government and (2) citizen participation in public affairs. Cities with a professional-participant form of political culture are most likely to have a relatively high level of planning commitment. Cities having a nonprofessional-participant political culture, on the other hand, also frequently have a high level of planning commitment, but this commitment is often short lived and relatively unstable. Cities with professional-nonparticipant forms of political culture may be able to develop technically competent plans, but without public support such plans are not likely to be implemented with any degree of success. Finally, cities which have a nonprofessional-nonparticipant form of political culture are likely to have a relatively low level of planning commitment or no commitment to the planning process at all.

Functional and Situational Factors

To summarize the conclusions drawn from this phase of the analysis, it would appear that the success of any planning effort is highly dependent upon a continuity of concepts and personnel (input factors). The fact that the directorship of the planning agency has changed hands since the comprehensive plan was completed may have little bearing on planning achievement. The length of service of the planning director, however, does seem to be of importance, as does the currency of officially adopted elements of the plan, including subsequent revisions. A larger planning staff, with a relatively high degree of professionalism, contributes to a higher level of planning commitment in two ways: (1) by increasing the likelihood that the plan and subsequent revisions will be prepared within the framework of local "expectations"; and (2) by increasing the points of contact between the planning agency and other public officials and agencies. These factors, taken together, increase the "sustaining power" of the original plan.

The conceptual character of the comprehensive plan seems to have little effect on the performance of the planning agency or the resulting level of planning commitment. A critical stage is reached in the level of planning commitment when the planning agency achieves a direct involvement in studies which have a direct input into the decision-making process. Of particular importance in this regard is agency participation in fiscal management activities.

These input factors and performance factors can be related to the general character of a planning agency's approach to the decision-making process. A planning agency that has a continuity of concepts and personnel is characterized by a high level of achievement in the areas of problem identification, innovation of alternative solutions, and design and implementation of programs to carry out public decisions. At the other extreme, an agency with a low level of continuity (continual turnover of personnel and parallel changes in planning concepts) and with limited participation in decision-making is confronted with the need to build a constituency that will be responsive to planning recommendations.

Between these two extremes are two other characteristic approaches. The first is the bureaucratic approach, in which concepts and personnel have relatively long-term continuity, but where members of the agency are content to remain in the background, secure in their position as technical experts and program administrators. In such instances, the approach is not to "rock the boat" by seeking more direct involvement in policy issues. As Parker and Daland observed in their study of planning strategies in the Piedmont area of North Carolina, "Where the planner's acceptance as a policy advisor is low, he has tended to avoid controversy and assumes the role of provider of technical information to decision makers. Where it is strong, he has undertaken commitments to particular solutions of current problems within whatever area of freedom the managers and planning commissions allow.[6]

The second approach might be termed the political-activist approach. This role for the planner has been suggested by the writings of various political scientists. Thus, Francine Rabinovitz asserts that ". . . only if the profession's image includes the picture of the planner as rightfully a political actor will the planner attain both professional rewards and the completion of concrete programs."[7]

Fundamental to this approach is a direct involvement of the planner in policy issues as a political confident to the chief executive and/or city council. Setting aside the question as to how this status is to be achieved, there are certain dangers inherent in this approach. As a result of this more intimate involvement, key personnel changes often accompany changes in political leadership; this, in turn, leads to a lack of continuity in planning concepts. Therefore the fundamental input factors necessary to achieve a high level of planning commitment are often lacking.

Communication

Although the data presented in this phase of the analysis are far from conclusive, some rather interesting findings can be noted with regard to the characteristic patterns of communication at the various levels of planning commitment. Perhaps first and foremost, this analysis lends support to the professional-participation typology suggested in the discussion of structural and contextural factors. The city manager, the budget director, and the public works director — positions frequently occupied by professionals — all provide important channels of communication for the city planner. These multiple channels of communication are most evident at the higher level of planning commitment. In the absence of these positions, the planner's task of becoming "established" in the hierarchy of government is a much more difficult one.

These data tend to support the primary hypothesis that there are measurable differences in the patterns of communication at each of the three levels of planning commitment. In cities with high commitment scores, for example, there is a greater frequency of communication between the planning and development sectors and between the planning staff and agencies in the planning support sector (with the exception of the planning commission). In cities with medium and low levels of planning commitment, there is an increased frequency of communication with the policy-formulation sector, and in particular with the office of the mayor. However, there is evidence to suggest that this communication is unidirectional, often originating with the planning director in an effort to establish his agency in the functional activities of city government.

There is relatively little evidence to support the corollary that the more effective planners are as communication intermediaries, the greater the likelihood of planning achievement. As has been noted, however, planners in cities with a high level of planning commitment do have more frequent contacts with other agencies in the planning support sector and in the development sector. The data also point up the fact that in cities with lower levels of planning commitment, the planning commission often uses other channels of communication, for example, the zoning officer and the city engineer, in their dealings with the policy-formulation sector.

Finally, it is important to note the differences in terms of the officials who provide coordination among the various sectors in local government. The city manager, the public works director, and the chief finance officer play a central role in cities with high commitment scores. In cities with medium levels of commitment, this role is frequently assumed by the public works director or the city engineer, while in cities with low commitment scores, the city clerk often serves in this coordinative role.

The Decision-Making Process

At the conclusion of his recent book, *The City Planning Process — A Political Analysis,* Alan Altshuler asserts: ". . . American city planners tend to have their horizons limited almost entirely by contemporary American practice and short-term estimates of political feasibility . . . when they do report historic and contemporary examples of "good" civic design, they tend to neglect analysis of the cultural, political, and economic factors which produced them. Until a serious effort is made to remove these blinders, the imagination of the American planning profession is bound to be severely confined, its perception of political opportunities and obstacles is bound to be quite shallow, and (probably most important) its sense of the difficulty of truly comprehensive evaluation — at the politician's level — is bound to remain rudimentary."[8]

With the passage of the Federal Housing Act in 1954, planning and its close kin, urban renewal and public housing, were elevated into the public-issue arena. Since that time, planning has provided fresh fodder for the political scientist and other disciplines concerned with the public decision-making process. A recent article by Rabinovitz has provided a concise summary of the basic tenets advanced by the majority of these studies: ". . . only if the profession's image includes the picture of the planner as rightfully a political actor will the planner attain both professional rewards and the completion of concrete programs." Until it casts off the "myth of apolitical action," planning is doomed to continue to be "an occupation in the process of attempting to be professionalized" — "a function in search of an identity."[9] Or so Dr. Rabinovitz and other writers would have us believe.

The authors are in complete agreement with the assertion that the planning profession must achieve a greater awareness of the political process. Plans are policies, and the making of policies in a democratic society must be equated with the political process. "That plans should be policies, political programs critically, self-consciously, understood as such and debated as such, will be clear gain for local democracy."[10] But the question remains: To what extent must the planner (or any professional in government) assume the mantle of the politician in order to effectively carry out his professional responsibilities?

The easy solution is to say, "If you can't beat them, join them." And undoubtedly professionals in government must begin to assume a more active "political" role. But this must not be the political role of compromise, of "incrementalism," and of maintaining the status quo which often characterizes a "good" politician. The role of the professional in government must continue to be to broaden the horizons of political and public concern by making the city aware of its problems and potentials. The scope of information and contacts available to the professional makes him particularly capable of serving in this capacity. If this means that he must, under certain circumstances, take the initiative and assume a more politically active role, then so be it. In striving to achieve his objectives of a fuller understanding and support for his proposals, however, the professional must not allow himself to become trapped by the politician's dilemma of trying to satisfy everyone, and thereby serving no one.

Planning Commitment and the
Model of Public Decision-Making

From the empirical evidence advanced in this and many other studies, it would seem apparent that the process of public decision-making seldom operates in reality in the manner outlined in the normative model presented in Chapter 15. There is evidence to suggest, however, that the systemic planning process can serve as a major contributor to the achievement of more rational decision-making. One of the primary functions of the systemic planning process is to increase or maintain the urban system's level of adaptation or adjustment to its environment. To achieve this, planning must serve as a *regulator* by striving to transform the competitive advantages of any problem situation into those states which are compatible to the stability of the urban system, while protecting the system from all incompatible or dysfunctional states by transforming them to neutral or functional states.

The maintenance of stability in the total system is dependent, however, upon the stability of the appropriate set of functions which serve in a regulatory capacity.[11] Thus, planning can serve most effectively as a regulatory device when it functions in a state of stable equilibrium. That is to say, if the planning function is undergoing continual changes as the planners try to "find themselves" (i.e., try to find their appropriate role in the operations of government), then planning is likely to operate less effectively as a regulator.

The findings of the empirical analysis would suggest that in cities with high levels of planning commitment, the planning function comes closest to approximating the role envisioned in the normative model. With a relatively high frequency, planners in cities with high commitment scores have a major responsibility for the identification of problems — the planning process serves as an important screening device in determining which decision demands are to be converted from *inputs* to *intakes.* Planners in these cities also serve an important role in the classification and definition of problem situations and in the establishment of boundary conditions. This phase of the public decision-making process is perhaps the least developed and most neglected. In the private sector, the establishment of constraints has achieved a fairly high level of sophistication, especially through the application of operation research techniques. It is in this area that the need for basic research in the public sector is most urgent.

The development of alternative courses of action or alternative solutions is the keystone of the systemic planning process. Here again, recognition of this function is most evident in cities with high planning commitment scores. The parallel activity of identifying goals and objectives and exploring existing policies as they might relate to these goals and objectives is less highly developed as a responsibility of planners.

The recommendation of a "best" solution or course of action also is most frequently recognized as a planning responsibility in cities with high levels of planning commitment. The divergency of responses between planning directors and chief executives in cities with medium commitment scores is important to reiterate. On the basis of this relatively limited data, it can be suggested that the expectations of chief executives in terms of these activities are not being met fully in cities with medium planning commitment.

The role of the planning agency in determining the action programs necessary to carry out decisions clearly differentiates between cities with high and medium planning commitments. This finding would indicate that a greater responsibility for the implementation of decisions accompanies a higher commitment to the planning process on the part of elected officials. Or conversely, planning agencies in cities with low and medium commitment scores have not achieved the status in the organizational structure of local government where they are called upon to develop programs necessary to carry out public decisions.

Finally, the continual monitoring of programs to determine the effectiveness of their performance is another area in which further research and development is required. The formulation of monitoring procedures would seem to be of particular importance in long-range planning, where changes in the problem situation can have far-reaching implications for the recommended solution.

Planning practitioners continually are faced with the dilemma of seeking to influence public policy without getting involved politically — of retaining the prestige of the technical expert, while at the same time, hoping to affect the course of public affairs through the political arena. This attitude, in part a product of the planner's professional training and the traditions that have grown up as the profession has struggled for its identity, produce a somewhat unstable set of conditions. This instability, in turn, reduces the effectiveness of planning as a regulatory device. There is a growing awareness that planning must involve more than the mere execution of decisions handed down from policy-making bodies. At the same time, planners have been unable to reconcile completely the degree of involvement in the political process necessary to make their activities more effective.

Prospects

We do not feel that it is necessary or useful to conclude this volume with pleas for the adaption and adoption of systemic planning theory and methods. Nor do we believe that it is desirable to offer promises to planners that systemic planning is a panacea or even an approach that will make their lives somewhat easier. We can only conclude on two notes. The first is that systemic planning is an interesting and innovative approach that merits consideration and application by planners of various ilks and preferences. Second, we would like to make several predictions of the likelihood of application of systemic planning in the short-term and in the long-term future.

The Short Term

For the short term, probably lasting no more than the next ten years, we foresee some extensive testing and development of scientific methods in urban and regional planning, and perhaps a merging of the various other types of planning such as corporate, military, and public, and even programming such as facilities production, tactics, and sales into a comprehensive form that will very likely take on many of the characteristics of systemic planning as discussed in this book.

The initial efforts, which already have begun in this country, will most likely be concerned with the settling of professional differences between classical planners, such as architects, city planners, engineers, and public administrators and the new breed of planners such as systems analysts, operations researchers, mathematicians, computer scientists, and social scientists. The most probable approach will be the highly rated interdisciplinary team, an idea which has emerged from interdisciplinary research and education programs in the universities. The interdisciplinary team utilizes the talents and skills of the many professions and fields that have something to offer to planning. The question of who leads the team is almost moot since the answer is the person with the best leadership qualities and understanding of the problems regardless of any other consideration. Planners who cannot accept the concept that no one person has an exclusive right or hold on the domain of planning are likely to find quickly that they are somewhat irrelevant.

Further efforts by professional craft guilds and special interest groups of state legislatures that attempt to pass rules and regulations saying that one group is to be given hold of the planning turf are archaic and most likely to be overruled, if not by institutions then by society. In fact, in our experience we have found that the sophisticated planners and members of the new and next generation not only welcome the interdisciplinary team approach but actively seek to encourage the practice. The interdisciplinary team approach will gain in popularity in the next few years, being adequately funded by such groups as the federal government, big business, and state and local governments, and it will become an established approach to planning, especially urban and regional planning. These developments will open the door to full testing of systemic planning concepts.

An extensive research and development effort can be expected in the short term for models, tools, techniques, and methods that will be useful for systemic planning. Current models are only first generation and little more than crude attempts to predict somewhat obvious developments. More and more attention will have to be paid to the development of better analytical tools to allow planners to test many possible futures and not simply those which are obvious. Analytical tools must also deal more with the nonquantitative factors of systems, since as we have repeatedly pointed out, there are few aspects of environmental systems that are quantitative, and most factors are based on such highly qualitative variables as human preferences, tastes, desires, and behavior. There is much to indicate that this thrust in research and development of analytical tools has already begun.

Basic mathematics, statistics, and data processing will most likely be improved to such an extent that analytical tools for planning will benefit. There are certain types of models that can be formulated today, but these models cannot be solved. Many types of mathematical programming models with nonlinear and dynamic relationships cannot be solved with today's mathematical knowledge. Perhaps it is true that scientific knowledge and technology have surpassed our abilities to utilize them, but there are clearly areas where the basic knowledge is inadequate for dealing with public planning problems. We would be remiss, further, if we did not add that the short-term advances in computer technology and software will certainly give further impetus to scientific and systems inputs to planning, since these advances can be regarded as the surrogate mothers of invention for better analytical tools and techniques for scientific endeavors in all fields.

Another perspective on the short-term future prospects for systemic planning is somewhat less precise. To be specific, we will have to enunciate better the goals and objectives that will lead us to a more complete understanding of what a good system is or can be. The generic objective of systemic planning is concerned with the optimization of systems, improving them to the highest potentials. Yet, for such systems as cities, very little, if anything, is known about what makes them good and not so good. It would be simple to say that the determination of a better definition of "good" systems depends on research, but there is much more to this task when human behavior acts as an intervening variable in both the systems themselves and in the environments in which systems must function. The task of determining what are good systems is bound up with the task of discovering what human drives, ambitions, hopes, and aspirations are basic and then, through planning, assuring that these goals can be attained within urban systems.

One further short-term prospect that is likely will be a wide acceptance of the scientific and systems approaches to planning. There are already signs that elected and appointed officials, professionals, and the general public, where it is interested in these matters, are impressed with the potential of the systems approach in planning. We cannot say that these people have been fully convinced, as of the present, but the job of education that is going on is formidable. Further, the early application of the systems approach to aerospace, military, and corporate planning leaves much to be desired in terms of a feeling of accomplishment by professionals working in these areas, and they will seek to extend its applications to more human, satisfying goals.

The Long Term

For the long term, or let us say by that magic year 2000, the approach of systemic planning may well be fully interwoven into the structure of public and private organizations. The very structures themselves will have been changed, to some degree, by the systems approach to planning. All omens that we have uncovered, and all seers and oracles we have consulted, lead us to reach the same conclusion: there will be much more systemic planning, not less. In the long term, the danger could be that systemic planning will be so institutionalized that it will be a battle to dislodge it for replacement by some higher, if still unknown, form of planning.

There are some long-term prospects for decision-making that merit our foremost concern and attention for the future. The major long-term issue becomes that of how far we should go with systemic planning or similar approaches to planning. At its ultimate, systemic planning could result in an automated planning function in the public and private sectors at the expense of the intuitive and judgmental qualities of leaders and decision-makers — the automated planning system, in the ultimate, might overrule the leadership. Is this an artificial issue or a self-fulfilling prophecy? We cannot answer that question, but we readily admit that, as most other people working in these areas, we have not devoted sufficient time and concern with such ultimate problems that surround any new methodology. Either our colleagues will have to be mustered around this issue or such disinterested fields as philosophy will have to be persuaded to take up the charge.

The ultimate form of systemic planning could be an automated planning system which is conservative and rather uninteresting. The ultimate of efficiency in planning would be so regularized and mechanized that most intellectuals would be uninterested in it as either a profession or a field of study — in fact, whether or not the system could eliminate the need for planners is an intriguing question. The system is more likely to be conservative than liberal in its automated direction. Liberal policies and decisions are rarely optimal or minimal — they are more likely to be maximal or utopian. Automation itself, as well as many forms of planning, are the antithesis of socialist theory, whereas most conservative theory, while not advocating planning, makes adequate leeway for it. Existentialists, we might add, are more likely to be liberals than conservatives. Thus, there is the danger in the long run that automated planning systems could exclude a full consideration of the ideology and philosophies of those of a liberal bent. This could mean conservative and highly efficient planning that is in reality quite sterile and unexciting.

A major confrontation between liberals and existentialists and conservatives and pragmatists may be expected in the future over such matters as systemic planning if the means (systemic planning) are allowed to become more important than the ends (an optimal environment that cannot yet be described fully). Our preference is for some sort of compromise solution, which is the basic tenet of our theory, so that systemic planning does not become an automated function, and decision-making continues to include the judgmental and intuitive. This is the stuff of human behavior and satisfaction, and we would not want to be any part of any effort to change that.

Several other factors, if not quite as heady as the above matters, merit consideration. Planning-programming-budgeting-scheduling systems, in our crystal ball, will be the major substantive achievement of the systems approach in the future. We do not believe that PPBS systems are a short-lived fad. We believe that they will become an everyday part of government and, very likely, long before the year 2000. The basic reason is that PPBS systems have output which is quite visible every day, quarter, year, and programming period. Politicians, voters, officers, and stockholders will all look at these results. If PPBS systems can achieve even minor advances in the next few years, their future existence is virtually guaranteed. Yet, we must issue our warning, once again, that PPBS systems are only the administrative and implementing mechanisms of systemic planning, or of any other planning process. To build sophisticated administrative and implementing mechanisms such as PPBS systems to carry forth inexact and suboptimal planning is similar to constructing an elaborate mining operation to gather copper pyrites for making gold jewelry — the operation may work well and even look good, but the profits will be small and the customers will know, sooner or later, that they are buying fool's gold.

Technology will also have a profound effect on the long-term evolution of systemic planning. Greater advances in technology related to automation can be expected which will probably occur at a rate faster than that of the discovery of new knowledge. A penchant for gadgetry that already is with us can be expected to continue, and perhaps to become somewhat extreme. We are concerned about this possible eventuality, but we are not alarmed. We really see little harm in building machines to do systemic planning at supernatural speeds as long as systemic planners retain the dominant decision-making authority to overrule machines at any time they believe they are justified on the basis of professional judgment and knowledge. We welcome, as do most of our colleagues, machines that economically perform mundane functions and leave planners with more substantial work — we too are attracted by big information system machinery and automated graphics, presentations, and problem-solving. Yet we demand that the machinery never reach a state of full automation in systemic planning.

Our last concern for the long term is that efforts be launched to ensure that the exotica and ebullition of systemic planning is not misconstrued to mean that planners must be less concerned with the values — which are more and more becoming demands — of the various groups in urban society, be they white or black, rich or poor, young or old, wise or unwise. Systemic planning can never, nor is it intended ever, to replace participation in the planning process.

It may seem trite, to say so, but planning is *for* people. One may say even that planning is *with* people if it is to be of any value. All those who seek to set up special towers from which they hope to control and plan the environment will quickly find the tower under siege and crumbling. Planners who want to be left alone to do planning are hopelessly out of touch with reality. If it seems as though we are saying that it is best to be an erudite systemic planner with a profound sense of human passion and concern; and it seems that we are asking a permanent paradox to be institutionalized; and if this all seems to make planning most difficult (and planners will likely find a longer work week while factory hands work less); then the reader has mastered much of our ideology. For the timid, we can offer little solace other than to say that we have told it like it is, and that systemic planning should be where it's at.

Retrospect

Scientific methods in city planning have been a fact for fewer than fifteen years. The Detroit Area Traffic Study (1954) was probably the first effort in city planning to implement a systems approach with mathematical modeling. Since that time until the present we can find no real instances of what we would call a smashing success in this effort. The only successes — if we can use that term vaguely and loosely — have been in certain areas of city planning that are relatively inflexible, such as transportation planning. Certainly there has been no evidence to date that the systems approach has been worth its cost in city planning. We believe, nonetheless, that a hybrid approach, such as systemic planning, will be successful in the long-term future.

It was perhaps presumptuous of us to develop a hybrid theory along with its jargon and techniques at so early a stage in the game. There are those who would argue that this book should have been written after the scientific and systems approaches to planning have been evaluated more fully, perhaps, in ten more years. We rejected this notion not as being unsound but as being too timid. There was no body of information on such matters as we have covered in this book, and we foresaw continued confusion unless there was some source of synthesis which educators and practitioners could embrace or deny, depending on their various dispositions. In retrospect, we firmly believe that there is justification in publishing a book on a new theory which has received some testing but is still in its embryonic state.

Notes

Notes

Chapter 1

1. Robert A. Walker, *The Planning Function in Urban Government* (Chicago: University of Chicago Press, 2nd Ed., 1950).

2. Charles Hitch, in *Analysis for Military Decisions,* ed. E. S. Quade (Chicago: Rand McNally, 1964), pp. 13—14.

3. G. H. Fisher, "The Analytical Bases of Systems Analysis," a talk presented at a symposium on "Systems Analysis in Decision-Making" sponsored by the Electronics Industries Association, Washington, D. C., June 23, 1966.

4. Peter F. Drucker, "The Effective Decision," *Harvard Business Review* Vol. 45 (January—February 1967), 92.

5. Peter F. Drucker, *The Practice of Management* (New York: Harper, 1954), p. 353.

6. Anatol Rapoport, "What Is Information?" *ETC: A Review of General Semantics,* 10 (Summer 1953), 252.

7. The concept of *equifinality* first was introduced by the noted biologist, Ludwig von Bertalanffy, in "Der Organismus als physikalisches System betrachtet," *Naturwissenschaften,* 28 (1940), 521.

8. Dagobert D. Runes, *Dictionary of Philosophy* (New York: Philosophical Library, 1960), p. 21.

9. *Threshold of Planning Information Systems,* selected papers from the ADP workshop conducted at the ASPO National Planning Conference, Houston, April 1967, p. 65.

10. Fisher, "Analytical Bases of Systems Analysis."

11. Wilbur A. Steger, "Urban Systems Simulation Flow Chart," *Journal of the American Institute of Planners,* 30 (May 1965), 145.

12. Roy F. Kenzie, "Urban Systems Methodology: Development to Data," a paper presented at Virginia Polytechnic Institute, June 8, 1969.

13. H. F. Swinburne, "Theoretical Model of the Architectural Process," *Journal of the American Institute of Architects* 47 (May 1967), 88—89.

14. As cited in W. S. Fowler, *The Development of the Scientific Method* (New York: Macmillan, 1964).

Chapter 2

1. Richard C. Snyder, "A Decision-Making Approach to the Study of Political Phenomena," in *Approaches to the Study of Politics,* ed. Roland Young (Evanston: Northwestern University Press, 1958), p.5.

2. See, for example, Chicago Area Transportation Study, *Final Reports,* Volumes 2 and 3 (Chicago: Chicago Area Transportation Study, 1962).

3. Britton Harris, "Plan or Projection: An Examination of the Use of Models in Planning," *Journal of the American Institute of Planners,* 27 (November 1960), 265—272.

4. Britton Harris, "The Limits of Science and Humanism in Planning,"

Journal of the American Institute of Planners, 32 (September 1967), 324-335.
   5. *Ibid.,* p. 326.

Chapter 3

1. Russell L. Ackoff, "The Development of Operations Research as a Science," *Operations Research,* 4 (June 1956), 265.
   2. Ackoff, *Operations Research,* p. 267.
   3. Ackoff, *Operations Research,* p. 287.
   4. Ackoff, *Operations Research,* p. 287.

Chapter 4

1. Norbert Wiener, *The Human Use of Human Beings* (New York: Doubleday Anchor Books, 1954), p. 17.
   2. David A. Easton, *A Systems Analysis of Political Life* (New York: Wiley, 1965), p. 21.
   3. Easton, *Systems Analysis of Political Life,* p. 28.

Chapter 5

1. John F. Cotton and Harry P. Hatry, *Program Planning for State, County, City* (Washington, D. C.: State-Local Finances Project, George Washington University, 1967), p.3.
   2. Frederick C. Mosher, *Program Budgeting* (Chicago: Public Administration Service, 1964), p. 5.
   3. David A. Page, "The Federal PPBS," *Journal of the American Institute of Planners* Vol. 33 (July, 1967), p. 257.
   4. David Novick, "Origin and History of Program Budgeting," transcript of talk filmed on August 11, 1966 for short course sponsored by the U. S. Bureau of the Budget and the U. S. Civil Service Commission on PPBS.
   5. Alan Walter Steiss, *A Framework for Planning in State Government* (Chicago: The Council of State Governments, 1968), p. 55.
   6. Novick, "Origin and History of Program Budgeting."
   7. Brian Herman and Selma Mushkin, *The Search for Alternatives: Program Options in a PPB System* (Washington, D. C.: State-Local Finances Project, George Washington University, 1967), p. 3.
   8. Daniel Alesch, "Government in Evolution: A Real World Focus for State Planning," *Public Administration Review,* Vol. 29 (May-June 1968) 264—267.
   9. U. S. Congress, Senate Subcommittee on Economy in Government of the Joint Economic Committee, *Hearings, The Planning, Programming Budgeting*

System: Progress and Potentials, 90th Cong. 1st Sess. (Washington, D. C.: U. S. Government Printing Office, 1966), p. 196.

10. Alesch, *Public Administration Review.*

11. Mosher, *Program Budgeting,* pp. 47–48.

12. Aaron Wildavsky, *The Politics of the Public Budgetary Process* (Boston: Little, Brown, 1964).

Chapter 6

1. Herbert A. Simon, *Administrative Behavior — A Study of Decision-Making in Administrative Organization* (New York: The Free Press, 1957).

2. Arthur Smithies, "Conceptual Framework for the Program Budget," in *Program Budgeting: Program Analysis and the Federal Budget,* ed. David Novick (Santa Monica, Calif.: The RAND Corporation, 1965), p. 17.

3. Smithies, "Conceptual Framework for the Program Budget," p. 18.

4. For a further discussion of the functions and responsibilities of line agencies, see Leonard D. White, *Introduction to the Study of Public Administration* (New York: Macmillan, 1955), pp. 195–223.

5. The authors are indebted to the pioneering work done in this area by Gene H. Fisher, and in particular his contribution to David Novick (ed.), *Program Budgeting: Program Analysis and the Federal Government* (Cambridge, Mass.: Harvard University Press, 1965), pp. 61–78.

6. Gene H. Fisher, "The Analytical Bases of Systems Analysis," a paper presented at a symposium on "Systems Analysis in Decision-Making" sponsored by the Electronics Industries Association, Washington, D. C. June 23, 1966.

7. For a discussion of Monte Carlo techniques, see E. S. Quade, *Analysis for Military Decisions,* R–387–PR (Santa Monica, Calif.: The RAND Corporation, November, 1964), pp. 407–414; and Herman Kahn and Irwin Mann, *Monte Carlo,* P–1165 (Santa Monica, Calif.: The RAND Corporation, July 30, 1957).

8. C. J. Hitch, *Appreciation of Systems Analysis,* P–699 (Santa Monica, Calif.: The RAND Corporation, August 18, 1955), p. 6.

9. Hitch, *Appreciation of Systems Analysis,* p. 7.

10. Fisher, "The Analytical Bases of Systems Analysis."

11. Smithies, "Conceptual Framework for the Program Budget," p. 18.

12. Smithies, "Conceptual Framework for the Program Budget," p. 24.

Chapter 8

1. Anthony James Catanese, "Automation in Planning: Some Perspectives on United States Experience," *Plan: Journal of the Town Planning Institute of Canada, 9* (March 1968), 24–31; "Automation of Town Planning: Problems and Potentials of the Coming Revolution," *Journal of the Town Planning Institute, 53* (December 1967), 448–452.

2. Britton Harris "How to Succeed with Computers Without Really Trying," *Journal of the American Institute of Planners, 33,* (January 1967), 11—17.

3. For example: "Geometric Design", *Highway Research Record Number 232* (Washington, D. C.: Highway Records Board, 1968).

4. For example, see M. L. Mannheim, *Highway Route Location as a Hierarchically-Structured Sequential Decision Process* (Cambridge: M.I.T. Civil Engineering Systems Laboratory, 1964).

5. Christopher F. Smith, "Graphic Data Processing," *Machine Design, 137* (May 27, 1965), 117—123; D. A. Curtiss, "Automated Drafting Where are We Now?" *Graphic Science, 7* (July 1965), pp. 13—15 ff.; David N. Keast, "Survey of Graphic Input Devices," *Machine Design, 39* (August 3, 1967), 114—120.

6. Frank Massey, Jean Dunn, and W. J. Dixon, *BIOMED Programs* (Los Angeles: Biomedical Data Processing Group of the University of California, 1964).

7. R. G. West and V. R. Reynolds, "Fortran Program for Plotting Two-Dimensional Graphs," *U. S. Government Research and Development Reports, 40* (August 1965), 102 (A).

8. U. S. Department of Housing and Urban Development, *Using Computers Graphics in Urban Renewal* (Washington, D. C.: U. S. Government Printing Office, 1963).

9. M. Adamowiez, "Graph Pak 1 — A Three Dimensional Manipulation Program," *STAR, 4* (March 23, 1966), 860 (A).

10. Jean-Charles Bernier, "How to Draw Perspectives by Computer," *Design Engineering, 10* (February 1964), 37—41.

11. D. G. Campion and K. G. Robey, "Perspective Drawing by Computer," *Architectural Review, 138* (November 1965), 380—386.

12. K. C. Knowlton, "A Computer Technique for Producing Animated Movies," *1964 Spring Joint Computer Conference* (Baltimore: Spartan Books, 1965), pp. 67—87; E. E. Fajec, "Computer-Made Perspective Movies as a Scientific and Communication Tool." *Communications of the Association of Computer Machinery, 7* (March 1964), 169—170.

13. F. G. Smith, "Three Computer Programs for Contouring Map Data," *Canadian Journal of Earth Sciences, 5* (April 1968), 324—327.

14. F. J. Rens, *A FORTRAN Program for Coordinate Mapping Using an IBM 7090 Computer: Government Document AD—611754* (Washington, D. C.: U. S. Government Printing Office, 1965).

15. Howard K. Fisher, *SYMAP* (Cambridge: Harvard Laboratory for Computer Graphics and Spatial Analysis, 1968).

Chapter 9

1. Seymour Lipschultz, *Set Theory* (New York: Schaum, 1964), pp. 1—16.

2. Charles H. Carr and Charles W. Howe, *Quantitative Decision Procedures in Management and Economics* (New York: McGraw-Hill, 1964), pp. 134—135.

3. Frederick E. Croxton and Dudley J. Cowden, *Applied General Statistics* (Englewood Cliffs, N. J.: Prentice-Hall, 1960), pp. 405–423.

4. W. J. Reilley, *The Law of Retail Gravitation* (New York: Putnam, 1931).

5. Wilber N. Thompson, *A Preface to Urban Economics* (Baltimore: Johns Hopkins Press, 1965), Chapters 1, 8, and 10.

6. Walter Isard et al., *Methods of Regional Analysis* (Cambridge: The M.I.T. Press, 1950), Chapter 11. F. Stuart Chapin, *Urban Land Use Planning* (Urbana: University of Illinois Press, 1964), Chapters 2 and 8.

7. Division of Planning, *Outdoor Recreation Plan* (Madison: Wisconsin Department Of Resource Development, 1966).

8. Basic sources of data: City Plan Commission, Dane County Planning Board, Madison Area Transportation Study, Wisconsin Department of Resource Development, Campus Planning Office, and Department of Urban and Regional Planning, University of Wisconsin. Data are available in raw form and in several publications, i.e., *Plan for Use of Land, Semi-Final Plan, Zoning Ordinance* (Madison: Madison City Plan Commission, 1965, 1966, 1967), etc., which are all public documents.

Chapter 10

1. D. M. Hill, D. Brand, and W. B. Hansen, "Prototype Development of a Statistical Land Use Prediction Model for the Greater Boston Region," *Highway Research Board Record* No. 114 (1966), pp. 23–35; Traffic Research Corporation, *Final Report: Land Use Forecasting Model for 626 Traffic Zones* (Boston: Traffic Research Corporation, 1967).

Chapter 11

1. Anthony J. Catanese, "Regional Development Alternatives: A Critique of New Towns," in *Proceedings of the Midwest Students Seminar on Urban and Regional Research,* ed. Alan Walter Steiss (Madison: University of Wisconsin, 1967), p. 75.

2. *Report of the United Nations Symposium of the Planning and Development of New Towns* (New York: United Nations publication no. 66.IV.3, 1966).

3. Lesley E. White, "The Social Factors Involved in the Planning and Development of New Towns," *Planning of Metropolitan Areas and New Towns* (New York: United Nations publication no. 67.IV.5, 1967), p. 195.

4. Lloyd Rodwin, *The British New Towns Policy* (Cambridge: Harvard University Press, 1956).

5. *The Planning of a New Town* (London: London County Council, 1961).

6. Wyndham Thomas, "New Town Blues," *Planning 1964* (Chicago: American Society of Planning Officials, 1964), p. 184.

7. See Willard Waller and Reuben Hill, *The Family: A Dynamic Interpretation*

(New York; The Dryden Press, 1956) for a further discussion of this relationship.

Chapter 12

1. Seward Hiltner, "Planning as a Profession," *Journal of the American Institute of Planners, 23* (1957), 166.

2. Hugh Pomeroy, "Some Thoughts on the Master Plan" (mimeograph), 1951

3. Robert T. Daland and John A. Parker, "Roles of the Planner in Urban Development," in *Urban Growth Dynamics in a Regional Cluster of Cities,* eds. F. S. Chapin and S. F. Weiss (New York: Wiley, 1962), p. 189.

4. The sources of this information, in addition to the mailed questionnaire and the various materials available from the Graduate Research Center of the Department of Urban and Regional Planning, University of Wisconsin, include various editions of *The Municipal Year Book,* reports, newsletters, and other materials made available by the Urban Renewal Administration of the Department of Housing and Urban Development, and reports of the ASPO Planning Advisory Service on expenditures, staff, and salaries of local planning agencies.

5. Robert O. Schulze has suggested, based on a study of a Michigan city, that managers of absentee-owned firms are less involved in civic affairs ("The Bifurcation of Power in a Satellite City," in *Community Political Systems,* ed. Morris Janowitz [New York: Free Press, 1961]). Pellegrin and Coates, employing different research methods, conclude that executives of national firms participate fully in local affairs (Roland J. Pellegrin and Charles H. Coates, "Absentee-Owned Corporations and Community Power Structure," *American Journal of Sociology, 81* [March, 1965], 413–419). Norton Long's conclusions as to the significance of the growing separation between the community and the large corporation tend to support those of Schulze (Norton E. Long, *The Polity* (Chicago: Rand McNally, 1962), Chapter 9).

6. Edward C. Banfield and James Q. Wilson, *City Politics* (Cambridge: Harvard University Press, 1965), p. 54.

7. E. L. Thorndike, *Your City* (New York: Harcourt, Brace, & World, 1939), pp. 33–34.

8. Oliver Williams, "A Typology for Comparative Local Government," *Midwest Journal of Political Science, 2* (May 1961), 150–164.

9. W. Ross Ashby, *Design for a Brain* (New York: Wiley, 1952).

10. Banfield and Wilson, *City Politics,* pp. 138–139.

11. Robert A. Walker, *The Planning Function in Urban Government* (Chicago: University of Chicago Press, 1941).

12. Francine F. Rabinovitz and J. Stanley Pottinger, "Organization for Local Planning: The Attitudes of Directors," *Journal of the American Institute of Planners, 33* (January, 1967), 28.

13. Banfield and Wilson, *City Politics* p. 168; Austin F. MacDonald, *American City Government and Administration* (New York: Thomas Y. Crowell, 1956).

Chapter 13

1. Francine F. Rabinovitz and J. Stanley Pottinger, "Organization for Local Planning: The Attitudes of Directors," *Journal of the American Institute of Planners, 33* (January 1967), 28.

Chapter 14

1. Robert T. Daland and John A. Parker, "Roles of the Planner in Urban Development," in *Urban Growth Dynamic in a Regional Cluster of Cities,* eds. F. Stuart Chapin and Shirley F. Weiss (New York: Wiley 1962), p. 189. This assumption is stated as a "fact" even though, to date, relatively little empirical evidence has been offered to support its validity. Other writers have suggested that this assumption represents what "ought to be" rather than what "is" (see Richard S. Bolan, "Emerging Views of Planning," *Journal of the American Institute of Planners, 33* [July 1967]).
2. Daland and Parker, in *Urban Growth Dynamic*, pp. 204–205.
3. *Ibid.*, p. 205.

Chapter 15

1. David Braybrooke and Charles Lindblom, in their book *A Strategy of Decision* (New York: Free Press, 1963), are guilty of this "sin of commission." By focusing on problem-solving situations, they conclude that the decision-making process is characterized by *incrementalism* and *mutual adjustment* or compromise. They fail to give adequate attention to the kinds of decision situations which cannot be dealt with effectively through the application of problem-solving techniques.
2. The dichotomy of programmed (routine) and nonprogrammed problem-solving, suggested by Herbert A. Simon, embodies the same perspective that is presented in this and subsequent discussions of routine, adaptive, and innovative responses to decision situations. (See *The New Science of Management Decision-Making* (New York: Wiley, 1960).
3. The notion of adaptive decisions meeting more immediate situations by providing temporary solutions is closely related to the concept of "satisficing" as formulated by Herbert A. Simon in his *Models of Man* (New York: Wiley, 1957). Unlike the economists' model of "maximizing man," "satisficing man" is moved by stimuli to search for alternatives; when he finds an alternative that is "good

enough" (i.e., one that suffices), he avoids spending further time, energy, and resources on additional search (i.e., he is satisfied).

4. W. Ross Ashby, *An Introduction to Cybernetics* (New York: Wiley, 1963), p. 206.

5. Filmer S. C. Northrup, *The Logic of the Sciences and the Humanities* (New York: Macmillan, 1947), p. 1.

6. David A. Easton, *A Systems Analysis of Political Life* (New York: Wiley, 1965), p. 38. Easton makes a distinction between authoritative outputs and associated outputs. The former includes "binding decisions, law, decrees, regulations, orders, and judicial decision," while the latter covers "policies, rationales, and commitments." In the present analysis, all outputs of the system are dependent upon a decision (including the "decision" not to decide). Therefore, the term "decision" can be substituted in this definition for "authoritative allocation."

7. For a further development of the concept of uncertainty in the human cognitative process, see John Dewey, *Logic, The Theory of Inquiry* (New York: Holt, Rinehart and Winston, 1938), pp. 105 ff.

8. David Easton makes the distinction between "inputs" and "withinputs," the latter referring to demands which are generated from within the system itself (Easton, *Systems Analysis of Political Life,* pp. 21 ff).

9. Anatol Rapoport, "What Is Information?" *ETC: A Review of General Semantics, 10* (Summer, 1953), 252.

10. Peter F. Drucker, "The Effective Decision," *Harvard Business Review, 45* (January—February 1967). pp. 92—104.

11. Robert W. Morell, *Managerial Decision-Making* (Milwaukee: Bruce Publishing Co., 1960).

12. Drucker, *Harvard Business Review,* p. 95.

13. Joseph D. Cooper, *The Art of Decision Making* (Garden City: Doubleday, 1961), pp. 15—16.

Chapter 16

1. Robert E. Coughlin, "The Capital Programming Problem," *Journal of the American Institute of Planners 26* (February, 1960), 39.

2. *Ibid.,* p. 39.

3. Francine F. Rabinovitz and J. Stanley Pottinger, "Organization for Local Planning: The Attitude of Directors," *Journal of the American Institute of Planners, 33* (January 1967), 27—32.

4. Herbert Gamberg, "The Professional and Policy Choice in Middle-Sized Cities," *Journal of the American Institute of Planners, 32* (May, 1966), 175.

5. See "An Analysis of City Managers," *Public Management* (January, 1954), pp. 5—9; George K. Floro, "Continuity in City Managers Careers," *American Journal of Sociology, 51* (November, 1955), 240—246.

6. Robert T. Daland and John A. Parker, "Roles of the Planner in Urban

Development," in *Urban Growth Dynamics in a Regional Cluster of Cities,* eds. F. Stuard Chapin Jr. and Shirley F. Weiss (New York: Wiley, 1962), p. 207.

7. Francine F. Rabinovitz, "Politics, Personality, and Planning," *Public Administration Review, 27* (March 1967) 19.

8. Alan Altshuler, *The City Planning Process — A Political Analysis* (Ithaca: Cornell University Press, 1965), p. 452.

9. Francine F. Rabinovitz, *Public Administration Review,* p. 19.

10. Norton E. Long, *The Polity* (Chicago: Rand McNally, 1965), p. 195.

11. W. Ross Ashby, *An Introduction to Cybernetics* (New York: Wiley, 1966), p. 233.

Annotated Bibliography

The two-letter symbols represent the predominant field from which the reference was extracted: i.e., DT, decision theory; SA, systems analysis; WP, work programming; and CY, cybernetics.

Abendroth, W. W. "The Research and Decision-Making Process." In Jesse Shera et al., *Documentation in Action,* New York: Reinhold, 1956. The author asserts that decision-making can be made into a science if the steps outlined as "Decision Calculus" are followed and if research techniques are used to reduce the area of projection based on insufficient data. DT

Ackoff, Russell L. "The Development of Operations Research as a Science," *Operations Research* (June, 1956), pp. 265–289. A bibliographic summary covering organization, decision theory, inventory theory, allocation process, queuing theory, routing process, replacement process, information-collection process, and competitive models. SA

———. *Scientific Method: Optimizing Applied Research Decisions.* New York: Wiley, 1962. The author's major work in the field of scientific method. A textbook covering the rudiments, principles, and concepts of the scientific method. SA

Andlinger, Gerhard, et al. *Operations Research: Challenge to Modern Management.* Cambridge: Harvard University, Graduate School of Business Administration, 1956. The past uses and successes of operations research are investigated and the future of this aid to decision-making is forecast. SA

Antill, James M., and Ronald W. Woodhead. *Critical Path Methods in Construction Practice.* New York: Wiley, 1956. A well-written introduction to CPM drawing upon the experience of the authors in Australian construction programs. WP

Archibald, Russell D., and Richard L. Villaria. *Network Based Management Systems.* New York: Wiley, 1966. An advanced treatment of network planning with special emphasis on the CPM technique, all within the perspectives of information science and systems. WP

Ashby, W. Ross. *An Introduction to Cybernetics.* New York: Wiley, 1963. A basic primer in the mathematics of cybernetics. Extensive development of the concept of feedback and its application to complex, stochastic systems. CY

Associated General Contractors of America. *CPM in Construction: A Manual for General Construction.* Washington, D. C.: Associated General Contractors of America, 1965. Another treatment of the use of CPM in building and construction, but written in a manner easy to understand. WP

Baker, Bruce N., and René L. Eries. *An Introduction to PERT/CPM.* Homewood, Ill.: Irwin, 1964. A widely used textbook with emphasis on the engineering and management of industrial organizations. WP

Baker, Robert F. "A Practical View of the Systems Approach," *Traffic Quarterly* Vol. 21 (October, 1967), pp. 471—489. A discussion of how the United States Bureau of Public Roads is using systems approaches for research and development. The outputs are a series of technological innovations for traffic control. SA

Battersby, Albert. *Network Analysis for Planning and Scheduling.* New York: St. Martin's, 1964. A descriptive textbook with several problems and solutions written by a highly lucid and literate Englishman. WP

Bertalanffy, Ludwig. "General Systems Theory," *Main Currents in Modern Thought* 1 (1955), pp. 1—10. A basic treatise on the concept of general systems theory, with particular emphasis on the distinctions between open and closed systems, the concept of equifinality, and the importance of organization as a counterforce to entropy. SA

Bock, Robert H., and William K. Holstein. *Production Planning and Control.* Columbus: Merrill, 1963. Chapters 6 and 7 are concerned with CPM and heuristic programming. In general, the work is a basic treatment of the general planning problem for industrial management. WP

Boguslaw, Robert. *The New Utopians: A Study of System and Social Change.* Englewood Cliffs, N. J.: Prentice-Hall, 1965. The author visualizes systems analysts as the new, "nonpeople" Utopians. Reviews basic constructs of systems analysis and concludes with a discussion of the role of systems in society. Distinctive because of its fine literary style. SA

Braybrooke, David, and Charles E. Lindblom. *A Strategy of Decision: Policy Evaluation as a Social Process.* New York: Free Press of Glencoe, 1963. An elaborate development of the concepts of "disjointed incrementalism" and "partisan mutual adjustment" as the prevailing form of decision-making. The authors challenge the synoptic or comprehensive form of problem-solving on the basis that it does not exist in reality. DT

Buchan, Joseph, and Ernest Koenigsburg. *Scientific Inventory Management.* Englewood Cliffs, N. J.: Prentice-Hall, 1963. Several examples are presented in this work of the use of computerized systems containing both analytical and heuristic elements for the purposes of inventory control. SA

Buckley, Walter. *Sociology and Modern Systems Theory.* Englewood Cliffs, N. J.: Prentice-Hall, 1967. A reevaluation of classical and contemporary social theory within the perspective of a systems approach. The author is concerned with the lack of a theoretical framework in contrast to the growth of empirical data in social sciences. SA

Calhoun, S. Reed, and Paul E. Green. "Simulation: Versatile Aid to Decision-Making," *Advanced Management* Vol. 23 (April, 1958), pp. 11—16. A basic discussion of the application of simulation modeling techniques as a tool for problem-solving in organization decision-making situations. DT

Carr, Charles R., and Charles W. Howe. *Quantitative Decision Procedures in Management and Economics.* New York: McGraw-Hill, 1964. An outstanding textbook on deterministic theory and applications. Includes discussions of mathematical model building, set theory, linear programming, quadratic programming, stepwise optimization, and Markovian processes. SA

Cartwright, Dorwin, and Leon Festinger. "A Quantitative Theory of Decision," *Psychological Review* Vol. 50 (1943), pp. 595—621. An early effort to develop a mathematical theory of decision which combines a topological analysis with a vectorial analysis of decision situations. DT

Catanese, Anthony J. "Regional Development Alternatives: A Critique of New Towns," *Proceedings of the Midwest Students Seminar on Urban and Regional Research.* Edited by Alan Walter Steiss. Madison: University of Wisconsin, 1967. An examination of the problems of the "new town approach" to regional planning using set theory as an organizational basis. SA

Charnes, A., and W. W. Cooper. *Management Models and Industrial Applications of Linear Programming: Volume I.* New York: Wiley, 1961. One of a few works dealing with applications of Linear Programming written by two of the pioneers of the technique. SA

Churchman, Charles W., Ackoff, Russell, and E. Leonard Arnoff. *Introduction to Operations Research.* New York: Wiley, 1957. A general introduction to methods concerning inventories, linear programming, queuing theory, replacement models, and so forth with an emphasis on the application of operations research to industrial problems. SA

Clarke, Roderick W. *An Introduction to Critical Path Analysis.* Stanford: Stanford University Press, 1961. One of the earliest intensive treatments of the subject but still useful for a basic understanding of the technique. WP

Clarkson, Geoffrey P., and Allan H. Meltzer. "Portfolio Selection: A Heuristic Approach," *Journal of Finance* 15 (December, 1960), p. 465. One of several studies developed to simulate the existing decision-making activities of an individual; in this case, a heuristic approach is applied to the investment of trust funds held by banks. DT

Clawson, Marion. *Methods of Measuring the Demand and Value of Outdoor Recreation.* Washington, D. C.: Resources for the Future, 1959. One of the best and perhaps only successful attempt to quantify variables for the measurement of outdoor recreation demand. SA

Clawson, Marion, and Jack L. Knetsch. *Economics of Outdoor Recreation.* Baltimore: Johns Hopkins Press, 1966. The finest work in the area of quantified analysis of outdoor recreation demand and supply. A useful planning book. SA

Collins, Frank Thomas. *Network Planning and Critical Path Programming.* Berkeley: Know How Publications, 1964. A non-technical, simplified approach making ample use of humorous cartoons and anecdotes. WP

————. *Manual Critical Path Techniques for Construction.* Berkeley: Know How Publications, 1965. Noncomputerized techniques for using CPM with special attention being paid to building and construction. WP

"Critical Path Programming: The New Way to Take the Guesswork Out of Scheduling," *House and Home* (April, 1963), pp. 106–109. An application for small home and apartment builders. A very interesting treatment in a limited space. WP

Cyert, Richard, Simon, Herbert A., and Donald Trow. "Observation of a Business Decision," *Journal of Business* (1956). This study presents an empirically derived model of the decision-making process in administration which illustrates some of the applications of heuristics. DT

Deatherage, George E. *Construction Scheduling and Control.* New York: McGraw-Hill, 1965. Several parts of the book give applications of the PERT-CPM techniques in construction. WP

Deutsch, Karl W. "Game Theory and Politics: Some Problems of Application," *Canadian Journal of Economic and Political Science* 20 (1954), pp. 76–83. An exploration of some of the limitations of game theory as it is applied in political problem-solving situations. The author asserts that insufficient consideration is given to dynamic factors and to value judgments. DT

———— . *The Nerves of Government.* New York: Free Press of Glencoe, 1963. An examination of cybernetic theory as it might be applied in the development of models for political communication and control. Emphasis is given to the role of learning, memory, feedback, and the establishment of goals and purposes. CY

Dooley, Arch R., et al. *Operations Planning and Control.* New York: Wiley, 1964. A casebook of planning problems prepared for use in the Graduate School of Business, Harvard University. Part 2 is concerned with the use of CPM techniques for operations. DT

Dreyfus, Hubert L. "Alchemy and Artificial Intelligence," *The RAND Corporation,* Vol. P-3244 (December, 1965). This work suggests some of the limitations to the use of heuristic programming in cognitive simulations. It is suggested that the best that can be achieved through research in artificial intelligence is computer approximation of decision-making through discrete operations. DT

Drucker, Peter F. *The Practice of Management.* New York: Harper, 1954. This book includes a highly developed analysis of the process of making decisions including the problem definition stage, the alternative development stage, and the action program stage. The author considers that the field of operations research is concerned with information processing rather than decision-making. DT

———— . "The Effective Decision," *Harvard Business Review,* Vol. 45 (January-February, 1967), pp. 92–104. A concise presentation of the author's further thinking on the procedures of decision-making. Particular emphasis is given to the distinction between generic and unique problem situations. DT

Duke, Richard D. *Gaming Simulation in Urban Research.* East Lansing: Michigan State University, Institute for Community Development, 1964. An extensive review and discussion of application of gaming techniques in urban areas. Included is a basic bibliography on gaming and simulation models. DT

Easton, David A. *A System Analysis of Political Life.* New York: Wiley, 1965. The second in a trilogy in which the author attempts to develop a general theory for political analysis. The framework presented draws heavily from systems analysis and includes a general cybernetic model for public decision-making processes. SA

Evarts, Harry F. *Introduction to PERT.* Boston: Allyn and Bacon, 1964. A good treatment of the subject. The book is part of a series on quantitative methods for business and economics. WP

Federal Electric Corporation. *A Programmed Introduction to PERT.* New York: Wiley, 1964. A textbook which employs the new "programmed instruction" approach, which allows for either self-teaching or computerized teaching. The treatment is highly technical, however, and does not go into depth on applications of the technique. WP

Flagle, Charles D., William H. Higgins, and Robert H. Roy. *Operations Research and Systems Engineering.* Baltimore: Johns Hopkins Press, 1960. A collection of papers originally presented as lectures in a course of the same title at the Johns Hopkins University. The work is distinguished by its succinct treatment of a large scope of subject matter. SA

Gore, William J. *Administrative Decision-making: A Heuristic Model.* New York: Wiley, 1964. An elaborate examination of the processes by which adaptive decisions are made through the use of heuristics or decision rules. Adaptive decisions are those for which there is a general agreement on goals and acceptance of a pattern of activities appropriate to achieving them. DT

Guetzkow, Harold. *Simulation in Social Science.* Englewood Cliffs, N. J.: Prentice-Hall, 1962. A discussion of the possible applications of simulation techniques in social science research. Simulation models are viewed as a set of criteria for selecting significant data and provide rules for applying logic to the distilled information. SA

Hadley, G. *Nonlinear and Dynamic Programming.* Reading, Mass.: Addison-Wesley, 1964. The basic textbook on nonlinear and dynamic programming, although it is not written for those with only a passing acquaintance with mathematics — strictly for the specialist. SA

Hansen, B. J. *Practical PERT Including CPM.* Washington, D. C.: America House, 1964. As the title implies, this treatment attempts to strip the intricacies of theory and mathematics away so as to allow for application. WP

Harris, Britton. "Urban Development Models: New Tools for Planning," *Journal of the American Institute of Planners,* Vol. 31 (May, 1965), pp. 90—95. The author attempts to suggest how simulation models can be applied as a means of calculating the optimal solution and evaluating alternative development strategies in urban planning. SA

Hart, William J. *A Systems Approach to Park Planning.* Marges, Switzerland: International Union for the Conservation of Nature and Natural Resources, 1966. An unusual book and source, but a very lucid and innovative general discussion of the possible areas of application of the system approach. SA

Hatry, Harry P., and John F. Cotton. *Program Planning for State, County, City.* Washington, D. C.: The George Washington University, 1967. The most important report to come out of the so-called "5—5—5 Project" at George Washington University on planning-programming-budgeting systems (PPBS). SA

Herrmann, Cyril C. "Systems Approach to City Planning," *Harvard Business Review* Vol. 44 (September-October, 1966), pp. 71—80. A discussion of the applications made of systems analysis techniques to urban renewal and redevelopment programs in the city of San Francisco. SA

Hill, D. M., D. Brand, and W. B. Hansen. "Prototype Development of a Statistical Land Use Prediction Model for the Greater Boston Region," *Highway Research Board Record,* No. 114. Washington, D. C.: Highway Research Board, 1966. A preliminary discussion of the principles of the Empiric model that is informative for specialists. SA

Hitch, Charles J. *Decision Making for Defense.* Berkeley: University of California, 1966. One of the best discussions of systems analysis as applied in the United States Department of Defense. Traces through the development of the systems approach of planning, programming, budgeting procedures (PPBS) formulated under the tutelage of Robert McNamara. DT

Hurwicz, Leonid. "Game Theory and Decisions," *Scientific American* Vol. 192 (February, 1955), pp. 78—83. A non-technical explanation of game theory, illustrated by simple mathematical problems. DT

Kilbridge, Maurice, and Leon Wester. "A Heuristic Method of Assembly Line Balancing," *Journal of Industrial Engineering* (July-August, 1961), p. 394. This study discusses the application of heuristic programming techniques to a production management problem of assigning elemental assembly tasks to work stations along a conveyor line; the problem of minimizing idle time among operators is analogous to the problem of "leveling-off" staff commitments. WP

Krasnow, H. S., and R. Merikallio. "The Past, Present, and Future of General Simulation Languages," *Management Science* 11 (November, 1964). This work explores the possibility of an all-purpose simulation language which would greatly reduce programming efforts and increase flexibility in the application of simulation techniques. SA

Lasswell, Harold D. *The Decision Process: Seven Categories of Functional Analysis.* College Park: University of Maryland, Bureau of Governmental Research, 1956. Develops seven categories of functional analysis — intelligence, recommendation, prescription, invocation, application, appraisal, and termination — and investigates each area in relation to the particular branch of government with which it is concerned. DT

Levin, Richard I., and Charles A. Kirkpatrick. *Planning and Control with PERT/CPM.* New York: McGraw-Hill, 1966. A recent work on the subject which places the technique within a very interesting framework of planning as a generic process. WP

Lockyer, K. G. *An Introduction to Critical Path Analysis.* New York: Pitman, 1964. An adequate treatment of the subject matter which will enable a general understanding. WP

Lowe, Cecil William. *Critical Path Analysis by Bar Chart: The Role of Job Progress Charts.* London: Business Publications, 1966. The author argues that small-and medium-sized programs do not require computerization. He develops a technique which incorporates the Gantt Chart into the CPM approach for ongoing control of programs. WP

Lowry, Ira S. "A Short Course in Model Design," *Journal of the American Institute of Planners* Vol. 31 (May, 1965), pp. 158—166. A succinct review of theories and uses of descriptive, predictive, and mathematical models. Extensive bibliography of model applications in the field of planning. SA

Luce, R. Duncan, and Howard Raiffa. *Games and Decisions: Introduction and Critical Survey.* New York: Wiley, 1957. This work attempts to communicate the central ideas and results of game theory and related decision-making models unencumbered by their technical mathematical detail. Examples are drawn from the social sciences with an emphasis on applications and theoretical concepts. DT

McCamy, J. L. "Analysis of the Process of Decision-Making," *Public Administration Review* Vol. 7 (1947), pp. 41—48. A basic discussion of decision-making as the center of the process of administration is presented from the point of view of a political scientist. DT

McKean, Roland N. *Efficiency in Government Through Systems Analysis.* New York: Wiley, 1957. An early discussion of potential transfers of systems techniques for defense applications to nondefense governmental functions. A case study of water resource management is included. SA

Meier, Richard L. *A Communications Theory of Urban Growth,* Cambridge. M. I. T. Press, 1962. A pioneering effort in the application of communications theory as a tool of analysis and prediction with regards to the patterns of urban growth. This study explores some of the long-range possibilities for the application of simulation procedures as a means of synthesis for complex problems. SA

————. *Developmental Planning.* New York: McGraw-Hill, 1965. A study of planned regional development for Puerto Rico, this report discusses the application of various techniques for simulation and guidance in the field of planning. SA

Meier, Richard L., and Richard D. Duke. "Gaming Simulation for Urban Planning," *Journal of the American Institute of Planners* Vol. 32 (January, 1966), pp. 3—17. The authors present an extensive survey of the applications of gaming simulation techniques in the field of planning. They conclude with a presentation of a "hybrid" model, which they suggest will achieve the most thorough compression of the real world while still retaining the flexibility for exploring widely divergent futures. DT

Miller, Robert W. *Schedule, Cost and Profit Control with PERT.* New York: McGraw-Hill, 1963. A guide for use of the technique in programs where cost and profit hold special significance to the manner in which jobs are undertaken. WP

Moder, Joseph J., and Cecil R. Phillips. *Project Management with PERT and CPM*. New York: Reinhold, 1964. The concern here is with short-term, complex problems and how they can be resolved by using the techniques of PERT and CPM. WP

Novick, David. *Program Budgeting*. Washington, D. C.: The Rand Corporation, 1965. A very good book of readings on the nature and principles of program budgeting in the federal government. SA

O'Brien, James J. *CPM in Construction Management: Scheduling by the Critical Path Method*. New York: McGraw-Hill, 1965. Another treatment of CPM in the building and construction context, but with some interesting discussion of managerial utility of the approach. WP

Operations Research, Inc. *Manual of Critical Path Theory and Practice*. Silver Spring, Md.: Operations Research, Inc., 1962. An early manual which serves as a textbook for three-day short courses on the subject which the firm contracts to present from time to time. WP

Optner, Stanford L. *Systems Analysis for Business Management*. Englewood Cliffs, N. J.: Prentice-Hall, 1960. A pioneering treatment of the systems approach for the management of private organizations. Emphasis is on EDP systems. SA

————. *Systems Analysis for Business and Industrial Problem-solving*. Englewood Cliffs, N. J.: Prentice-Hall, 1965. A refinement, as well as generalization, of Optner's first book. The EDP orientation is replaced by a general systems perspective of more interest to public organizations. SA

Orcutt, G. H., M. Greenberger, J. Korbel, and A. M. Rivlin. *Microanalysis of Socio-Economic Systems – A Simulation Study*. New York: Harper, 1961. The most important large-scale simulation in the social sciences to date. A worthwhile book on this important experiment. SA

"Performance Design," *Progressive Architecture* (August, 1967). A concerned analysis of systems analysis by the architecture profession, seeking its meaning, as well as possible applications, for urban design. SA

Polya, Gyorgy. *How To Solve It*. New York: Doubleday, 1957. This study offers a further discussion of the philosophical basis of heuristic problem-solving and its applications within the field of logic. SA

Riggs, James L., and Charles O. Health. *Guide to Cost Reduction Through Critical Path Scheduling*. Englewood Cliffs, N. J.: Prentice-Hall, 1966. A modification of the basic technique to include (1) a matrix formulation of problems, (2) a probability basis for time estimates, and (3) an improved communication of findings. A very advanced and sophisticated treatment. WP

Schlaifer, Robert. *Statistics for Business Decisions*. New York: McGraw-Hill, 1961. This book offers an excellent summary of statistical decision theory, linear programming, and machine problem-solving, translating theory into useful propositions. SA

Shaffer, Louis R., J. B. Ritter, and W. L. Meyer. *The Critical Path Method*. New York: McGraw-Hill, 1965. An adequate treatment of the subject which is well written and illustrated. WP

Sieloff, Richard O. *The Economics of Outdoor Recreation in the Upper Midwest.* Duluth: University of Minnesota, 1963. An interesting attempt at quantification and analytical solution of outdoor recreation needs. SA

Simon, Herbert A., and Allen Newell. "Heuristic Problem Solving: The Next Advance in Operations Research," *Operations Research 6* (January-February, 1958). pp. 1–10. This article offers a good introduction to the concepts of heuristic programming and its potentialities for solving ill-structured problems through computer simulation. DT

Smith, Kenneth M. *A Practical Guide to Network Planning.* London: British Institute of Management, 1965. A succinct discussion of network planning written from the perspective of the British railroad system. WP

Stires, David M., and Maurice M. Murphy. *Modern Management Method: PERT and CPM.* Boston: Materials Management Institute, 1962. A guide prepared for the Corporation for Economic and Industrial Research CEIR for three-day short courses. WP

Stires, David M., and Raymond P. Wenig. *PERT/COST.* Boston: Industrial Education Institute, 1964. A modification of the basic programming techniques to include cost-reduction objectives. The manual was prepared for contractors to the Department of Defense and National Aeronautic and Space Administration who are required to perform such analyses of their programs. WP

Shubik, Martin. *Readings in Game Theory and Political Behavior.* New York: Doubleday, 1954. A collection of readings on the application of game theory in the context of political and social science, this book includes a selected bibliography of writings in game theory. DT

Thompson, Victor A. *Modern Organizations.* New York: Knopf, 1962. This work marks the emergence in the literature on organization and theory of a recognition of heuristic processes as being of equal importance to the more formal aspects of the decision system. DT

Traffic Research Corporation. *Final Report: Development and Calibration of the EMPIRIC Land Use Forecasting Model for 626 Traffic Zones.* Boston: Traffic Research Corporation, 1967. The definitive work on the development of a land-use model which is operational — perhaps the only major land use model to be made operational so far. SA

U. S. National Aeronautic and Space Administration. *PERT 'C' Computer Systems Manual.* Washington, D. C.: U. S. Government Printing Office, 1964. The basic operational guide which NASA introduced for computerized scheduling and network planning. WP

Van Kruegal, E. "Introduction to CPM," *Architectural Record,* Vol. 136 (September, 1964), pp. 337–341. A brief description and application to architectural practice and building supervision. WP

Waldron, James A. *Applied Principles of Project Management and Control.* Haddonfield: Privately printed by author, 1966. The author is a planning consultant who published this work to introduce organizations to the benefits of CPM as part of a general management control system. WP

Wiener, Norbert. *Cybernetics; or Control and Communication in Animal and the Machine.* New York: Wiley, 1948. The author presents the concept of cybernetics as a new field of control and communication based on statistical mechanics. Statistical methods and quantum mechanics are discussed as they can be applied to the problem of predicting the future of a system. CY

_____. *The Human Use of Human Beings: Cybernetics and Society.* Boston: Houghton Mifflin, 1954. The theories of Wiener's earlier book are restated in nonmathematical terms, and the ethical and social implications are examined. The implications of cybernetics are explored in a wide range of human endeavours. CY

Wiest, Jerome D. "Heuristic Programs for Decision-Making," *Harvard Business Review* 44 (September-October, 1966), pp. 129–143. This article provides an extensive review of various applications of heuristic programming in the field of business, including location allocations, site selection, job-shop scheduling, engineering design, and large project scheduling where such planning and scheduling techniques as PERT and CPM are widely used. DT

Subject Index

Subject Index